Highway maintenance handbook

Highway maintenance handbook

Edited by

Ken Atkinson, CEng, MICE, MIHT

 Thomas Telford Ltd, London

Published by Thomas Telford Ltd, Thomas Telford House, 1 Heron Quay, London E14 9XF

First published 1990

British Library Cataloguing in Publication Data
Atkinson, Ken
  Highway maintenance handbook.
  1. Roads. Maintenance and repair
  I. Title
  625.7′6

ISBN: 0 7277 1577 1

This book is published on the understanding that the author is solely responsible for the statements made and opinions expressed in it and that its publication does not necessarily imply that such statements and or opinions are or reflect the views or opinions of the publishers. Every effort has been made to ensure that the statements made and the opinions expressed in this publication provide a safe and accurate guide; however, no liability or responsibility of any kind can be accepted in this respect by the publishers or the author.

Typeset in Great Britain by the Alden Press, Oxford, London and Northampton
Printed and bound in Great Britain by Redwood Press Ltd, Melksham, Wiltshire

Contents

Introduction

In recent years, highway maintenance has become a relatively high profile topic, due perhaps to the greater travel potential of the general public, and also to the impact of roadworks on commerce since the swing away from rail transport has gathered momentum. From being a specialized but none the less 'Cinderella' occupation, maintenance is now being treated as a deservedly important consideration in the overall cost of providing highways. For most construction, the maintenance requirement can be predicted in terms of a series of actions required to keep the initial components in a state of acceptable serviceability. This usually entails the establishment of appropriate intervention levels in the lifespan of each material or member, allowing recovery of its performance before such time as full replacement is needed. Unfortunately, the dual pressures of workload and resource limitation frequently prevent this idealized procedure from taking place, and economies are lost. Such loss of performance and potential savings are not surprising given the long-term nature of maintenance and the difficulties of persuading the controllers of finance that attention is needed, which may not be apparent to the layman.

The purpose of this book is to give an insight into some of the facets of highway maintenance, which are practised or under development, to aid both the engineer engaged in the discipline, and those needing to know more about this field of activity. With such a diverse and often complex subject, the full range of topics cannot be covered, but a selection has been made to show the areas of 'general maintenance' in which most money is commonly spent. Reference is also made to techniques used to establish the basic needs and programmes. The authors have drawn from experience gained in local government, contracting and academic research fields, and most chapters also offer sources of further information.

1.1. The highway scene

Failure to provide and maintain vital communication links affects every household, either directly in terms of travelling time, or indirectly in the mounting costs of supplying goods, vehicle damage, accident costs, and the loss of competitive edge against vying commercial interests elsewhere. Roads have assumed an increasingly important role in this process, particularly during the past 20 years, and as a result of the motorway building programme. In total some 340 000 km of public road serve the nation, and

Table 1.1. Public road length — all surfaced roads: 1987[1.1]

Country	Class					
	Trunk roads: km	Classified		All trunk and classified roads: km	Unclassified roads: km	All roads: km
		Principal roads: km	Non-principal roads: km			
England	10 469	24 721	80 135	115 325	153 132	268 457
Wales	1 702	2 554	12 418	16 674	16 038	32 712
Scotland	3 135	7 725	17 393	28 253	22 872	51 125
Great Britain	15 306	35 000	109 946	160 252	192 042	352 294

these are divided into various categories as shown in Table 1.1.[1.1] Improvement in major road links has encouraged the transfer of bulk haulage from traditional rail transport to such an extent that predictions of road life expectancy, using estimates of the cumulative totals of standard axles, have been far exceeded. A recent report by the Audit Commission[1.2] illustrates this growth in terms of road category, as shown in Fig. 1.1. In addition the character of vehicles in use has altered towards the larger and heavier end of the spectrum. Inevitably, this large increase has shortened the life of roads, and has increased the cost and frequency of maintenance needed to keep them serviceable. The overall condition of most roads has, however, deteriorated during the past ten years, despite the considerable efforts of government and highway authorities.

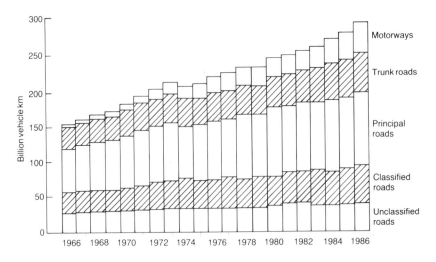

Fig. 1.1. Traffic increase (by total of 92%) for the period 1966–86 on each class of road. (Source: Audit Commission analysis of Department of Tranport data.)

Table 1.2. Commuting levels into London

Year	Public transport	Private transport	Overall
1982	770 000	234 000	1 004 000
1987	925 000	190 000	1 115 000

Forward planning and the estimation of traffic needs is difficult, and subject to many indeterminate changes — Table 1.2 shows changes that have occurred in London in the period 1982–87.

This switch of some 20% away from private transport, as shown in Table 1.2, is indicative of the difficulty in travelling by road, and the increasing attraction of commuting by public transport. A further change in attitudes has been the willingness of commuters to travel extended distances, balancing the extra cost against perceived improvement in environment, and lower prices in the more remote positions. Many factors will influence future trends in road usage, including

(a) the success of policies to divert development to less crowded areas

(b) the impact of physical and political changes in Europe, such as the Channel tunnel, and trade barrier legislation.

Against this background of variables and uncertainties, politicians and their advisers face the task of determining levels of finance and activity, which will maximize the benefits, and minimize the disadvantages of the road network. Not least among these factors are the emphasis and resources to be allocated to the important category of highway maintenance. There are clear signs that the time for giving priority to this work is now, before the escalation in road damage reaches uncontrollable proportions. Dependence on a natural process of deterring travel by the sheer difficulty involved, may well work for non-essential journeys, but in the process has disastrous effects on necessary commerce.

Current thinking suggests that transport efficiency will once again come to rely on the railway system, but this will require a considerable change in the outlook of users, who have become accustomed to the flexibility and convenience of door-to-door transport. Such a reversal of attitude will not take place quickly enough to stem the increasingly costly effects of road congestion.

The environmental impact of major new building has prompted ideas such as the use of rail routes for elevated roads, and restricted finance has led to consideration of sources other than the public sector for road and bridge building. Schemes involving ways in which prime locations can be priced and/or restricted, greater flexibility in working hours, and reduction in the benefit of company car use have all been included in appraisals of the traffic problem. Highway maintenance is undoubtably a key factor in all such deliberations, including all works within the highway which have an effect on either traffic or the integrity of highway structure. Whatever the evolutionary changes in transportation practices and methods, commonsense dictates that the under cared for and over used elements of the existing system need to be nursed in a structured programme of repair for the foreseeable future.

1.2. Relevant facts

During the past decade, spending on local roads has fallen by 5%, whereas traffic has shown a marked increase of about 20%.

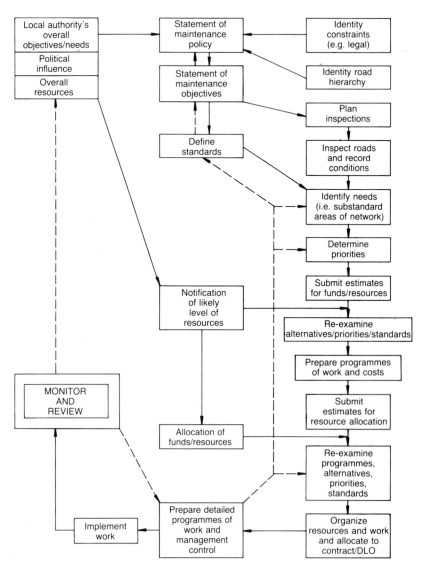

Fig. 1.2. Maintenance management flow diagram

The number of licensed vehicles is approximately 20 million, and this total is expected to rise.

The trend towards the use of heavier vehicles is expected to continue, and it remains to be seen whether this will lead to a decrease in the total numbers of goods vehicles.

At present, 85% of all goods are carried by road, and in the short term this method is likely to continue.

Spending on highway maintenance in 1986–87 was at an annual level of £200 million for trunk roads and motorways and £1150 million for county roads.

The average expenditure per kilometre for principal roads is £9100 and for non-principal roads is £3200.

The results of the National Road Maintenance Condition Survey (NRMCS) indicate that some 20% of urban principal roads and 10% of rural principal roads have a residual life of less than five years.

1.3. Definition of highway maintenance

In engineering, the term 'maintenance' is used to describe the processes of sustaining construction elements in a safe and usable condition. There are also benefits to be gained from regular attention, in appearance and cleanliness. From the time of production, construction components begin to decline as a result of weathering, use, and changes occurring in physical and chemical conditions. The aim of maintenance is to carry out protective and repair measures designed to limit the detrimental effects of these natural or imposed processes, thereby prolonging the useful life of the construction. The effectiveness of maintenance is improved if action is taken before major deterioration takes place, and is likely to be most efficient if done in a preplanned manner.

For most components, a relatively long life is expected in the highway context, ranging from say five years for surface dressing of carriageways to perhaps some hundreds of years for major structures, such as bridges and tunnels. Each aspect and item forming the highway therefore needs consideration in developing a programme involving inspection, design of remedial treatments, contract preparation, implementation and monitoring of results. Also, with the exception of accident damage, the process of decline permits a variable response timescale and introduces the need to choose between frequent minor attention and less frequent but more costly major work. Such decisions, made jointly between the maintenance engineer and the owning authority, form the crux of the art maintenance, and may be summarized as follows.

(a) Identify and assess conditions.
(b) Define and cost alternative actions and respective consequences.
(c) Obtain necessary approvals and finance.
(d) Institute a programme of work including the frequency of intervention and the scale of regular work required.
(e) Carry out periodic monitoring of the results achieved. Figure 1.2 shows a typical management flow chart.

1.4. Importance of records and monitoring

Adequate records of item (*e*) form the basis of experience on which reliable future judgements can be made, and without which sensible comparisons between methods, materials used and costs become difficult. Care is needed to avoid false economies, which in the short term offer savings, but result in a shortened lifespan or inferior service. While structures often demonstrate a surprising capacity to withstand the ravages of time and abuse, it is unwise to depend on such characteristics without carrying out systematic inspections and assessments.

Figure 1.3 shows a small arch bridge in London, built in the 12th century, and today carrying full highway loading without apparent distress.

Figure 1.4 shows a Victorian bridge of more elaborate form, which, due to material and structural changes, is now limited to a maximum loading of 2 tonnes and requires constant surveillance. Such examples illustrate the difficulty in predicting future conditions at the design stage. A further well known case is the early motorways, where design assumptions were exceeded within one-third of the anticipated lifespan in some cases. Present generations owe a debt to predecessors, whose wisdom, and investment, provided a generous capacity in design, and high quality in construction. This is not to say that design should automatically be over-conservative, but that the sensitivity of costings to increase in design capacity should be related to a timescale.

1.5. New techniques and materials

The development of new techniques and materials is an important feature of maintenance work, and requires cooperation between producer

Fig. 1.3. Clattern Bridge Kingston, London

Fig. 1.4. Albert Bridge, London

and user. In highway maintenance this means mutual assistance between client authorities at county and local level, research organizations such as the Government's Transport and Road Research Laboratory (TRRL) at Crowthorne, consultants in the field of materials testing, specialist contractors, many of whom conduct programmes of research and development, and manufacturers, who again give support and advice in the choice and use of available and developing products. A typical sequence of events is

(*a*) the identification and production of a new commodity

(*b*) laboratory and initial field trials, perhaps extending over months or even years

(*c*) engaging the help of a highway authority and carrying out limited scale trials in a working location, and under full exposure to traffic, using normal operatives and plant, and carefully monitoring the work results

(*d*) full-scale use of the product under working conditions, again with a recording of method and performance.

Such trials may be at the expense of the supplier, or in the later stages can involve the client authority in a reasonable part of the costs, preferably with the protection of a guarantee clause in the arrangements.

1.6. Usage of the highway

With the exception of motorways and certain designated special roads, highways are available for use by all classes of traffic, including cyclists, pedestrians and horses. Legislation covers the manufacture and use of vehicles and all aspects of street furniture, signing and the behaviour of road users. Practitioners of highway maintenance need to be familiar, for instance, with the requirements of Chapter 8 of the Traffic Signs Manual[1.3] covering temporary road works signing. Overall, highway authorities have a duty, under section 41 of the Highways Act 1980,[1.4] to ensure that roads are in a safe condition for traffic likely to use them. In recent years a pronounced change has occurred in the methods of distributing goods, resulting in a major increase in the number and gross weight of traffic using the highway. The current maximum vehicle weight permitted without special consent is 38 tonnes, but a further upward increase may well take place to unify the types of vehicle used in Europe. The majority of roads are all purpose facilities, serving both local and through traffic. The carriageways and footways are also available to statutory authorities for the laying and maintenance of necessary pipes and mains, under powers conferred by the Public Utilities and Street Works Act 1950.[1.5] Although all these activities are subject to controlling powers by the highway authority and agent authorities, the overall effect presents the maintenance engineer with a considerable challenge.

1.7. Funding of highway maintenance

Government expenditure on roads is derived from a three-year plan of public expenditure, which is reviewed annually. The Department of Transport minister responsible for roads will compete with other demands made on the available money, and arrive at a listing of approved schemes or cash levels for allocation. Unsuccessful items are deferred for later consideration the following year, or reintroduced if further money becomes available. Strict control is exercised over the total amount of public spending. Councils receive funds from rates generated finance, Rate Support Grant (RSG) and Transport Supplementary Grant (TSG).

RSG is supplied by Government and is calculated by a formula according to such factors as population, road mileage and numbers of children of school age. While this item is intended to cover local road maintenance the councils are not obliged to allocate in the same ratio as the formula,

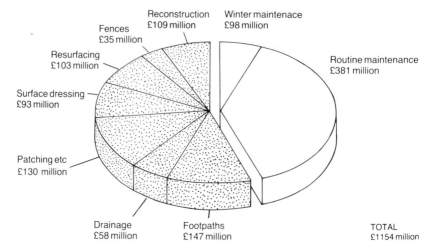

Fig. 1.5. Expenditure on highway activities

and frequently set priorities with a different emphasis. The total grant was £13 775 million in 1988–89, some £1264 million being the allowance for road maintenance. Previous experience has been that some of this grant is diverted (12% in 1987–88).

TSG relates to expenditure on capital works, i.e. for projects of more than local importance. Such schemes are identified in prepared lists of

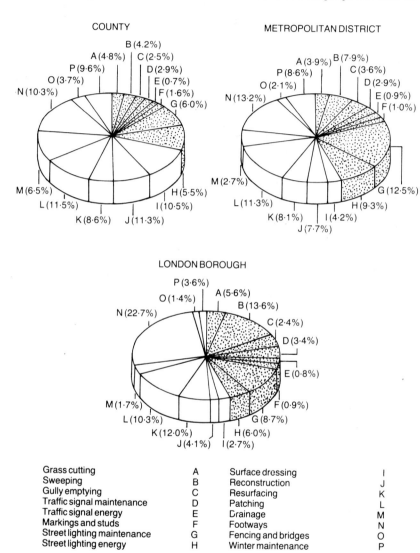

Fig. 1.6. *Typical make-up of the budget for each type of highway authority. Routine maintenance activities (shaded) make up a large proportion of the budget*

Transport Policies and Programmes submitted to the Department of Transport, and giving details of schemes for the next financial year and outlining plans for a further four years. Trunk road maintenance, carried out generally by highway authorities acting as agents for the Department of Transport, is funded separately according to a programme of capital renewal and current maintenance estimates. All other road maintenance is funded from RSG and local rates income. There are also isolated instances of income from toll charges and bridge funds. Arguments are sometimes presented for the acceptance of certain maintenance schemes as qualifying for capital expenditure.

These procedures will change as a consequence of the Local Government Bill and the introduction of community charges in 1990–91, but a new form of roads grant will be introduced, the Roads Programmes Grant.[1.6] An indication of the level of expenditure on the various highway activities is shown in Fig. 1.5,[1.7] and this illustrates the relatively high proportion spent on routine, and the unpredictable winter maintenance elements. A comparison between typical distributions for different locations is given in Fig. 1.6, also taken from an Audit Commission report.

One difficulty arising from the present system is that the allocation of funds within the overall budget is at the discretion of the elected members, whose perception of priorities and decisions may not reflect the most cost effective actions from a road maintenance point of view. It is the job of the maintenance engineer to develop and present arguments to illustrate the importance of this work, and the disproportionate costs of undue delay in carrying out repair treatments. Elements which affect judgement include

(*a*) perceived road condition
(*b*) trends in traffic usage
(*c*) changes in vehicle design and use, particularly with regard to potential damage factors
(*d*) accident statistics
(*e*) incidence of public complaint and litigation
(*f*) plans for development.

The maintenance engineer will need to be aware of these influences, and indeed will be required to input data into the management system used.

1.8. Monitoring road conditions

The importance of reliable information cannot be overestimated, and this is fully appreciated at the national level. Considerable efforts are made to develop and improve methods and equipment to assist in this field. The TRRL in concert with practising County Engineers developed a system for evaluating the general condition of the road network, and the following brief description shows the development of that system.

1.8.1. National Road Maintenance Condition Survey (NRMCS)

Government and highway authority concern about the condition of roads nationwide, was focused by the publication in 1970 of the Marshall Report.[1.8] Adoption of standards recommended in the report were followed for trunk roads and motorways, but these were not implemented elsewhere due to cost. The need for condition information, and a sound basis for applying available road maintenance funds, however, resulted in the setting up of a Standing Committee on Highway Maintenance in 1975, which was charged with the task of developing a workable system for road condition assessment. Commencing in the spring of 1977 (base year) the NRMCS[1.9] has been carried out each year since by participating County Engineers, assisted in the processing of data and interpretation of results by the TRRL and Department of Transport statisticians.

1.8.2. Form of survey

The base year assessment, whatever the condition of the roads at that time, was to be the datum. Clearly this meant that subsequent indications of deterioration would be set against differing starting points in different areas, and might not reflect the true scale of need. In the interests of simplicity and speed, this disadvantage was to be accepted.

Each class of road — trunk, urban principal, urban classified, urban unclassified, rural principal, rural classified, rural unclassified — was to be examined by a system of sampling, and reported separately. Half the sites chosen were to be changed each year in a random manner to avoid bias or pre-knowledge by inspectors. The sites were to be either at equal intervals of total mileage of road type divided by the number of sites required or by selection at random from grid squares.

The condition was to be assessed by experienced engineers and reported on a standard form to ensure, as far as possible, uniformity of approach and reliable results, which were above suspicion.

Data recording was in the form used for the Computerized Highway Assessment of Ratings and Treatments (CHART), and the number of inspections, governed by statistical requirements, originally totalled 3914×100 m lengths. As experience was gained, this figure almost doubled, and obviously the costs of the survey increased. Nevertheless, this approach was regarded as a logical and necessary way of gaining an overall view of the road system, and a vital prerequisite to sensible spending on road maintenance. Results were to be published and to take the form of an analysis of the various defects, weighted by a programme devised by the TRRL, and illustrated by bar charts indicating the confidence limits for each result, as shown in the example in Fig. 1.7.

Successive annual reports resulted in increasing confidence in the validity of the method, and by plotting the mean of each result, an indication of the trend in condition could be gained, both nationally and for individual counties.

The importance of the survey is that arguments can be supported

(*a*) at the ministerial level
(*b*) at committee level
(*c*) at officer level in the allocation of funds to each class of road.

In addition to inspection, some authorities have carried out surveys of structural strength and life expectancy on major roads using the

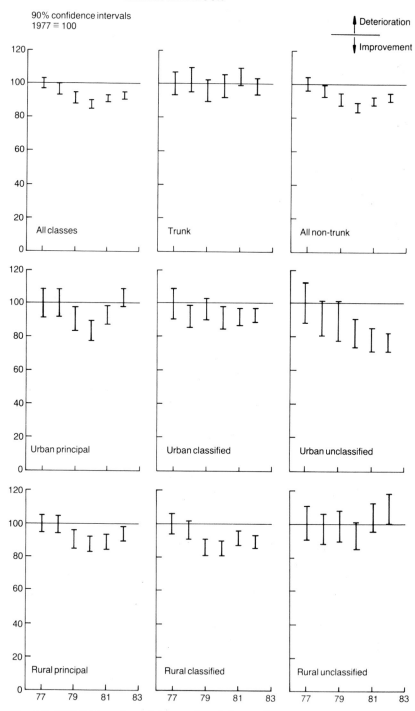

Fig. 1.7. NRMCS road condition results: defects index

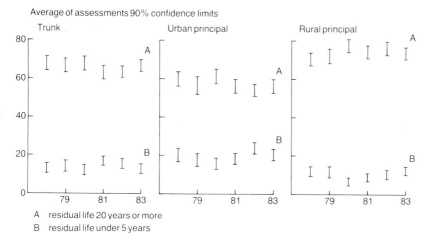

Average of assessments 90% confidence limits

A   residual life 20 years or more
B   residual life under 5 years

Fig. 1.8. NRMCS Deflectograph results: percentage of road length by residual life, 1978–83

deflectograph. This information, shown in Fig. 1.8, has been incorporated in the NRMCS and provides valuable further evidence of highway conditions. (Copies of the full report[1.9] can be obtained from the Department of Transport.)

Initially, the reliability of the results was questioned, and the effects of short-term remedial measures, such as surface dressing, were thought to be influential. With further data, sufficient confidence in the dependability of the method has been built up for reliable conclusions to be drawn. The emerging trend is one of deterioration for most categories of road, due to shortfall in funding and/or maintenance activity, as reported by the Institution of Civil Engineers in 1988.[1.10] An aim of this book is to enliven appreciation of the long-term costs of inappropriate maintenance management, both as direct additional costs, and also the resultant community costs, including accidents, delays, and increased vehicle damage.

1.9. Budgets and planning

At the local level each authority collects information, by means of inspection, concerning the conditions of roads in the area. In the case of major roads, and agency duties for trunk roads, these inspections will involve a systematic method such as CHART. For lesser roads, a visual inspection and the historical knowledge and judgement of the engineers is usual. From this information, a list of required work can be developed, against which estimates are prepared. A review of the overall workload and its cost is then carried out and a preferred order of priorities formulated. Bids are then made either to transport committees or to the Department of Transport, for funding in competition with other demands on finance. The success of these bids determines which schemes go forward to the preparation stage.

For larger maintenance projects, one of the difficulties is the lead time required to reach a stage where a contract can be let, and this problem is further compounded by the arrangements governing each year's cashflow. Since the financial year begins each April, the desirable aim of carrying out works during the summer months is seldom practicable, except for smaller jobs, surfacing operations, and those jobs for which preparation has been done in advance of the work being sanctioned, which entails the risk of abortive effort. The effect of these influences can be that work is opted for which is quick to implement, but this approach may not reflect the most cost effective use of resources. A more flexible attitude from those controlling the allocation of money and its timing should be aimed for.

1.10. Working arrangements and resources

Maintenance has in the past largely depended on direct labour organizations (DLO) employed by the County or District Authority, and under the control of the County Surveyor or his/her equivalent. This method has many advantages, and has developed as a result of the piecemeal nature of many maintenance tasks, and the need for a flexible response to emergencies and variations in weather conditions. In parallel, certain works, which could be clearly defined as contracts, would be tendered for and carried out by contractors supervised by local authority staff or consulting engineers. Examples of such work are carriageway resurfacing, bridge painting and specialist materials testing and repairs.

A further method, which proved satisfactory for the maintenance of principal road structures in London, was the appointment in competition of a term contractor. A schedule of rates, agreed at the time of tender, was prepared for items of plant as used and held on standby, and labour rates based on the Federation of Civil Engineering Contractor's Schedule of Dayworks[1.11] formed a basis for payment. The tender included percentage variations on the listed rates. This arrangement had the advantage of drawing on the resources and skills of a large contracting organization, without incurring the costs of full time employment. For maintenance work, where workload and the type of work can vary considerably, this system can offer benefits, but needs care in the preparation of documents, and an experienced supervisory team.

1.11. Sources of work

Each highway authority has responsibility for the roads within its area, and the nature of maintenance work and specified requirements will usually vary according to the ownership and importance of each route. Definitions of the various categories of road are given in the Highways Act 1980, Chapter 66,[1.4] and provisions for maintenance costs are defined. Work to the highway results from

(a) routine inspections and assessment procedures
(b) accident reports
(c) public complaint.

The size of workload will also change due to

(a) handover of new construction
(b) boundary changes

(*c*)   dedication of privately owned streets or structures

(*d*)   adoption of highway items from other owners, for example, transfer of railway or canal bridges.

Maintenance organizations need a system for the handover and registration of all new responsibilities, so that the boundaries and cost allocation can be defined at the outset. The condition of all new acquisitions should form part of the negotiations, and all available record information should be included in the transaction. Such a system needs developed links between legal, valuation and maintenance departments, and a constant review of highway property and information is necessary. Changes in highway status are the subject of orders issued by the Minister of Transport, and copies should be provided to the maintenance organization.

1.12. Staffing

There are a number of alternative arrangements to be considered when deciding the allocation of staff to maintenance functions, and the advantages of each are not necessarily common to all systems. Judgement is therefore needed to suit the framework and operational system to local circumstances. Controlling factors are as follows.

(*a*)   The size of the maintenance workload.

(*b*)   Estimation of finance across a number of years, and the profile and dependability of these estimates.

(*c*)   Availability of existing staff and potential for transfer from other duties.

(*d*)   Opportunity for recruitment of any staffing shortfall.

(*e*)   Availability of backup organization such as administrative staff, design and contract preparation units, legal advice, labour and plant resources, inspection staff and facilities, and materials testing facilities.

Large organizations are likely to be supported in many of the above areas by specialist departments, but they, and smaller authorities, engage the services of consultants and contractors to level out peaks in demand, and for specialist activities.

The initial step is to decide whether the work is to be undertaken directly or to be delegated, wholly or in part, to others. In recent years, legislation has been passed which is designed to ensure that works such as highway maintenance are subject to competition (Local Government Planning and Land Act 1980),[1.12] and the thresholds above which works have to be tendered for has been progressively lowered. The requirements are at present that all works costing more than £25 000 and at least 60% of works costing less than £25 000 (since 1 April 1988) shall be subject to competitive tendering.

The Department of Transport has also carried out experimental contracts (lane rental schemes) in which the time taken to complete a scheme is compared with that allowed in the contract, and rewarded or penalized for under or over running. Clearly an emphasis on workmanship and safety standards is necessary to gain full advantage from this approach.[1.13]

Many offices integrate maintenance activities with design and construction teams. This has an advantage in conserving resources, and can help to ensure that early feedback of design faults takes place. Such direct involvement in the whole-life appreciation of structural integrity is likely to show long-term economic benefits, and lead to improvements in the initial detailing of projects.

1.13. Measurement of performance

Whichever system of works implementation is used, management is responsible for ensuring the quality of the work done, and the payment of the appropriate costs. The system of control must be capable of demonstrating that acceptable standards in these areas are achieved. The County Surveyor, or equivalent, will be required to produce evidence of the satisfactory working of his maintenance procedures to audit staff within his own authority, and on occasion to the District Auditor. Where possible, yardsticks of performance should be developed and agreed between management and staff representatives. Of fundamental importance is the preservation of records covering work done, and labour, plant and materials used. Such records also form valuable reference information when reviewing the effectiveness of working methods and techniques, and as an aid to future costing. Larger organizations will benefit from the compilation of computer records and retrieval systems for this type of long-term storage of information.

For most work, a vital factor in assuring quality is the availability and use of a materials testing facility. For works of any scale, a preplanned programme, stating the frequency and methods of testing to be adopted, should be prepared, and such plans must also indicate the action to be taken in the event of sample failure.

1.14. Maintenance administration

The response needed from maintenance organizations can be summarized as follows.

(a) To examine and validate their own appraisals of local conditions.
(b) To prepare realistic works programmes in order of priority.
(c) To determine levels of finance required.
(d) To prepare arguments that justify proposed schemes and costings, together with the consequences of alternative courses of action.
(e) To ensure that actions taken demonstrate the advantages claimed.
(f) To check and regulate the management and working practices to give best return on investment, with particular reference to proven competitiveness.
(g) To improve the gathering, recording and use of available data concerning all areas of responsibility.

Many factors impinge upon the achievement of the above criteria, some of which are discussed in later chapters, and it is necessary for the engineer

Table 1.3. Public utility activity as quoted by the National Joint Group for 1982–83

Public utility	New and replacement mains: km	New and replacement services	Small openings
Electricity	4 000	200 000	217 000
Gas	5 457	767 000	544 000
Telecommunications	3 150	467 000	74 000
Water	3 200	230 000	536 000
Sewers	2 500	—	—
Total	18 307	1 664 000	1 371 000

engaged in maintenance to be aware of the broader issues affecting the success of his bids. To this end, information on government and local council policies should be circulated.

1.15. Impact of public utility works

In addition to wear and tear from traffic, carriageways and footways are subject to disruption by statutory authorities in the course of laying and maintenance of their pipes and mains. Considerable research has been carried out to find ways of countering the severe damaging effects of trenches within the highway, and model specifications have been developed[1.14] to guide contractors in this work. The results have been disappointing, and the level of concern was such that a review panel was set up to examine the operation of the Public Utilities and Street Works Act 1950 chaired by Professor Horne. A report was formulated giving recommended changes in the procedures, and proposing a change in the liability for the reinstatements.[1.15] These recommendations are as yet unadopted. An impression of the scale of disruption can be gained from Table 1.3.

If the proposals contained in the report are translated into law, there will be a need for improved inspection routines, sophisticated registration of works, and control systems for all works affecting the highway. Future developments are likely to be a greater need for highway assessment techniques, and research and development methods for installing services with less disruption, such as trenchless excavation and purpose made comprehensive service ducts. Considerable changes are necessary in the collection and dissemination of data affecting the highway, and the coordination of consecutive operations within and adjacent to roads, which are seen by the public to be both destructive and wasteful of time, effort and materials, must be improved.

References

1.1.   DEPARTMENT OF TRANSPORT. *Transport statistics for Great Britain*, 1977–1987. Her Majesty's Stationery Office, London, 1987.

1.2. AUDIT COMMISSION. *The management of highway maintenance.* Audit Commission, Bristol, 1988.

1.3. *Traffic signs manual*, ch. 8. Her Majesty's Stationery Office, London, 1965 (plus amendments).

1.4. *Highways Act 1980*, section 41. Her Majesty's Stationery Office, London.

1.5. *Public Utilities and Street Works Act 1950.* Her Majesty's Stationery Office, London.

1.6. BLANKS H.J. The financing of roads. *J. Instn Highw. Transpn*, 1988, **35**, 8–9.

1.7. AUDIT COMMISSION. *Improving the condition of local authority roads.* Audit Commission, Bristol, 1988.

1.8. MARSHALL A.H. *Report of the Committee of Highway Maintenance.* Her Majesty's Stationery Office, London, 1970.

1.9. DEPARTMENT OF TRANSPORT. *National road maintenance condition survey.* DTp, London, 1977 (and annually since).

1.10. INSTITUTION OF CIVIL ENGINEERS. *The state of roads and bridges in the United Kingdom.* ICE, London, 1988.

1.11. FEDERATION OF CIVIL ENGINEERING CONTRACTORS. *Schedule of Dayworks.* FCEC, London, 1983.

1.12. *Local Government Planning and Land Act 1980.* Her Majesty's Stationery Office, London.

1.13. BODNAR V.A. Lane rental — the DTp view. *J. Instn Highw. Transpn*, 1988, **35**, 22–26.

1.14. DEPARTMENT OF THE ENVIRONMENT. *A model agreement and specification.* Her Majesty's Stationery Office, London, 1975.

1.15. HORNE M.R. *Roads and the utilities.* Her Majesty's Stationery Office, London, 1985.

2

High profile maintenance

For the general public, nothing attracts attention more, or with more notable success, than the neglect of the following general maintenance activities

(*a*) highway cleansing
(*b*) drainage
(*c*) grass cutting, hedge trimming and tree pruning.

Such reaction is understandable in political terms, but the allocation of funds should also be considered in the context of overall spending, and relative importance to the maintenance criteria discussed in Chapter 1. In grouping these topics together, the intention is to draw attention to a number of interacting aspects. Annual expenditure on the group amounts to some 12% (County) and 15% (Metropolitan District) of the respective highway budgets, and the relationship to other work can be seen in Fig. 2.1.

2.1. Cleansing

Neglect of cleansing soon leads to a poor appearance, and of greater importance are the effects that this can have on safety. Among the factors to be considered are the following.

(*a*) Accumulated debris on the highway can obscure signs, causing driver uncertainty.
(*b*) Such debris, aided by rainwater, forms a grinding paste, which erodes the microtexture necessary for good low speed skidding resistance, thereby shortening the acceptable life of the existing surfacing.
(*c*) Vehicle tyre wear is increased.
(*d*) The risk of vehicle damage, particularly windscreens, is increased with a consequent increase in accident potential and associated costs.
(*e*) Highway drainage is adversely affected in both freedom of run-off and accelerated silting of gullies and pipework.
(*f*) Resulting ponding on the carriageway can be a traffic hazard, causing aquaplaning at high speeds, and the formation of potentially dangerous ice in winter months.

(*g*)   Sensitive areas, such as bridge expansion joints, become obstructed and self destructive (see Chapter 11).

(*h*)   High levels of litter are not only unsightly, but can also form an environmental health risk, particularly when generated from food products. Unattended rubbish in litter bins and the ubiquitous thin plastic bags become targets for rodents and similar scavengers, causing further problems.

Clearly a strong case exists for effective, regular highway cleansing. There are also advantages to be gained if cleansing staff develop a system of reporting obvious defects, such as accident damage, to the relevant maintenance section.

2.2. Operational needs and problems
Efficient cleansing depends on overcoming many of the following factors

(*a*)   traffic densities and speeds — in many urban areas, cleansing can only be accomplished by night work

(*b*)   obstruction from parked vehicles

(*c*)   the supply of appropriate equipment for the job

(*d*)   design of cleansing routines which ensure coverage of the planned routes at the required intervals and to agreed standards

(*e*)   procedures which ensure safety of operatives and the public at all times

(*f*)   system of monitoring which identifies shortfall in standards or

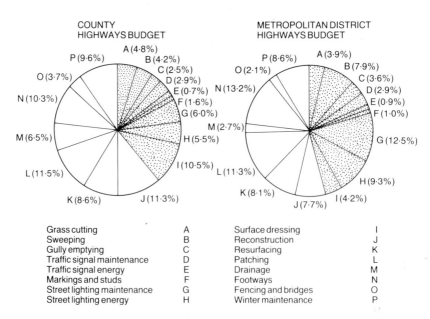

Grass cutting	A	Surface dressing	I
Sweeping	B	Reconstruction	J
Gully emptying	C	Resurfacing	K
Traffic signal maintenance	D	Patching	L
Traffic signal energy	E	Drainage	M
Markings and studs	F	Footways	N
Street lighting maintenance	G	Fencing and bridges	O
Street lighting energy	H	Winter maintenance	P

Fig. 2.1. Division of the highway maintenance budget

particular problems, e.g. special measures to be taken in areas which cannot be reached by normal cleansing vehicles, such as pedestrian subways, footbridges and enclosures between guardrails

(g) guidance in dealing with special problems, such as graffiti (see section 11.21.3).

Some areas demand preliminary scavenging before employing say grass cutters, or may require particularly frequent clearance, e.g. street markets, approaches to sports stadia and transport termini, or highway areas of special significance to tourism. Agreement of the standards to be adopted, between the Council and/or highway authority and the maintenance managers, is fundamental to the preparation of a cleansing system.

2.3. Legal aspects of cleansing

Highway cleansing is divided into two broad categories

(a) amenity cleansing — that needed for environmental and health reasons

(b) the highway element — that needed for the safe operation and the preservation of the fabric of the highway.

The Control of Pollution Act 1974[2.1] imposes a duty on the highway authority for the *highway* element of the cleansing, and on the district or borough authority for the *amenity* element. The work may, however, be delegated by the highway authority to agents. Division of costs cannot be accurate because the distinction between similar work is blurred and affected by local policies. Many authorities adopt an agreed formula to solve the problem, which is applied to the summation of all related cleansing costs.

Cleanliness tends to be a subjective assessment of the public's requirements, and will vary considerably even for similar locations, due to differing reactions to financial constraints, activities within the area, and the tolerance or otherwise of the inhabitants.

Justification of standards and the ability to demonstrate a reasonable compliance with legislation depend heavily on the preparation of a clear system.

2.4. Cleansing needs

Highway cleansing needs depend on several factors

(a) the action of rainfall, and the drainage regime, e.g. whether the road is kerbed or not

(b) the action of traffic — high speed densely trafficked roads tend to be self cleansing except for heavier objects, which need to be scavenged

(c) the policy objectives as perceived by the local politicians and their advisers

(d) the location of the road considered, and any adjacent activities, e.g. building developments, farming activity, market sites and tourist areas.

Table 2.1. Highway cleansing frequency (LAA Code)

Class of road or location*	Cleansing frequency
Rural Unkerbed — no positive drainage Kerbed — with positive drainage Category I and II Category III and IV	As the need arises Twice per year Once per year
Urban Town centres and principal shopping centres as defined locally Category II and III Category IV	Weekly Monthly Four times per year

* Category I: motorway.
 Category II: primary routes.
 Category III: main and secondary distributors.
 Category IV: local roads.

The standards and routines adopted need to reflect these variations and to be adjusted according to local experience, and the cost parameters decided upon. However, an indication of average requirements is given in the LAA (Local Authority Association) Code of Good Practice Section 17,[2.2] which divides activity by class of road and between urban and rural locations as shown in Table 2.1.

2.5. Cleansing methods and costs

Cleansing methods depend on the scale of work (area/mileage of carriageway), the frequency proposed, and the standard to be achieved in relation to known local conditions. The majority of cleansing is carried out by lorry mounted brush/suction equipment, but footways, town centres, and areas with restricted access will require hand or light machine methods. The factors outlined in section 2.2 will have a major influence on the cleansing plan, especially in urban areas. Route length is a function of vehicle capacity, the position of disposal points and past experience of the volume of solids to be expected, and may also be affected by cross boundary and dual carriageway rationalization considerations between adjacent authorities. The aim of the cleansing plan is to achieve efficiency by

(a) achieving the target standards set
(b) remaining within the cost levels allocated
(c) regular review of labour, plant and methods in relation to (a) and (b).

The monitoring of performance against clearly defined targets was emphasized in a study of routine maintenance[2.3] and significant factors were seen to be as follows.

(a) The availability of comparative costs between direct and contract labour.

(b) The provision of an inventory on which to base achievement monitoring.

(c) Comparison of actual work done with that registered as done ensuring adherence to specified standards.

An important conclusion was that considerable savings could accrue from the introduction of improved control and from a systematic approach based on a more informed appraisal of the size of the task, and that such savings could be of critical benefit to areas of structural maintenance.

Highway designers should consider the future needs of cleansing when preparing schemes, and realise that the inclusion of irregular surfaces and areas, which cannot be reached by normal cleansing machinery, will add to the overall cost of maintenance.

Cleansing costs are subject to wide variation, due to differences in adopted standards, location and methods. Some indication of the range of costs can be seen in Table 2.2.[2.3]

2.6. Drainage

The importance of adequate drainage to the structural integrity of a road has been appreciated for many centuries. Roman engineers ensured the longevity of their constructions by attention to this aspect, and the use of self draining materials continues to this day for sub-base construction. The study of pavement drainage for both flexible and rigid forms has resulted in the conclusion that the construction should be treated as a series of permeable layers, and that added precautions are necessary to protect the sub-grade.[2.4,2.5] The introduction of membranes has helped to control the migration of fine material from the sub-grade (pumping), and also indicates that relatively small migrations of fines from the sub-grade

Table 2.2. Cleansing costs

Activity	Location	Average: £	Lowest: £	Highest: £	Lower quartile: £	Upper quartile: £
Mechanical sweeping (costs per channel km swept per occasion)	Counties	7·95	3·32	13·79	5·85	9·63
	London boroughs	5·95	1·12	14·24	2·90	7·00
Gulley emptying (cost per gulley emptied per occasion)	Counties	1·73	0·72	2·81	1·42	2·01
	London boroughs	2·78	0·99	6·68	1·59	3·53

into voids in the sub-base can seriously reduce the capacity of the sub-base to act as a lateral drain.[2.6] Road Note 29[2.7] advises that the water table should be prevented from rising to within 600 mm of the formation level, and emphasizes the need for effective subsoil drainage in frost susceptible materials. In carrying out works to surfacing, care must be exercised if these drainage features are to be preserved.

Some examples affecting the maintenance engineer are

(a)   ensuring clearance of sub-surface drain holes in gulley frames
(b)   being aware of the presence and purpose of 'no fines' concrete kerb bedding, which permits lateral drainage from lower levels of road construction
(c)   ensuring that water traps are not formed at transverse joints by metalwork
(d)   similarly, sub-surface ponding can result from changes in bituminous material permeability, and thought needs to be given to the drainage falls where this is likely to occur.

These aspects relate to the structural integrity of the road pavement. Increasingly, the maintenance engineer will be called upon to take responsibility for the effects of surface water discharge, with particular reference to pollution control. Obvious examples, such as the accidental spillage of dangerous transported substances are at one end of the scale, and usually attract sufficient local attention to ensure some remedial action. Precautions may also be taken to exclude such possibilities, as in the case of some vehicular tunnel by-laws. At the day-to-day level, there is increasing concern, particularly in areas adjacent to heavily trafficked roads, about the steady flow of pollutants such as lead, zinc and chemical fertilizers, which are known to be carried into the land drainage system. Analysis of dust samples taken adjacent to the M4 in London, and at the Aston Expressway in Birmingham, has indicated significant levels of lead in highway detritus. Attention to methods of filtration is a factor to be included in future highway maintenance for such problem areas.

2.7. Categories of drainage

Highway drainage falls into two distinct categories

(a)   subsoil drainage — to sustain the stability of pavement support within the design tolerances
(b)   surface water run-off — to remove water from areas of the carriageway or footway, where its presence would be harmful or dangerous to users or lead to deterioration.

In category (a) are measures such as porous pipes, lateral and vertical layers of granular material and man-made fabrics and membranes. Such drainage techniques are largely built-in features of the design, and do not lend themselves to routine maintenance. Their presence and the intended mode of operation must be known and understood by the maintenance engineer, since most systems become clogged in five to ten years, and will need replacing. Obvious surface signs, such as flooding, or instability of pavements, may be the first warnings of system failure. Perhaps the most critical aspect of this drainage is the provision of detailed 'as-built' information to reduce the risk of inadvertent disruption of the intended operation during subsequent maintenance works.

Category (*b*) can be summarized as the routine cleansing of gullies, pipework, chambers and ditches forming the immediate highway drainage system.

2.8. Legal aspects of drainage

Some legal aspects concerned with drainage are included in the Highways Act 1980.[2.8]

(*a*) Sections 100 and 101 confer powers to enable the construction, diversion, or filling of drains and ditches necessary for the preservation of the highway. These clauses also cover drains on adjacent land, which could endanger the highway, and the payment of compensation for damage suffered by an adjacent landowner as a result of highway authority actions.

(*b*) A general liability for maintenance and removal of obstructions is covered by clauses 41 and 150, and persistent flooding could lead to litigation.

(*c*) Clauses 151 and 163 confer powers on a 'competent authority' to take action with regard to soil or refuse being washed into the streets, and in particular causing blockage of drains, and powers to control water falling from buildings on to highway users and 'so far as is reasonable practicable' to prevent water from flowing on to the highway from adjacent premises.

2.9. Water on the highway

Water on the highway has many implications and, in the main, is undesirable because for traffic

(*a*) friction between tyre and road surface is reduced
(*b*) contact between tyre and road surface can be reduced at higher speeds (aquaplaning)
(*c*) in freezing conditions, an even greater risk of skidding arises
(*d*) ponding can create sudden and dangerous changes in road holding
(*e*) spray affects visibility

and for the highway structure, the ingress of water can

(*f*) lead to disruption on freezing (frost heave)
(*g*) cause corrosion, particularly when carrying corrosive elements, such as de-icing salts
(*h*) promote aggregate/alkali reaction in concrete
(*i*) weaken underlying foundations
(*j*) cause unsightly staining
(*k*) encourage weed and algae growth.

The aim of most highway surfacings, therefore, is to be impervious. The majority of surface water run-off is carried to the sides of the road by

Table 2.3. Example of drainage falls required in rolled asphalt carriageways to BS 594

For roads with a straight cross fall
   not more than 3%
For cambered roads, the average fall from crown to channel
   not more than 3%
   not less than 2%
Longitudinal fall in channels
   not less than 0·8%

design falls, discharged into ditches, or contained by kerbs and directed to gullies along graded channels (see Table 2.3). The design of drainage is beyond the scope of this book, but the maintenance engineer should have a working knowledge of drainage principles, available fittings, and equipment. Most drains rely either on the self cleansing flow of water, or are designed to be sufficiently oversized to permit a reasonable time lapse between cleansing operations without impairing their effectiveness. Many drains are fitted with gulley pots incorporating grit traps, and these are intended to delay the need for cleansing. Whatever the composition of the system, cleansing routines should indicate clearly the work to be done, the frequency for that work, the equipment and labour to be used, and most importantly any safety measures and equipment required.

2.10. Gully cleansing

The frequency of cleansing will ensure, ideally, that gullies are emptied before pipework becomes blocked. Wide variations in need result from position, gully design, volume of run-off and cleanliness of the highway.

It is not practicable to assign individual frequencies, and a routine for each area will be based on local experience, unless prescribed, as for instance where agents act for the Department of Transport. Many authorities will base their routine on the LAA Code of Good Practice[2.2] which suggests a frequency of twice per year on average. However, there is clearly a difference in circumstances between a rural location and a busy shopping centre, and the aim should be to provide a service based on a measurable level of need. One proposal given in a recent review was to calculate the ratio of the number of blockages reported to the total number of gullies, and to use this as a yardstick of cleansing performance. Table 2.4 indicates the present requirements of the Department of Transport, and this could also be used as a basis for planning non-agency work routines.

2.11. Pipework

Maintenance of the system is largely the inspection and clearance of any blockages found. Smaller pipes are rodded or jetted, and larger pipes may require manual clearance. Inspection techniques include direct observation, the use of lights and mirrors, and increasingly the employment of trolley-mounted video cameras. Whenever chambers or drainage systems

Table 2.4. Drainage system cleansing frequencies

Item	Inspection frequency*	Correction of defects†	
		Category 1‡	Category 2§
(a) Surface furniture	Annually	Immediate — 24 h (temporary) 28 days (permanent)	6 months or more in programmed works
(b) Pipes	Once every 10 years	As (a)	12 months or more in programmed works
(c) Gullies, catchpits and interceptors	As (a)	Immediate — 24 h	As (b)
(d) Ditches	Once every 5 years	As (c)	As (a)
(e) Piped grips and grips	No set interval	As (a)	As (a)
(f) Filter drains	As (d)	As (d)	As (b)
(g) Culverts over 3 m dia. or 2 to 3 m dia. but less than 1 m cover or 0·9 m dia. in corrugated metal, all including aprons and headwalls	As (a)	As (a)	As (a)
(h) Balancing ponds 1. No outflow control	Once every 2 years	As (a)	As (a)
2. With outflow control	6 monthly	As (a)	As (a)
(i) Sluices and tidal flaps	6 monthly	As (a)	As (a)
(j) Pumps	According to manufacturers' instructions		

* Inspection frequencies shown are the normal requirements of the Department of Transport, and variations are subject to agreement.

† All action taken to be promptly recorded and retained for 6 years.

‡ Defects which require prompt attention, because they represent an immediate or imminent hazard, or because there is a risk of short-term structural deterioration.

§ All action taken to be promptly recorded and retained for 6 years.

are to be entered, safety procedures and equipment must be considered, since accumulations of gas have proved fatal. In some systems, remote storms can lead to sudden surcharging of drains, and an advance warning drill must be instituted. Staff must, therefore, be trained and alerted to the potential hazards of this work, and be provided with the necessary protective equipment, and a means of communication.

2.12. Street furniture

Many designs are available for direct and side entry drainage, and special types are manufactured for restricted sites, such as bridge decks and underpasses. A recent innovation for general highway use is the precast kerb unit incorporating the drainage pipework ('Beany Block'). From the maintenance aspect, important features for any furniture are ease of access, ease of replacement, availability, cost of replacement, safety (particularly with regard to pedestrians and cyclists), compatibility with normal cleansing methods and durability.

Although designed to take highway loading, gulley and manhole frames will suffer if the bedding proves inadequate, and depressed or broken fitments will result. The designer can assist, when siting the drainage system, by positioning surface covers out of the wheeltracks, thus enabling work to be carried out without double lane closure or risk to operatives. The maintenance depot needs to keep a stock of standard furniture, together with plates and signing for emergency temporary actions.

2.13. Highway landscaping

Highway landscaping is seen by some as a wasteful extra to essential engineering requirements. There is no doubt, however, that carefully planned 'soft' treatments can both enhance appearance, blend the harsh lines of a highway into the surroundings, and provide cheaper protection against erosion than alternative materials. Trees and hedges also serve as useful demarcation, and can inhibit off-road parking and fly tipping. The disadvantages are mainly concerned with increased maintenance, and these will be a function of

(a)   the type of cover chosen, e.g. grass, gorse or trees
(b)   the sensitivity of the site in terms of public perception
(c)   engineering considerations such as safety hazards, root effects on drains and structures, blockage by leaves and accessibility for machinery.

Many of these are covered by legislation, which may be considered under the headings of

(a)   obstruction to vehicles
(b)   obstruction of highway visibility
(c)   damage to adjacent property.

2.14. Legal aspects of landscaping

Although the maximum height of a vehicle is not prescribed in the Construction and Use Regulations, the Highway Authority must ensure that damage is not caused to vehicles by overhanging vegetation. Section 154 of the Highway Act 1980 requires that, 'Any tree or vegetation, which in the view of a competent authority forms a hazard or interferes with the view of drivers or obstructs lighting, may be the subject of a notice by the authority for removal within 14 days, failing which the authority may remove and recover costs from the person in default.'

Section 79 confers powers on the Highway Authority enabling it to serve notice on landowners for the removal of trees, shrubs, or other vegetation, which is regarded as an obstruction to necessary sight lines at corners and junctions.

The planting of tree shrubs and grass verges within the highway is controlled under sections 64 (2b and 2d) and section 96, and of particular importance are sub-sections 96 (6, 7 and 8) covering obstruction to the highway and damage to adjacent property. Further control may be exercised under section 141, where planting has taken place in the highway or within 15 feet ($\simeq 4 \cdot 6$ metres) of the centre line of a made-up carriageway. Adjacent landowners may however, plant within the highway, subject to the issue of a licence by the highway authority under section 142.

Hedge trimmings, and particularly those of the hawthorn variety, can be a nuisance if left in the carriageway. The Cyclist's Touring Club has drawn attention to this[2.9] and recommended the use of section 148(c) of the Highway Act 1980[2.8] and section 1 of the Litter Act 1983[2.10] in any claims for injury or damage. The attention of contractors and hedge owners is drawn to this legislation, the liability for clearance of trimmings being initially on the person carrying out the work.

2.15. Grass cutting, and the trimming of trees and hedges

Grass cutting, and the trimming of trees and hedges may be divided into two aspects — safety and amenity — and the cost of work will as a result fall either into the highway budget, or as a public health element. Maintenance policy will be determined by location and the level of finance allocated, since densely populated residential areas may demand a higher level of attention than say motorway embankments. A cycle of maintenance will therefore aim to satisfy public opinion as well as necessary safety needs. In recent years, the need for economy has reduced the frequency of routine cutting, especially on motorways, and an indication of the present recommendations for this type of work is as follows.

2.15.1. Department of Transport code of practice for routine maintenance

The DTp code of practice for routine maintenance[2.3] recommends that

(a) grass should be cut not more than once per season, unless agreed or in locations where sight lines, signs or safety are jeopardized, in which case action should be taken within five days

(b) the use of chemical sprays and retardants should be strictly controlled and used only as permitted by the DTp and on such weeds as prescribed in the Weeds Acts 1959;[2.11] attention to the agreed areas of conservation should comply with agreements made with the relevant bodies

(c)   trees and hedges should be inspected annually, with the adjacent highway and in detail every five years to check stability and soundness; they should be cut only as necessary to preserve sight lines, safety at bends and visibility of signs.

2.15.2. County and local roads (LAA Code of Good Practice)

Rural practice as recommended in the LAA code of good practice[2.2] is that

(a)   grass should be cut to provide visibility areas and pedestrian refuge, according to the rate of growth; all other areas should be cut at least once in three years
(b)   chemical sprays should be used to a minimum to achieve specific results, and in accordance with manufacturers' instructions
(c)   trees and hedges should be trimmed once a year, or when required to preserve visibility; trees, whether privately owned or the responsibility of the highway authority, should be inspected annually and pruned to maintain headroom and safety; notice of required action should be given to adjacent tree owners.

In urban areas grass cutting is required more often to produce a standard acceptable to the public; a minimum of five times per year is likely to be needed. The recommendations for the use of chemical sprays and the trimming of trees and hedges in urban areas are as for rural practice.

The importance of specialist inspection of trees means that engineers should have access to an arboriculturist, both to confirm safety aspects, particularly after storms, and to advise on such matters as pruning, root pruning and suitable varieties for restocking in the highway context.

2.16. Costs of grass cutting

The costs of the grass cutting will vary widely due to factors such as

(a)   the size of the area covered
(b)   the ratio of rural to urban area
(c)   seasonal growth rates and rainfall influences
(d)   decisions on the methods and equipment to be used
(e)   frequency adopted for each operation.

Table 2.5 indicates present unit costs for urban and rural locations.

Table 2.5. Unit costs for grass cutting (derived during review by the Audit Commission in 1988)

Activity	Location	Average: £	Lowest: £	Highest: £	Lower quartile: £	Upper quartile: £
Grass cutting (m^2 of urban grass per occasion)	Counties	1·9	0·7	3·9	1·1	2·7
	London boroughs	1·2	0·5	3·0	0·7	1·5

2.17. Guard railing and fences

Guard railing, barriers and fencing may be divided into several types, according to purpose, as follows

(a) those designed to absorb vehicular impact, which are used most extensively on the median strips of high speed roads, and as protection to vulnerable items, such as bridge piers and lighting columns, or to retain traffic on elevated structures and bridges

(b) those designed to restrain or guide pedestrian movement, usually in urban areas at controlled crossings, and in busy shopping centres on multi-purpose roads

(c) those designed to enclose highway land, for instance to prevent the straying of animals on to motorways, or to act as a boundary to the highway.

Category (a) is further divided into tensioned beams (i.e. tensioned corrugated beams and rectangular hollow section beams) and untensioned beams (i.e. open box beams and blocked out beams). Details of the required methods of fixing and positioning for these types are given in Department of Transport Technical Memorandum H9/73. From a maintenance point of view, it is most important that repairs are carried out in strict accordance with the design details included with the above document, with particular regard to retensioning tensioned beams and the use of approved components. Following damage, inspection and emergency action to clear distorted sections is necessary, and the condition of adjacent posts and rail sections should be inspected. If, for any reason, it is suspected that the safety fence has not performed satisfactorily, then these initial inspection reports could be important in establishing the behaviour of the fence. Category (c) may also be used as an anti-glare or sound barrier installation.

Maintenance of all these types of fencing consists of

(a) routine paint or preservative treatments. In many cases, fencing will be galvanized on delivery, and will be left unpainted at least for a period. This assists with the adhesion of any subsequent protective painting, otherwise, an etch primer is necessary before undercoating new zinc coatings (see BS 5493:1977 (para. 11.3.2))

(b) inspection and reporting of defects and damage

(c) repair and replacement of damaged sections, posts and foundations or holding down bolts.

Persistent damage to sections of fencing should be investigated, and the possibility of protective measures considered. For instance, the use of high safety kerbs on corners can prevent damage from over riding vehicles (see Chapter 4, Fig. 4.20, for this type of kerb).

2.18. Other sources of complaint

Several other topics attract regular public attention, among the most frequent being noise and vibration. Complaints usually emanate from roadside dwellers, concerned about deterioration in living conditions, or the suspected effects on property. Measures which may be tried to alleviate such problems include the following.

(a) Improving the road surface (e.g. laying a more expensive wearing course such as friction course material, see Chapter 3, Part II) may be beneficial. This treatment not only improves the riding quality, thereby reducing vehicle generated noise and vibration, but has also shown marked reduction in tyre noise.

(b) Monitoring of roadside structures may indicate whether damage is continuing, but some historical information concerning crack development, traffic patterns, and other buildings in the area, should be sought. Studies indicate that damage from traffic vibration is rare if the building is adequately constructed, and other reasons for deterioration should be investigated.

(c) The erection of noise screens, constructed in timber, concrete or metal panelling, either free standing or attached to existing guard railing, has offered some relief, as do trees and shrubs in the growing season.

(d) Complaints should always be investigated to establish the cause of noise, since this can be a valuable early warning of potentially costly or dangerous developments. Common examples are insecure expansion joint plates, loosened lighting column outreaches and broken or depressed manhole covers.

In urban areas, splashing of pedestrians can be troublesome and is a function of traffic speed, surface condition, weather, and the effectiveness of surface water drainage. The judgement of the maintenance engineer is needed when assessing the relative merits of competing road improvement schemes, and the use of aids, such as surface profile measuring equipment, may help to quantify such amenity factors. The pressures exerted by the public are also a viable means of arriving at priorities, since they pay the cost, but are best backed up with measurable criteria and information.

2.19. Special highway problems

The presence of travellers and homeless people camping within the boundaries of the highway, in some cases within and under highway structures, can represent a safety risk and will usually lead to additional maintenance duties. Although, initially a matter for the police and magistrates, in terms of possible obstruction and trespass, such situations are likely to escalate into politically sensitive issues, in both the urban and rural locations. From the point of view of the maintenance organization, there are the following considerations

(a) potential damage to the highway, or structures over the highway, particularly from fire

(b) the development of a health risk due to accumulation of rubbish, and in some cases excreta

(c) danger to encamped people and highway users due to the proximity of traffic, and unrestrained animals.

Among the practical steps which have been taken to alleviate the above problems, are

(*a*)   the provision of properly constructed parking areas for travellers
(*b*)   defensive measures and modifications to the highway design such as mounding, ditches and additional fencing or heavy duty posts.

In the event of unauthorized occupation of highway property, action by the Sheriff's Office may take place, in which case, some back up services may be called on from the maintenance organization to install some of the measures described in (*b*). Such duties need to be handled sympathetically, and the aftermath can involve considerable clearance of rubbish. In extreme circumstances, care is needed to protect the workforce from any health risks, and these duties are best performed by machine plant. An increased frequency of inspection, cleansing of covered areas, and liaison between affected parties, including representatives of the people directly involved, is normally necessary.

References
2.1.   *The Control of Pollution Act, 1974*. Her Majesty's Stationery Office, London.
2.2.   LOCAL AUTHORITY ASSOCIATIONS. *Highway maintenance code of good practice*, section 17. Association of County Councils, London, 1983.
2.3.   AUDIT COMMISSION. *The management of highway maintenance*. Her Majesty's Stationery Office, London, 1988.
2.4.   GRACE H. Sub-surface drainage of road pavements. *Symposium on unbound aggregates in roads*. University of Nottingham, 1981.
2.5.   ROY M. Drainage of a road pavement. *Symposium on unbound aggregates in roads*. University of Nottingham, 1981.
2.6.   INGOLD T.S. The role of geotextiles in sub-surface drainage of pavements. *Symposium on unbound aggregates in roads*. University of Nottingham, 1981.
2.7.   DEPARTMENT OF TRANSPORT. *Road note 29*, 3rd edn. Her Majesty's Stationery Office, London, 1970.
2.8.   *Highways Act, 1980*. Her Majesty's Stationery Office, London.
2.9.   CHURCHMAN J. A thorn in the side. *Cycletouring*, 1988, Oct.–Nov. C.T.C., Godalming, Surrey.
2.10. *The Litter Act, 1983*, section 1. Her Majesty's Stationery Office, London.
2.11. *The Weeds Act, 1959*. Her Majesty's Stationery Office, London.

3

Carriageway maintenance

The design of roads is not within the scope of this book, but will obviously affect road longevity and maintenance needs. Many authorities find that the integration of maintenance duties with general design has advantages, from resource levelling, training, and passage of information viewpoints. It is in any event important that maintenance engineers develop procedures for relaying information on the field performance, installation difficulty, accessibility and costs of servicing materials and components specified in the initial design documents. Roads designed for the Department of Transport need to comply with Road Notes and Technical Memoranda, and these documents will in many areas be the basis for the design of other roads. Such data are subject to regular review and amendments, and the maintenance organization must institute a system for the revision of library information. A feature of maintenance is that much of the work inevitably deals with past specifications and design codes, and a judgement has to be made concerning the storage of outdated material, which could be of use in dealing with older constructions. Microfilming is one method of reducing the bulk of stored data. A further peculiarity is that staff need to be conversant with both metric and imperial unit systems, when dealing with dimensions and calculations.

Even before the opening of a road to traffic, the process of deterioration has commenced with the effects of weathering. The notional design life of 20 or 40 years, depending on the form of construction, will be related also to the type of traffic envisaged. Research indicates that damage is approximately proportional to the fifth power of the axle loading, thus a doubling of the load can lead to some 30 times the destructive effect on the carriageway. Clearly there is a need to control vehicle weights and loading patterns, and legislation covering vehicles made in Great Britain aims to do this.[3.1] However, trade with Europe and elsewhere introduces a further complication in the control requirements, and vehicles entering the country have to be monitored and subjected to dockside load readjustments to ensure compliance. Despite the systems of control, much countrywide abuse of regulations occurs, and overloaded vehicles are regularly found in checks carried out by police and local authority inspectors. Advances in roadside weighing equipment will assist in the control of axle loads, and also provide more information on the spectrum of loads and configurations of axle using the highway at chosen locations.

A perennial source of damage to the highway structure is the excavation of trenches by public utility companies in the installation and maintenance of their pipes and mains, as mentioned in Chapter 1. Until improved working methods are devised and adhered to, the constant disturbances of the carriageways and footways cannot fail to produce a costly and sometimes hazardous situation.

The definition of carriageway defects and maintenance categories is useful in determining the method to be used for repairs, but it is essential if comparisons of unit costs and value are to be considered. For instance, the use of the term 'patching', to cover areas ranging between $1 m^2$ and perhaps several hundred square metres distorts cost comparisons because it involves hand laying as against machine, and also a scale factor in materials. Although many engineers will argue that a broad classification offers some flexibility in the annual budget distribution, it is suggested that an overall benefit would result from closer identification of working methods and their costs, and changes in the financial arrangements. Investigations carried out by the now defunct Greater London Council within London boroughs, and more recently by the Audit Commission,[3.2] indicate wide variations between apparently similar operations, and one reason for this is undoubtedly the differences in definition of work.

The following sections deal separately with the more common forms of construction and maintenance for concrete and bituminous roads, but as is made clear in the text, many roads successfully combine the two types of materials, and indeed most areas will contain lengths of road built in various combinations and specifications of these basic materials. Investigation of faults and choice of remedy depend on recognition of the construction form and mode of failure of each type, and further information is given on this in Chapter 8.

PART I. CONCRETE PAVEMENTS
3.1. Background

An engineer responsible for the maintenance and repair of any pavement has far less freedom in the choice of available options than the engineer responsible for the original design. The maintenance engineer has to do his best with the pavement as it exists, often under the difficult working conditions of keeping traffic flowing, poor site access and possibly other restraints, such as limited headroom at bridges. To do his job well, the maintenance engineer must have a clear understanding of the behaviour of the pavement being maintained, be able to diagnose the reasons for the development of any faults and select the appropriate repair method to rectify the problem.

This part of the book reviews the background to different design and construction aspects of concrete roads and briefly describes their *modus operandi*, before detailing various repair techniques.

Some repairs are the responsibility of the contractor, who may be required to carry out certain repairs before the road is opened to traffic, and at the end of the maintenance period. Others will be the concern of the maintaining authority and work may not be required for a long time.

An important duty of the maintenance engineer is to carry out regular condition surveys, to examine both the present and change of condition of the road and to predict when permanent repairs will be needed.

These surveys will also provide the basic data required to develop a Bill of Quantities for any proposed repair contract, although the difficulty of surveying 'live' motorways and trunk roads means that obtaining accurate estimates of quantities is rarely possible. Methods of making surveys and

Table 3.1 (below and facing page).
Symbols for recording defects

Type of fault	Data recorded during survey	Standard symbol	Fault Ref.
Shallow spalling	Length, width and depth		J1
Deep spalling	Length, width and depth		J2
Defective joint seals	Length		J3
Cracks at joints	Length and width	20mm	J4
Opening of longitudinal joints	Length and width		J5
Stepping (faulting)	Difference in level across joints or cracks	H L	J6
Vertical movement at joints and cracks	Dynamic movement or vibration, mud-pumping, staining	Pumping	J7
Transverse cracks	Length and width, i.e. W, M and N		ST1
Longitudinal cracks	Length and width, i.e. W, M and N		ST2
Diagonal cracks	Length and width, i.e. W, M or N		ST3
Corner cracks	Length and width, i.e. W, M and N		ST4
Cracks associated with inclusions	Length and width, i.e. W, M or N		ST5

recording the results are explained in Chapter 8, but a list of preferred symbols for recording faults in concrete pavement, mostly taken from Mildenhall and Northcott,[3.3] is given in Table 3.1. Records of surveys will be used for many years and it is therefore essential that a standard way of describing and recording faults is used, in order to maximize the benefits of the surveys and develop long-term records showing how different repair methods perform in different situations.

Type of fault	Data recorded during survey	Standard symbol	Fault Ref.
Settlement	Degree of settlement, area, any associated cracking	Settlement	ST6
Reinforcement corrosion	Rust staining on the surface		RS1
Compression failures	Extent of affected area		ST7
Inadequate surface texture	Extent of area excessively worn	STW	SU1
Surface irregularity	Subjective assessment — good, fair, poor. Note any deterioration since last inspection		SU2
Surface scaling	Extent of affected area		SU3
Surface crazing	Extent and degree		SU7
Plastic cracking	Extent and degree, i.e. minor, moderate or severe		SU4
Poor surface drainage	Location	Ponding	SU5
Miscellaneous surface defects	Type of defect		SU6
Missing road stud	Type, number and location	Stud missing	MR
Previous repairs	Type, number and condition	O.K.	PR
Sealed crack		As appropriate	PR

3.1.1. Where are the concrete roads?

In urban areas concrete is probably the most common roadbase material; its use is also extensive for major rural roads, mainly in the form of lean concrete, now known as CBM3[3.4] or some other form of cement bound material. This wide use of concrete is often overlooked, because the concrete is hidden by bituminous surfacings, ranging in thickness from a few millimetres to 200 mm or more. The performance of bituminous materials is structurally enhanced by being laid on a rigid layer, as surface deformation due to trafficking is then limited to the bituminous layer. There is, however, a greater risk of cracking of the surfacing due to expansion and contraction of the roadbase, although not all cracks in the surfacing originate from the slab.[3.5] Historically, most urban concrete roads were built of short, unreinforced slabs, surfaced soon after casting and before being opened to traffic. This form of construction is still used today, offering advantages by spanning over the numerous underlying service trenches, which hinder adequate compaction of rolled roadbases.

The third edition of Road Note 29, published in 1970,[3.6] recognized the benefits of composite pavements, especially for city streets and other very heavily trafficked carriageways, and also for pavements built on very variable sub-grades, as a simple means of providing pavements needing minimal maintenance. This edition of the Road Note, for the first time, gave design recommendations for continuously reinforced concrete roadbases, surfaced with 90 mm or more of bituminous material, the thickness selected being dependent on the design life and anticipated commercial traffic volume. These thin surfacings were considered practical because cracking of the roadbase would be frequent and well controlled by the reinforcement. The Department of Transport, when issuing new design recommendations, in 1987,[3.7] retained the basic design with only a marginal increase to 100 mm in the minimum surfacing thickness.

Although less common, there are a number of highways with concrete running surfaces, some dating back to the 1930s. A well built concrete road has a very long potential life; using conventional designs the tensile stresses, developed within the slabs due to traffic loadings, are less than 50% of the maximum tensile strength of the concrete, resulting in very low fatigue stresses and a theoretically infinite life. A small increase in slab thickness substantially lowers the stresses developed, so a conservative design is economically viable, and because of that most concrete pavements have a reserve of strength and are able to carry traffic well in excess of the original design assumptions.

Nearly all failures of concrete pavements are due to detailing or construction faults, most commonly in the vicinity of joints. Concrete pavements therefore rarely degenerate overall, but develop discrete faults, some brought on by weathering, others by trafficking. To avoid these problems, especially for very heavily trafficked roads, continuously reinforced, jointless concrete pavements (CRCPs) are becoming more common. To date, CRCPs have generally performed well and there is not a great deal of experience of their repair. Two possible risk areas exist — corrosion of the reinforcement and 'punch-out', which are due to a local failure of the sub-base, causing a small, unsupported area of the slab to fail also.

3.2. Stresses

3.2.1. Over-stressing of the concrete

Stresses are developed in concrete slabs by the contraction and expansion of the concrete due to moisture and temperature changes as well as to traffic loadings. The integration of stresses from these different causes is difficult to predict and calculate. However, to understand the principles of design and causes of fault development in concrete roads, it is helpful to understand how the various stresses are developed.

3.2.2. Stresses caused by moisture and temperature changes

After a slab is cast, several factors will cause its dimensions to change. Initially there will be a loss of moisture; with efficient curing this will mainly result from some of the mixing water going into chemical combination with the cement, but when curing ceases it will be mainly due to evaporation losses. Any loss of moisture will result in a general reduction in the dimensions of a slab. After a concrete has 'set' (i.e. has hardened sufficiently to be considered as an elastic solid, rather than as a plastic) and it contracts, tensile stresses will develop, as there will be some degree of movement restraint due to friction between the underside of the slab and its supporting layer. If these tensile stresses exceed the tensile strength of the slab, it will crack (see Fig. 3.1).

A study of cracking in relation to time of construction, showed that slabs cast in the forenoon, during an English summer, cracked significantly more than slabs cast in the afternoon. The reason for this is simple to explain: as the ambient temperature fell at night the slab temperature also fell, adding to the contraction caused by moisture loss. Slabs cast in the

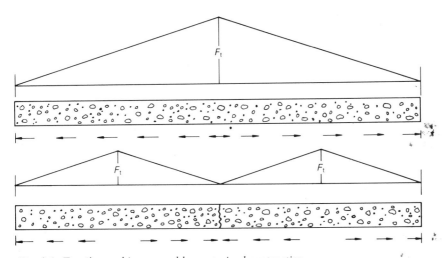

Fig. 3.1. Tensile cracking caused by restrained contraction

forenoon had by night time developed some, but not a high, strength and modulus and were stiff enough to crack, while the slabs cast in the afternoon were still in the plastic state and could strain rather than crack. During the following day, slabs cast the previous afternoon had had more than a further day to gain strength, so that during the second night they were generally strong enough to withstand the tensile stress development.

If random contraction cracking is to be avoided there is a limit to the length of slab that can be constructed. Before the 1940s, most concrete roads were constructed by the alternate bay method, all joints being day-work joints. This technique was viable because nearly all roads were built manually, mechanization being limited to the mixing of the concrete. In the last 40 years most concrete roads have been constructed as continuous strips, divided by contraction joints. In other words, contraction joints are premeditated contraction cracks and their spacing has to be sufficiently close to ensure that there will be no intermediate, unwanted cracking. With unreinforced slabs this results in a maximum joint spacing of about 5 m unless the coarse aggregate is limestone, when the spacing can be increased to 6 m. This increase in spacing is because of the relatively low coefficient of thermal expansion (contraction) of limestone, compared with that of other road making aggregates. Joint spacing can also be increased if reinforcement is included in the slab. The reinforcement does not prevent cracking, but controls it, so that any crack width is limited, and in practice the majority of such cracks are rarely visible.

Concrete also expands, and this expansion can generate large forces, sufficient to move bridge abutments, walls, and the surrounds to underground chambers. Allowance for expansion is essential at these locations and also at tangent points on sharp horizontal curves. The maximum expansion depends on many variables, including most significantly the temperature range, between that at which the concrete 'set' and the maximum slab temperature subsequently reached. In general terms, the total expansion achieved is not likely to exceed the total contraction, and therefore expansion stresses are well below the compressive strength of the concrete. For this reason the Department of Transport Specification[3.4] does not require expansion joints in any road built between the 21 April and 21 October.

All joints need to be sealed to prevent surface water run-off reaching the sub-base or sub-grade and weakening them, and to minimize the amount of detritus entering the joint. If joints are not adequately maintained, detritus will build up in them, preventing closure, which in a few years will result in increased expansion stresses. These higher stresses may disclose weaknesses in the slabs, shown by joint arris spalling, longitudinal cracking or slabs buckling, resulting in the so-called 'blow-up'. If a blow-up occurs, the affected part of the pavement has to be rebuilt and an expansion joint formed (see section 3.19).

3.2.3. Stresses due to traffic

In 1926 Westergaard[3.8] showed that if a load was applied to the surface of a rigid rectangular slab, itself supported on an elastic homogeneous

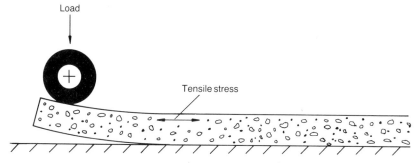

Fig. 3.2. Warping caused by temperature/moisture gradients

layer, the greatest stresses were developed when the load was applied at a corner, and almost as great if the load was applied at an edge. Translating this into wheel loads applied to concrete slabs meant that the slab thickness had to be selected to keep corner stresses low enough to prevent cracking. The problem of stress generation is aggravated when slabs warp due to temperature, and/or moisture gradients (see Fig. 3.2). Alternative ways of keeping stresses at acceptable levels are either to (i) keep wheels clear of edges and corners or (ii) provide load transfer at joints. Load transfer devices, across adjoining slabs, can be designed to restrain warping and also to transfer load and thereby reduce the stress in any one slab. Providing that cracks do not open, aggregate interlock, resulting from the irregular vertical faces created by cracking, restrains warping and provides a degree of load transfer. At joints, which must be free to open and prevent contraction cracking, more positive forms of load transfer are needed in all but the most lightly trafficked roads.

Over the years a host of different load transfer devices have been developed, but the dowel bar system is the only one that has gained wide acceptance. In this, dowel bars are cast into the concrete, spanning the joint, so that their shear strength transmits load from one slab to its neighbour, as shown in Fig. 3.3. The dowels also restrain warping at a joint. In practice the spacing of dowels is constant (300 mm centres), but their diameter is increased with higher traffic loadings. Also, larger

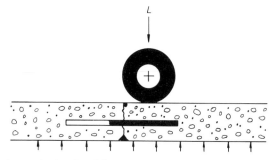

Fig. 3.3. Load transfer by dowel bars

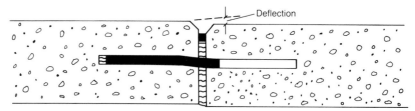

Fig. 3.4. Expansion joint–dowel bars subject to bending

diameter bars are required in expansion than contraction joints, because those in expansion joints will be subject to bending as well as shear (see Fig. 3.4). The major problem with the construction of any dowelled joint is to ensure that all the bars are parallel to each other, to the pavement surface and to the pavement centre line. Ways of doing this are described in many publications, e.g. refs 3.9 and 3.10.

3.3. Cracking

The development of cracks in a slab can be from a variety of causes, and every attempt should be made to ascertain the particular cause, to ensure the correct choice of repair method. In this respect it is also very helpful to know when a fault first developed. For example, brine created when de-icing salts are dissolved can, over many years, cause corrosion of dowel and tie-bars. When these fail, the deflections of slabs arising from the passage of vehicles is greatly increased, causing increased stress and ultimately cracking, most likely in the joint vicinity. Again, good mainte-nance of joint sealants is therefore important.

On the other hand, if a wide transverse crack develops in a reinforced slab within a few months of construction, this indicates a probable construction fault, such as inadequate overlap of reinforcement mats.

3.3.1. Classification of cracks

Cracks are classified by a description of their general direction and their width. Cracks fall into five main types: transverse, longitudinal, diagonal, corner and miscellaneous. The width of cracks, measured at the pavement surface, is classified as narrow if less than 0·5 mm, medium if 0·5 mm to 1·5 mm, and wide if greater than 1·5 mm.

3.3.2. Significance of crack width

The structural significance of any crack depends on its type, width and whether or not the slab is reinforced. Narrow transverse cracks in rein-forced concrete slabs are normal and their presence is of no concern, as aggregate interlock will be retained. However, spalling of such cracks indicates a loss of interlock and yielding of the steel, in which case the crack should be treated as 'medium', rather than 'narrow' and sealed, as described in section 3.18. Wide transverse cracks in any concrete road require earliest possible attention, the fault being rectified by means of a full depth reconstruction, as described in section 3.19.

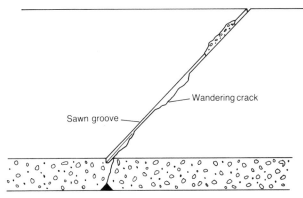

Fig. 3.5. Premature cracking due to late sawing

3.3.3. Transverse cracks

Transverse cracks may result from any one of the following causes

(a) excessive bay length, in relation to the amount of reinforcement used

(b) lack of adequate reinforcement overlap

(c) joints not moving freely

(d) too late sawing of contraction joints

(e) too high restraint at the slab/sub-base interface

(f) corrosion of reinforcement due to brine solution entering a medium or wide, unsealed crack

(g) lack of load transfer at a joint.

Causes (a) and (b) will usually result in cracks some way from a joint. If the joint design includes a bottom crack inducer (see Fig. 3.5), a crack caused by too late sawing will most likely be located near the sealing groove, but it may also develop somewhere else.

The extent of cracking due to excessive sub-grade restraint can range from a large number of narrow cracks to a few wide ones.

Cracking due to cause (f) will not occur for some years in service and results in a loss of aggregate interlock. It can be rectified by 'stitching', in the form described in section 3.14.

If fault (g) develops within the first five years of service, the fault is most likely due to the omission of the dowel bars. The development of dowel bar locating equipment[3.11] means that this error will be improbable in the future. It also means that both the presence and the alignment of dowel bars can be checked at the time of construction, reducing the risk of fault (c).

Depending on the standard of joint sealant maintenance, after some 15 years or more, it is possible for dowel bars to corrode and fail. If this happens, stresses within the concrete due to traffic loads will be greatly increased, and the slabs will warp more freely, both increasing the risks of transverse or corner cracking near the joint. In this case the joint will need to be reconstructed (see section 3.19).

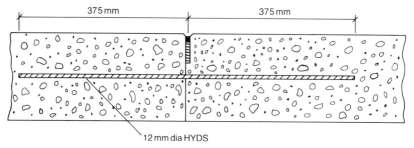

Fig. 3.6. Longitudinal tied joint

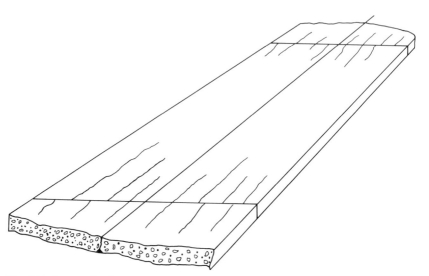

Fig. 3.7. Longitudinal cracking due to compression stresses

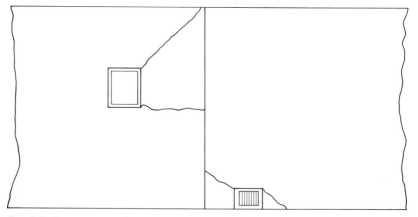

Fig. 3.8. Some causes of miscellaneous cracking

3.3.4. Longitudinal cracks
Longitudinal cracks can result from one of the following

(a) excessive slab width: it is not common practice to reinforce slabs transversely, although it has been done on an airfield to reduce the number of longitudinal joints. With normal reinforcement mats the transverse steel is very light and only serves to locate the main reinforcement, laid longitudinally along the slab length

(b) incorrect location of bottom crack inducer: for major works, pavements are often constructed two or more bays wide, being divided by formed longitudinal joints in a similar manner to that used for contraction joints, the major difference being that the longitudinal joints have tie-bars, rather than dowel bars (Fig. 3.6)

(c) uneven longitudinal support: drainage faults and excessive changes in the moisture content of the sub-grades, especially clay sub-grades, can result in uneven support, encouraging longitudinal cracking

(d) compression stress: if there are no expansion joints and the contraction joints have become permanently opened, due to detritus, there can be considerable build up of compression stress which, because of the Poisson ratio effect, results in tensile stresses capable of causing longitudinal cracking (see Fig. 3.7).

Longitudinal cracks are not expected in any form of concrete road construction and their existence denotes something amiss. Because they are not tied, longitudinal cracks often widen and lengthen and if they are in the wheeltracks will degenerate quickly. Any form of longitudinal cracking detected should be dealt with as soon as possible.

3.3.5. Diagonal cracking
Diagonal cracking is uncommon and is most likely to be caused by a major change in the quality of support offered by the sub-base or sub-grade, e.g. a trench back-filled with a much stronger material than the surrounding sub-grade. Repair methods range from just sealing, to stitching and sealing, or even slab replacement, depending on the degree of cracking and the traffic intensity.

3.3.6. Plastic cracking
Plastic cracking is entirely different from the forms of cracking discussed previously. It occurs very soon after compaction of the concrete, sometimes in well under an hour. Plastic cracking appears as a group of short, approximately parallel cracks, oblique to the line of the slab. Individual cracks taper at each end, and rarely are they deep or do they extend to the edge of the slab. They are caused by a rapid loss of moisture from the slab surface and mostly occur on sunny days when there is also a drying wind. An excess of dry 'rock fines' in the aggregate, which absorb water quickly, also increases the risk of occurrence of the problem. Experience shows that plastic cracking is very uncommon when the concrete is air-entrained.

Very narrow plastic cracks are self-healing and need cause no concern, however, it is prudent to seal wider plastic cracks by pouring in a low viscosity latex emulsion. When plastic cracking occurs, extra attention should be given to

(a) curing, including protection from the wind and sun
(b) keeping down the mix moisture content
(c) stricter control of entrained air content.

3.3.7. Miscellaneous cracks

Other cracks can form at intrusions, such as gully frames, usually in one of the forms illustrated in Fig. 3.8. They are caused either as a result of poor detailing or by the slab being supported locally on, e.g. a gully chamber. If the cracks are narrow, remedial works are not necessary; medium cracks should be sealed, as described in section 3.18. Slabs suffering wide cracks should be made good by a full depth repair, in the form described in section 3.19. It must be recognized that, in the case of reinforced concrete slabs, medium cracks will soon become wider and slab replacement should therefore be undertaken as soon as possible, redesigning the joint layout to avoid a repetition of the problem. If a slab is supported locally, it should be cut through, removing the cracked area, and rebuilt, isolating it from the support.

3.4. Surface water spray, skidding resistance and surface damage

Because concrete slabs do not rut, surface water drainage does not become impaired, which helps to minimize both the extent of surface water spray, and the risk of skidding accidents. The transverse grooves, formed in a concrete surface by using a stiff-bristle broom or with a grooving machine, provide the shortest possible drainage paths, which aids surface water drainage, as well as providing good skid resistance.

3.4.1. Skid resistance

Provided that a suitable sand was used in the concrete, the micro-texture will be retained, ensuring good resistance to low-speed skidding for many years.[3.12] If the sand used for making the concrete contains a high proportion of acid soluble material the road surface will polish rapidly, even under light traffic and this particular fault can only be resolved by slab replacement or by using some form of overlay.

For high-speed traffic, the macro-texture is important in helping with clearing water in front of vehicles tyres. After many years and under very heavy traffic the macro-texture could be worn away. Methods of restoring it are described in section 3.16.8.

3.4.2. Surface damage

Surface damage can result from a number of causes — frost damage, late finishing, trowelling-on of a 'topping' after the main slab has been compacted and found to be low, or 'mechanical damage' caused by freshly placed or hardened concrete.

Concrete surfaces sometimes scale as a result of using de-icing agents for snow and ice clearance. The application of a de-icing agent to a pavement that is already covered with ice or snow causes it to lose a large amount of heat rapidly. This extracted heat melts the ice and snow, but at the same time causes freezing of any water already entrapped in the road surface. The application of de-icing agents thus increases the number of freezing and thawing cycles. De-icing salts, applied prior to a concrete road being covered with ice or snow, will not cause damage to the surface, as they contain little to harm concrete directly, although they may cause steel corrosion in the long term. If a road slab was made with an excessively wet concrete, bleed-water would have evaporated from the surface, and the top few millimetres of the slab will have a high content of voids, and a higher than average water:cement ratio. The voids can easily become saturated and when frozen, tensile stresses are developed resulting in scaling of the slab surface.

It is well established that air-entrainment, within the mortar fraction of the concrete, greatly reduces the risk of frost damage, probably by providing microscopic, discrete air bubbles, which act as 'expansion' chambers, preventing the generation of stresses when any entrapped water freezes. If a concrete road is known to be constructed with either non-air-entrained concrete, or concrete with too little air it is prudent to apply de-icing salts before ice has formed on the surface. A short-term method of preventing freeze–thaw damage to non-air-entrained concrete is by soaking the surface with linseed oil, to fill the voids. Longer term repair methods are described in section 3.16.

Mechanical damage, no matter how it arises, can most readily be repaired by using a bonded topping technique, as described in section 3.12. This method can also be used to repair holes caused by clay 'balls' left in aggregates used for making the concrete.

3.5. Arris spalling

Joint arrises can spall for different reasons and to different depths. For convenience these are dealt with separately as shallow, and deep spalls.

Spalling, also known as ravelling, can result from workmanship faults in making wet-formed joints, or sawing too early. These faults may not be disclosed until the pavement is in service, and some local stresses induced at the weakness.

3.5.1. Shallow spalling

Wet-formed contraction joints are often created by pushing a strip of material into the surface, to act as a crack inducer/groove former. Untreated timber should not be used for this purpose, as it will swell as it absorbs water from the concrete, and set up stresses, in the joint vicinity. Local cracking, as shown in Fig. 3.9 may then be induced. For this reason non-swelling materials are preferable as top crack inducers, although their use does not remove the need for care. It is common practice to form a crack-inducing groove by vibrating a blade into freshly compacted concrete, and then to insert a strip of plastic material to prevent the groove

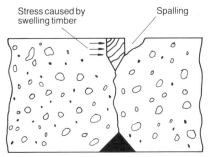

Fig. 3.9. Spalling due to swelling groove former

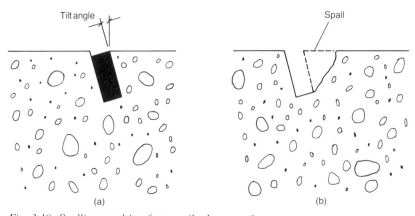

Fig. 3.10. Spalling resulting from a tilted groove former

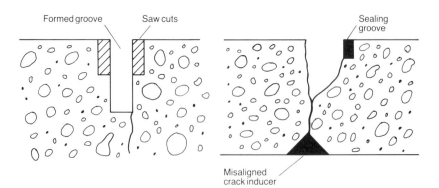

Fig. 3.11. Widening a sealing groove by saw cuts

Fig. 3.12. Deep spalling due to misaligned crack inducer

closing. On small jobs the groove forming blade is often just hammered into the freshly compacted concrete. However the groove is formed, the concrete close by is disturbed, and therefore it has to be revibrated to rectify any induced weaknesses. This revibration must be done carefully to avoid the groove retaining strip being tilted and creating an angled sealing groove, as shown in Fig. 3.10(a). If the angle of tilt from the vertical exceeds 10°, the fault must be rectified, to prevent the later spalling of the 'over-hanging' concrete at the joint (Fig. 3.10(b)).

Because it avoids interruption in construction, the sawing of sealing grooves is undoubtedly the best way of making top-crack inducers, but this method is not always viable. The main restriction to sawing is the type of coarse aggregate. Flint aggregates are very hard and also have a large coefficient of expansion, which means that sawing has to be delayed to ensure that the cement–paste matrix is strong enough to prevent the stones being plucked out, instead of being cut. However, if sawing is delayed too long, the joint will crack before it is sawn, as shown in Fig. 3.5.

Concrete at slab edges needs extra attention, especially at day-work joints. Sharp arrises, which are considerably weaker than the body of the slab should be 'rounded off', with an arrising tool, or chamfered, when the concrete is strong enough, with an angle grinder. Not all joint spalling is caused by construction faults. If stones become jammed into joint sealing grooves, high local stresses can develop when the slabs expand, resulting in shallow spalling. Sawing offers a simple and effective means of dealing with shallow spalls, by increasing the width of the sealing groove, as illustrated in Fig. 3.11, otherwise the arrises have to be reformed, as described in section 3.13.

3.5.2. Deep spalling

This type of spalling extends well below the normal depth of the sealing groove, even below dowel bars. It is caused by one of the following

(a) misalignment of bottom crack inducer and the sealing groove, as shown in Fig. 3.12
(b) a build up of detritus in the full joint depth
(c) misaligned dowel bars

Deep spalling can only be rectified by full depth reconstruction, as described in section 3.19.

3.6. Slab rocking and settlement

3.6.1. Rocking slabs

Undowelled slabs constructed on unbound sub-bases can develop 'steps' at joints, the main cause being movement of the sub-base. As a vehicle travels over a joint, the slab on the approach side is deflected downwards and when the wheel leaves, it quicky deflects upwards, creating a zone of low air pressure between the slab and the sub-base, drawing material from beneath the departure slab to the other side of the joint. After many passages of vehicles a significant amount of material is moved across the joint, resulting in 'stepping'. The problem can be recognized as the slab displacement always results in a 'stepping downwards' pavement. The road develops an unsatisfactory riding quality and if left will ultimately lead to slab cracking, because of the uneven support.

Slabs may also rock due to uneven ground support, a situation which will soon result in cracking of the slabs.

Both these faults can be rectified by pressure or vacuum grouting to fill the voids and thereby provide a more uniform support. The extended life afforded by these remedies, which are described in section 3.15, depends greatly on the ground conditions beneath the pavement and is difficult to predict.

3.6.2. Slab settlement

Consolidation of the ground beneath a slab or major movements due, for example to collapse of abandoned mine workings, can result in major uneven settlements. Reliable methods of raising slabs, to counteract this problem have been developed and are described in section 3.15.

3.7. Loss of riding quality

The riding quality required depends on the purpose of the road. The higher the traffic speed, the greater the riding quality expected by drivers. An inadequate riding quality may result from poor construction, slab movement, surface scaling or 'stepping' of joints. Faults arising from poor construction can be rectified, either by bump cutting or slab replacement, but if riding quality is generally poor, an overlay may be the most economic answer. There are several forms of overlay that can be adopted, the choice of which depends on the purpose of the road and the possible merit of strengthening. The different types of overlay are described in section 3.16.

3.8. Trench openings

Repairs to damaged concrete roads resulting from the need to break into slabs to repair or install underground services can be carried out in a permanent form from the time of the original trench reinstatement. If reinstatement is considered prior to the slab being broken into, both time and effort can be saved, but an equally effective repair can be achieved even if this is not done. Methods of carrying out this work are described in section 3.17.

3.9. Joint sealant failures

Joints are, or should be, very active parts of any concrete pavement and as a result the sealing material suffers considerable stress and strain, both diurnally and annually. The physical dimensions of the sealing groove are of great importance in optimizing the performance of any sealant.

Sealants come in two basic forms, preformed and applied, the latter being subdivided into those that have to be heated, to melt them prior to application, and those supplied as two-part or three-part packs, which are mixed and poured at ambient temperature, and set due to a chemical reaction.

3.9.1. Preformed materials

These are basically some form of tube, made of elastic materials, such as polychloroprene elastomers, complying with BS 2752.[3.13] Other materials that comply with ASTM D2628[3.14] are also permitted in the Department of Transport Specification.[3.4] Microcellular sealants, made of ethylene–vinyl acetate, can also be used for sealing tied joints, where the amount of movement is relatively small.

Compression seals must be kept under compression at all times, even when the slabs are fully contracted. It is suggested that the maximum width of the fully opened joint sealing groove should not be more than 70% of the uncompressed sealant width, and also that the groove width should not exceed 30 mm. The specification[3.4] requires that at least 20% of the depth of the sealant groove walls is in contact with the sealant at all times. As with poured sealants, a compression seal should also be set 5 mm below the slab surface, so that there is little risk of it being pulled out by traffic or vandals. It is the usual practice to apply a lubricant-cum-adhesive to the sealing tube to assist first with its installation and later to help its retention. This form of sealing has not proved popular in practice, possibly because the sealing grooves have to be of a very uniform width throughout, to ensure the seal's reliability. This uniformity of width is difficult to guarantee before the start of paving, and this is possibly the reason why they are rarely specified. With correct installation however, there appears to be no fundamental reason why this form of sealing should not have a long life.

3.9.2. Applied and poured sealants

The performance of these depends almost entirely on the design of the sealing groove and the correct application of the sealant. They fail for two reasons — peeling from the walls of the sealing groove or splitting along the length of the seal, due to excessive strain.

Figure 3.13 shows a section through a sealed groove; the ratio of width to depth, known as the shape factor, should not be less than 1:1 nor more than 2:1. The opening of the joint causes the sealant to strain

$$\text{Strain (\%)} = \frac{\text{joint opening} \times 100\%}{\text{joint width, when sealed}}$$

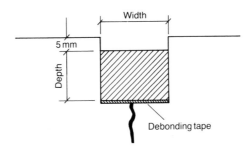

Fig. 3.13. Section through a sealed groove

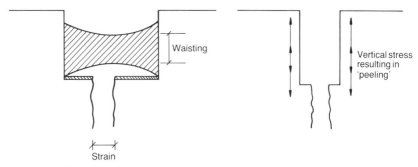

Fig. 3.14. 'Waisting' due to straining of   Fig. 3.15. Vertical stress caused
the sealant   by horizontal strain

The greater the percentage strain, the greater the risk of the sealant peeling from the groove walls and/or splitting. To reduce this risk the groove should be designed to minimize the strain.

If the sealant is stuck to the base of the groove, its strain will be concentrated over the crack width and therefore be very high, which will result in the early splitting of the sealant. To prevent this the base of the groove should be separated from the sealant by sticking tape along the base length, before the sealant is installed.

As a joint opens, the shape of the sealant cross-section changes, developing a waist near the centre, as shown in Fig. 3.14. If the groove is narrow (i.e. has a shape factor of less than 1), the extensive waisting increases the risk of both splitting, at the narrow part of the cross-section, and peeling from the walls because of the large vertical stresses at the interfaces (see Fig. 3.15).

If the groove dimensions result in a shape factor outside the width-to-depth ratio range 1–2, the groove must either be widened or, if it is as wide as practical, the bottom must be caulked to limit the sealant depth. Theoretically, the amount of movement can be calculated knowing the coefficient of expansion of the concrete, the slab length and the maximum range of slab temperature likely from the time of pouring the sealant to the predicted minimum. To assist the calculation of average joint movements,

Table 3.2. Typical coefficients of expansion of concrete. Aggregate:cement ratio = 6:1

Types of aggregate	Coefficient of expansion ($\times 10^6/°C$)
Dolerite	7·9
Granite	7·7
Gravel	11·7
Limestone	5·9
Sandstone	8·6
Quartzite	11·7

typical values of the coefficients of expansion of concrete, made with different natural aggregates, are shown in Table 3.2. These values were taken from ref. 3.15. For a host of reasons, accurate calculation of individual joint movements is not possible. The actual joint movement is likely to be less than determined by calculation, but as not all the joints will move uniformly, some will open more than anticipated. It is suggested that ideally the average maximum sealant strain should be designed to 20%, but in no case should it exceed 25%.

Poured and applied sealants are practically incompressible, so when a joint closes, relative to its width when first sealed, they will squeeze upwards. Therefore, if they are placed level with the road surface, they will ultimately project upwards, and then be either pulled away from the joint walls, or spread over the road surface by traffic. For this reason it is necessary to underseal joints by some 5 mm. Methods of resealing joints are described in section 3.18.

3.10. Overlays

Overlays may be used for a variety of reasons

(a)   for aesthetics
(b)   to restore riding quality, lost due to major surface damage or slab movements
(c)   to overcome loss of skid resistance
(d)   a need to strengthen the pavement.

3.10.1. Bituminous overlays

Bituminous overlays, ranging from surface dressing, which is useful for sealing a porous surface, to thick overlays are dealt with in Part II and these overlays in their different forms serve to resolve many of the deficiencies cited above.

3.10.2. Concrete overlays

Concrete overlays can also be used for any of the needs listed. If the surface has suffered scaling, or the old concrete was made with an unsuitable sand that polishes quickly under traffic, it can be repaired with either a thin bonded or an unbonded overlay. These overlays not only overcome the immediate problem but can also improve the structural strength of the pavement.

3.10.3. Block and brick overlays

Both concrete block and clay brick pavers have been used to overlay concrete and bituminous surfaces. Originally they were used to improve the aesthetics of roads in conservation areas, but it has been shown that block overlays add considerably to the strength of existing pavements.[3.16]

3.11. Repair methods

The types of faults that develop in concrete pavements, and their causes, were described in section 3.2. It is always advisable, but not always possible, to ascertain the cause of any problem before undertaking a repair; as with a sound diagnosis, the chances of achieving a long term and effective repair are greatly increased. Few repairs to concrete are cheap, but they can be effective and long lasting. Even so, it should also be borne in mind that for most repairs the cost of initiating the work and controlling the traffic are far greater than the cost of the repairs themselves, and therefore it is well worth time and effort to ensure their effectiveness. Some repair techniques are applicable to several types of fault.

3.12. Thin bonded toppings

The bonding of new concrete or mortar to old concrete can be done with great confidence and one can be sure that the bond strength is at least equal to the tensile strength of the concrete. The technique can be used to remedy polished surfaces (section 3.4.1), the repair of scaled and mechanically damaged surfaces (section 3.4.2), spalled arrises (section 3.5.1) and for the creation of bonded concrete overlays (section 3.10.2).

3.12.1. Preparation for repair

It is essential to ensure that the old concrete is sound and clean before the new material is applied. Preparation of concrete to receive a bonded topping is analogous to repainting wood, where the quality and the life of the new work depends entirely on not painting over flaking paint or rotting timber. This analogy is also true for the relative cost, preparation in both cases being the major time and cost element, the repair materials and their application being relatively cheap.

Usually the limits of any surface scaling extend beyond that which can be seen, and for a fully effective repair, the areas of incipient failure must be found. An effective way of locating the true area of surface scaling is to bounce the end of a heavy steel rod on the pavement surface around the already scaled area; a 'hollow' sound denotes a detaching surface. Having identified the extent of potential scaling it is prudent to mark out an area

Fig. 3.16. Cutting around an area to be scabbled   *Fig. 3.17. Concrete crack cutter*

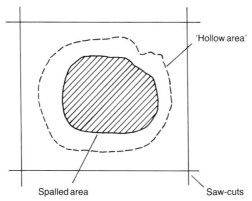

'Hollow area'

Spalled area   Saw-cuts

Fig. 3.18. Effect of sawing around a spalled area

somewhat greater, say 100 to 150 mm beyond the identified limits. For convenience of the reinstatement work, the area should be approximately rectangular. The next stage is to cut along the marking-out lines (see Fig. 3.16) with either a saw or router, see Fig. 3.17, to a depth of at least 10 mm. Both methods of cutting have been used successfully and each has its advocates. The saw gives a sharper arris for the repair, but the cuts have to extend beyond the corners of the area (Fig. 3.18). Also, if the concrete has been made with a very hard aggregate, such as flint, the vertical sides of the saw cuts can be highly polished, not an ideal surface for bonding to the overlay material. Once the edges have been cut out the rest of the area is removed with a multi-headed scabbler (Fig. 3.19), or high pressure hydraulic cutter (Fig. 3.20). Cutting must continue until all unsound material is removed, and a 'flat', not a 'stepped' base, is produced, as shown in Fig. 3.21. If the base of the area to be resurfaced is stepped,

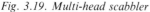

Fig. 3.19. Multi-head scabbler   *Fig. 3.20. High pressure water cutter*

Fig. 3.21. Cross-section of scabbled area

shrinkage of the repair material will be restrained locally and as a result a visible crack will be formed. There is no merit in going deeper than is necessary for the removal of any defective concrete. When a damaged surface has been previously repaired with a bituminous material all traces of the bitumen must be removed before making the new repair. This can be done by grit or high water pressure blasting, or scabbling. If a repair is to be permanent a similar standard of preparation is needed, no matter what repair material is used.

If a repair is at the edge of a slab and there is no kerb, formwork will be needed to retain the repair material, while it is being placed. The formwork must be set rigidly to ensure the correct level of the final repair. Similarly, if a repair is at a joint a temporary groove former has to be installed to prevent the repair material flowing into or spanning the sealing groove.

3.12.2. Repair materials

A wide range of materials has been used successfully for repairs and when choosing which to adopt, several factors must be considered

(*a*) compatibility with the base concrete
(*b*) cost
(*c*) ease of usage on site
(*d*) suitability for use in different weathers
(*e*) speed of opening the repair to traffic
(*f*) durability, i.e. resistance to weathering, polishing and/or breakdown under traffic
(*g*) availability.

The priority order of this list will depend on a variety of circumstances, and the list is intended only to indicate the factors that the maintenance engineer should consider, before selecting any repair material to be used.

Trying to meet certain needs, such as very early opening, has led to the development of 'miracle' materials which are generally expensive but are not always compatible with the base concrete. Preference should be given to using cementitious materials, which are likely to satisfy more of the requirements, including compatibility with the base concrete, which is not always true of resin-based mortars and concretes.

At the other end of the scale, fine cold bituminous materials are readily available, quick to apply and carry traffic, and for these reasons are often used for emergency repairs. Unfortunately, bituminous materials are sometimes placed in an unprepared 'hole' and considerable reliance placed on compaction by the traffic. Repairs made in this way do not last long, and should therefore only be considered as short-term emergency repairs, rarely a bargain! It has also been claimed that bituminous repairs encourage more scaling to occur, but it is more probable that the fault results from lack of preparation, and the concrete surrounding the filled area being loose but attached, before the hole was filled. With good preparation, by using a bituminous tack-coat on a surface free of water, and placing the material at a temperature of not less than 5°C, this type of repair can be expected to last at least several months. A correctly made repair with a cement mortar or concrete will last for many years, probably for the design life of the pavement.

The long curing time often specified has discouraged the greater use of cementitious repair materials, despite their reliability. These delays are not always necessary. For example in North America, it is accepted that mixes containing between 380 and 500 kg/m^3 of rapid hardening cement (Type III, containing 2% calcium chloride), entrained air and minimal water, can be opened to traffic within four to five hours, without structural damage or loss of surface texture, providing that the air temperature is not below 10°C.[3.17] Lilley[3.18] reported that, once the strength of cubes made from the repair mix material, and stored at the side of the pavement being repaired, showed a minimum strength of 10 N/mm^2, a thin bonded repair could be safely trafficked. He also found that repairs trafficked at much lower cube strengths remained structurally sound, but their surface texture was rapidly abraded. This, and other research, shows that with a suitable mix design, and except in cold weather, concrete repairs can be trafficked within less than 24 hours. There are, therefore, few situations where relatively cheap, cement based materials cannot be used.

The mix proportions recommended in the Manual,[3.3] have been used for many years in the UK. For repairs up to 20 mm deep a 3:1 sharp sand:cement mix is suggested and for deeper repairs a 2:2:1 10 mm washed aggregate:sharp sand:cement mix. The sands should be within either C or M grades of Table 5 of BS 882.[3.19] The water:cement ratio of either mix should not exceed 0·45, to ensure both long-term durability and low shrinkage. Although the use of air-entrained concrete is always recommended for paving works, experience has shown that the high cement content, low water:cement ratio mixes used for repairs are durable, without the entrained air. This is fortunate, as good control of the air content of the small batches used for repairs would be extremely difficult.

For thin bonded, ordinary Portland cement toppings, the Manual[3.3] recommends a minimum curing period of three days, plus one day for every night of frost. This is a prudent recommendation, and should always be adopted unless the strength development is monitored, as outlined previously. The hydration of cement can be accelerated by different methods, such as heating the aggregates and/or the mixing water. However, it must also be remembered that the total mass of the materials used in a thin bonded topping is small, when compared with the mass of the base concrete, which acts as a 'cold sink', absorbing most of the heat stored or generated in the surfacing material.

The optimum amount of calcium chloride, to form an accelerator, is 2% by mass of cement. The use of calcium chloride in reinforced concrete is now known to be dangerous, as chlorides cause rusting of any nearby steel. With thin bonded repairs, as long as there is no steel near the repair, there is no reason why it should not be used. If the presence of reinforcement is found during preparation of the area being repaired, or is shown by a cover-meter to be within, say 50 mm, mixes containing calcium chloride should not be used.

Where very early openings to traffic are essential, concretes made with magnesia–phosphate cement (MPC) have proved successful. These cements, marketed by specialist firms, are phosphates blended with selected fine aggregates and packed ready for use. After water has been added and mixed in, setting is rapid. Depending upon the ambient temperature the mixed mortar will remain workable for 10 to 60 min. With ambient temperatures over 5°C, repairs are reported to be opened to motorway traffic in less than one hour.[3.20]

3.12.3. Batching and mixing

Good quality control of both batching and mixing is essential for all repair materials. To simplify control, the aggregates and cement are often preweighed and bagged. This is recommended for thin bonded toppings and spall repairs, as it is difficult to set up a practical and reliable weighing and batching system on site, when only small quantities of material are being produced throughout a day.

Portland cement repair mortars and concrete, with their high cement contents and low moisture contents, cannot be mixed thoroughly in small free-fall mixers.[3.21] Pan or trough forced action mixers should always be used.

Mixes made with MPCs become more free flowing the more they are mixed, and therefore free-fall mixers can be used in this case.

3.12.4. Placing, compaction, and texturing

Repairs to any area should be completed within 48 hours of it being prepared, in order to minimize the risk of carbonation of the cement at the bond interface. If a longer delay occurs, the prepared surface should be 'cleaned' by washing with a 10% solution of hydrochloric acid, applied using a water can with a sprinkler rose. Protective clothing and goggles should be worn when preparing the acid, and when brushing it over the surface being cleaned. For a few seconds the acid will react with the cement, and when the effervescence stops the surface should be washed thoroughly with clean water, removing any loosened debris. At this stage, the acid will have been neutralized by the cement and the washing can safely be allowed to run to waste. An acid treated area must be thoroughly washed before the acid has a chance to form a gel.

An area that is being repaired with a Portland cement mix should be well wetted with water, ideally overnight, to minimize suction. Immediately before placing the mix, any free water on the surface should be removed, first by brushing and then by blowing the area with oil-free, compressed air. Oil traps on the compressors must be checked daily, as oil blown on to the surface at this stage will result in the preparation work being abortive.

Some engineers like to apply either a neat cement or 1:1 sand:cement grout, often with styrene–butadiene rubber (SBR) added, to act as a bonding aid. The author has not found this necessary, but if grouts are used, they must be brushed out, to a very thin layer, which *must not* dry out before the topping mortar or concrete is placed. Probably the main benefit of a grout is that it coats any small particles that have blown on to the prepared surface and allows them to combine with the body of the repair material, without harm. The repair mix should be spread evenly, and with a surcharge above the surrounding surface level of 25% of the final repair depth. Suitably sized battens, placed on the sides of the repair area aid striking-off to a uniform level, and spreading. The repair mix is then compacted by intensive surface vibration, this being necessary to fluidize the low workability mix, and to flow the paste fraction into the rough surface texture of the base concrete. Once compacted, the surface is trowelled to match the levels of the main slab, and then textured, usually by transverse brushing, and is finally cured.

Because they are self-levelling, MPC mixes do not need to be vibrated and are just trowelled into place.

3.12.5. Curing

The importance of good curing of any cement based product cannot be overemphasized. Without curing, water will escape from the surface, which will leave voids and stop the cement hydrating. The end result will be a loss of surface strength and durability, which means a reduction in both abrasion and freeze/thaw resistance. With thin bonded toppings, curing is of even greater importance, as both the layer thickness and volume are small, so that even a marginal loss of water will be very serious. For this reason it is common practice to duplicate curing, first by spraying the surface with a reflective resin curing membrane, and in hot or windy weather additionally covering it with polythene sheeting or wet hessian. Curing should continue for as long as possible, up to say seven days, unless earlier opening is necessary.

3.12.6. Synthetic resin mortars

Synthetic resin mortars are used to a limited degree to repair scaled surfaces, but in the author's experience they do not always perform well, at least for external work, probably because of the differences in their thermal and other physical properties, when compared with those of the base concrete. Where they are used, because of a need for very early opening, the same degree of surface preparation is as essential as for cementitious repairs. Conversely, however, the surface of the concrete must be dry, and the suppliers recommendations on surface priming, materials batching, mixing and placing, must be strictly adhered to. Resins are most likely to be used for the repair of spalled joints, and for very small areas of surface damage.

3.13. Spalled joints

Joint arrises can spall for different reasons and to different depths, as explained in section 3.5. For convenience, the repair of these is described separately, as shallow and deep spalled joints.

3.13.1. Shallow spalling

Shallow spalls can often be removed, while at the same time creating a groove of uniform width, by sawing along a line outside the limit of the spall, as illustrated in Fig. 3.11, otherwise the arris has to be reformed, as described below.

3.13.2. Reforming shallow spalled joints

If the technique described in section 3.12.1 cannot be used, because it would create a too wide sealing groove, or the spalled length is short in relation to the total joint length, the arris can be reformed. Before reinstating the spalled concrete, the concrete near the joint should be 'sounded' with a steel rod and the prepared area cut back some 100 mm beyond any 'hollow' areas, and in any case at least 100 mm back from the joint, if a resin respair is intended, or 150 mm for a cementitious repair. The cutting-out should be as deep as the deepest spalling and should form a 'flat' base to the area. This can be done in the manner already described in section 3.12.1, for the repair of scaled surfaces, but usually all the work can be done with a single-headed scabbler. A collapsible joint filling strip is then installed, projecting below the bottom of the cut area, to ensure that the repair material cannot bridge the joint (see Fig. 3.22). Unprotected timber should not be used as a joint groove former if the repair is with cementitious material, since it will absorb water, swell, and put the newly set repair under stress, which can be sufficient to damage it, as well as making the timber difficult to remove. If both sides of a joint have spalled, there is no reason why both sides cannot be reformed at the same time, but again the bottom of the groove former must be set below the level of the deepest spalling to ensure that there will be no 'bridging' of the groove.

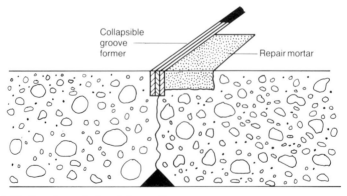

Fig. 3.22. Repair to shallow joint spall

The same Portland cement mixes as recommended for thin bonded toppings are best for these repairs, except for small areas, or where very rapid opening is essential. In these cases repairs can be effected with the aforementioned MPC mixes or synthetic resin mortars, strictly in accordance with the supplier's instructions.

3.13.3. Deep spalls

These go well below the sealing depth and are usually D shape in plan. No matter what the cause, this defect can only be rectified by making a full depth repair, as described in section 3.19.

3.14. Cracking of slabs

In section 3.3, cracks were classified by their direction and width, and probable reasons for their formation were also given. Because the crack classification, and whether or not the slab is reinforced, influences the choice of the best form of repair to adopt, repair methods for different types of cracks are discussed separately.

3.14.1. Narrow transverse cracks

In reinforced pavements narrow cracks need not cause any concern. Cracks of any width should not exist in unreinforced slabs, and if found, the list of causes of transverse cracking given in section 3.3.3 should be examined in an attempt to ascertain the cause. Repairs should be undertaken as soon as practicable. If the cause is excessive bay length, the cracked slab has to be broken-out and recast, creating a contraction joint midway between the existing joints.

If the cause is thought to be excessive sub-grade restraint, again the slab has to be broken-out and rebuilt. The opportunity should be used to examine both the sub-base and the slip-membrane and, if need be, they should be made good.

Cracking resulting from either too late sawing, or joint locking, also makes it necessary to remove the slab, and reconstruct. After the slab is broken-out, the dowel bars at the joints on either side should be examined. If the dowels are found to be outside the specified alignments, it may be possible to bend them to correct the alignment, in both the horizontal and vertical planes. If this can be done, the bars should be realigned, sheathed, and the slab recast. If the dowels are too badly misaligned to straighten, they will need to be sawn-off and replaced, as described in section 3.19, before the new slab is cast.

Some engineers consider it prudent to install reinforcement in a replacement slab, although not strictly necessary, as an insurance against a repetition of the problem.

3.14.2. Medium transverse cracks

If medium transverse cracks exist in unreinforced slabs they must be dealt with as described in section 3.14.1. They are simple to deal with in reinforced slabs, as the reinforcement will still be retaining aggregate interlock, but it is necessary to protect the steel by sealing the crack. To do this the top of the crack needs to be widened. The simplest way of widening is with a crack cutter, Fig. 3.17, and the groove formed should be at least 13 mm wide and 18 mm deep. This is to allow the sealant cross-section to be 13 mm × 13 mm and 5 mm below the road surface (see section 3.18). Alternatively, the crack can be widened with a single-head scabbling machine or, if it is sensibly straight, by making two parallel saw cuts straddling it.

3.14.3. Wide transverse cracks

Wide transverse cracks are a cause for concern and should be dealt with as quickly as possible, invariably by slab replacement, as described in section 3.19.

3.14.4. Longitudinal cracks

Possible reasons for longitudinal cracks are given in section 3.3.4. If they result from too great a slab width, uneven slab support, or the development of tensile stresses, due to compression along the pavement length, the cracks can be stitched.

This process is essentially the installation of tie-bars to prevent the crack opening. The bars are introduced through slots cut across the cracks. The slots, 25 to 30 mm wide and 470 mm long, are cut at 600 mm centres along the length of the crack and at approximately 90° to it. The depth of the slots should be about half the slab depth. Most chase cutting of this type has been with a single-head scabbler, as dry cutting is preferred, because the tie-bars are to be bedded on an epoxy resin mortar. The next stage is to drill vertical holes, 50 mm deep, at the ends of each slot. The debris is then removed, by blowing with oil-free compressed air. The holes, and the base of the slots, are then primed with resin and covered with an epoxy resin mortar, into which hooked, 16 mm dia., high yield deformed bars are pushed, until covered with mortar. Finally the slot is refilled to the road surface with either fine concrete or more resin mortar, which is then cured. The stitching should be continued in line with, and some 1 to 1·5 metres beyond, the end of the visible crack.

Once stitching has been completed, a sealing groove is chased or sawn, whichever is the most appropriate, along the line of the crack, which is finally sealed, as described in section 3.18.

Figure 3.23 shows a cross-section through a stitch repair, and Fig. 3.24 a plan view.

Cracking due to a misplaced bottom crack inducer can result in a wandering crack in the vicinity of the longitudinal sealing groove. This fault means that the longitudinal crack is now the joint, and the original sealing groove is redundant. A simple repair is made by chasing-out the crack, so that it can be sealed. Where the crack crosses the original sealing groove there is a risk of spalling, particularly if the angle of the intersection is acute. Any minor spalling that is caused when chasing-out the sealing groove can be made good with epoxy resin mortar. Although the original sealing groove is redundant it should be kept sealed to prevent detritus entering and causing it to spall.

3.14.5. Plastic cracks

These may be visible within an hour, or even less, of casting a slab. If seen, action should be taken to check the concrete production, particularly the entrained air content, and slab protection, to prevent more plastic cracks forming. Where plastic cracking does occur, it rarely penetrates the concrete to any great depth, at least initially. There is little evidence that the existence of plastic cracking reduces the performance of the slab, although when found it nearly always causes concern. Some engineers believe such cracks to be a point of incipient weakness, and that they will get deeper with the normal slab movements caused by the weather and traffic stresses. Plastic cracks rarely extend beyond the level of any rein-forcement and are commonly self-healing. To protect the steel, plastic cracks can be sealed by pouring in rubber latex emulsion, but this must be done soon after the fault is found otherwise the cracks will be filled with fine detritus, preventing the emulsion from entering.

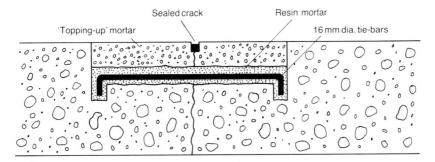

Fig. 3.23. Section through a 'stitched' repair

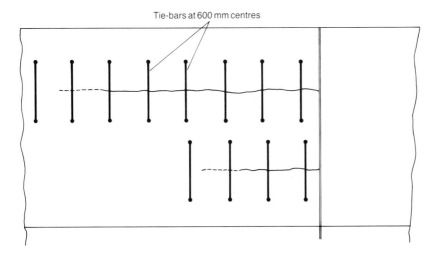

Fig. 3.24. Plan of 'stitched' cracks

Table 3.3. Effect of an acute angle on the stress caused by corner loading

Angle of corner	Stress: %
90°	100
80°	120
60°	175
40°	175

3.14.6. Miscellaneous cracks

Other cracks are normally corner cracks or cracks arising as a result of poor detailing, such as those that originate from gullies and inspection chamber positions. Corner cracks are most likely at undowelled joints, and if the slabs contain acute angles. Loads applied near corners cause the greatest stress but if the corner is acute the stress will be greatly magnified, as shown in Table 3.3.

If cracking results from the presence of an acute angle in a slab, steps must first be taken to correct the cause, one possible solution being illustrated in Fig. 3.25. First full depth saw cuts are made to allow removal of the concrete containing the crack. The vertical faces of the slab are then drilled to a depth of 200 mm, to receive 20 mm dia., high yield deformed steel tie-bars, at about 500 mm centres and at mid-slab depth. The tie-bars are bonded into the main slab with epoxy resin mortar. Before casting the new slab a sealing groove former is glued to the main slab.

The acute angle still exists in the reinstatement, but as this is a small slab it is subject to less stress than the original.

If the corner crack results from the absence of dowel bars, or a gross underestimate of traffic, it is necessary to make a full depth repair, as described in section 3.19, installing dowel bars at the same time.

Cracks originating from an intrusion into the slab, such as those illustrated in Fig. 3.8, can be sealed and/or stitched and sealed as described in sections 3.18 and 3.14.4. If the cracking is severe it could be more

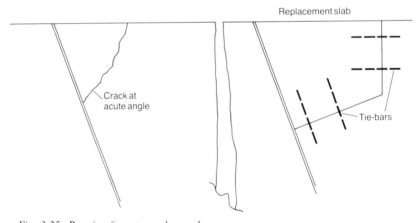

Fig. 3.25. Repair of acute angle crack

practical to reconstruct the whole slab, at the same time separating the service cover(s) with their own slab concrete surround. Surrounds should be reinforced and separated from the main slab by an expansion joint filler-board, the joints being sealed.

3.15. Rocking and settled slabs

Where sub-bases have become displaced resulting in 'stepping' at joints, or if excessive relative vertical movements of adjoining slabs occurs, the slabs will need to be underpinned. Slab movement can, in severe cases of sub-base displacement, be seen as a heavy vehicle passes by. More often it can be felt by the vibration of the slab, caused by traffic. Advice Note HA 6/80,[3.22] details a method of measuring the relative vertical movement of slabs, consisting of mounting a pair, or pairs of displacement gauges, straddling the joint, and driving a heavy vehicle slowly across the joint. Such testing can be useful in ascertaining the potential risk of slab fracture, or the risk of cracking of any overlay that may be applied.

Slab movement, on a larger scale, can occur due to major sub-grade settlements, also resulting in an unacceptable loss of riding quality.

Both joint movements and slab settlement can be rectified by the introduction of grout beneath the slabs, although this will not prevent further ground movements. There are two methods of introducing the grout, by pressure, or by vacuum, the latter in the UK being limited to one specialist firm, who operate in competition with pressure grouting specialists. Alternatively, settled slabs can be raised on support frames, and then stabilized by filling the resulting void with either concrete or grout, depending on the void size.

3.15.1. Pressure grouting

It is first necessary to estimate the extent of the void beneath the slab, and then to drill 50 mm dia. vertical holes through the slab, in a 1 metre grid pattern, starting about 0·5 metre from the slab edges, and extending over the void area. Next an airline is attached to the highest hole, and air is blown through to remove any water beneath the slab. This process is repeated at each drilled hole, working along and across to the lowest point. In addition to escaping from drilled holes, water may also escape from slab edges or through joints, which shows that their sealing is defective. Once any water has been removed, grout, normally cementitious, is introduced at the highest hole under a pressure of 3–4 bars (45–60 lb/in^2), care being taken to ensure that the slab is not raised, and that the grout is restricted to filling the void. Excessive line pressure can result in slab lifting. A simple and effective way of detecting if a slab is being lifted is to place pats of plaster across joints. If these crack, it indicates relative slab movement. Should such movements be detected, grouting can continue, but at a lower line pressure. When grout is seen exiting from adjoining holes in the slab, the inlet pipe(s) can be moved on. Once grouting is completed the holes can be filled and trowelled-off to road level. While grouting is in progress, care must be taken to determine where the grout is going to ensure that it is not entering the local drainage system, or service ducts.

Although it is possible to lift slabs intentionally by pressure grouting, the amount of lifting is difficult to control. Once a slab has been raised it cannot be lowered, therefore a mechanical lifting system (see section 3.15.3) is preferable.

3.15.2. Vacuum grouting

Vacuum grouting is a more recent method of feeding grout beneath slabs, developed by Balvac-Whitley-Moran Ltd. It results in a far better control of grout location. The slab to be underpinned is drilled in the same way as for pressure grouting, the holes being drilled in straight lines across the slab. Alternate lines of holes are then covered with steel or aluminium channel sections, laid as inverted Us, to form air ducts. The whole area is then covered with a plastic sheet, held down and sealed at its edges, usually with strips of wet clay. Vacuum tubes are attached to holes in the channels and through the plastic sheeting, and any underlying water is sucked out. Once the water flow stops, grout is fed in through the drilled holes between the vacuum ducts, and the plastic sheeting, as shown in Fig. 3.26. Once the void around a feed hole is filled, denoted by grout entering the vacuum line and trap, the line is disconnected and the process is repeated at the next duct, until void filling is completed. The plastic sheeting and channels are then removed and all the holes are topped up.

The equipment for vacuum grouting is mobile and relatively small, so that the amount of interference with traffic movement is minimal. Under-

Fig. 3.26. Vacuum underpinning

Fig. 3.27. Slab lifting frame

pinned areas can be opened to traffic soon after the completion of the operations.

3.15.3. Slab lifting

The lifting of slabs mechanically allows them to be raised to precise levels. If the settlement is large, the slabs can be lifted in a series of stages each of 50–60 mm. Lifts totalling heights well in excess of 300 mm have been carried out successfully.

The lifting device is essentially a number of space-frames, resting on hydraulic jacks. The slabs to be lifted are first drilled, for both the vacuum

Fig. 3.28. Full depth sawing

process, described earlier, and to receive anchor bolts, which are attached to the lifting points of the space-frames (see Fig. 3.27). The space-frames are currently designed to span a single slab width, although developments are in hand to allow complete carriageway widths to be lifted in one. Before lifting a single slab width, it is necessary to cut, by full-depth sawing, any tie-bars across longitudinal joints. This is illustrated in Fig. 3.28. Once slabs have beeen attached to the lifting frames, they are raised by manually operated hydraulic jacks, and before the void is filled, the exact height of the slab can be finely adjusted. If the lift is small, the created void is filled with grout by the vacuum process, which, as it packs the void, relieves the load on the jacks as shown by pressure gauge readings. If the void is large, it can be filled by blowing in fine dry concrete, which supports the slab, initially due to its mechanical stability, and later by the setting of the cement, dampened by the moisture from beneath the slab. The setting of the cement prevents the concrete migrating, as a result of traffic movements.

Once the slab has been lifted to the desired level and underpinned, the lifting frames removed and the holes filled with grout, it is ready for trafficking.

It would seem prudent to reinstall tie-bars between adjoining slabs. At the time of writing, this precaution had not been applied as part of the lifting process, but if it is adopted it could be done using the stitching process described in section 3.14.4.

3.15.4. Grouts used for underpinning

Grouts used for underpinning are usually cementitious, although synthetic resin grouts have also been used. They need to be very fluid to allow them to be blown or sucked into position. If too stiff, they will not be well dispersed beneath the slab, and may cause blockages in the pipework, and if too fluid they will flow too readily away from where wanted. Mixing is usually carried out in a colloidal mixer, and to improve the fluidity of the grout without using excess water, plasticizing agents are often added. To limit shrinkage the water:cement ratio should not exceed 0·45.

To reduce costs, and increase workability, mixtures of cement and pulverized fuel ash are often used, in the proportions of 1 part cement to 3 parts ash. Because both the neat cement and cement:pfa grouts are made entirely of fine materials, they are suitable for filling both small and large voids.

Both pressure and vacuum grouting are specialist techniques under continuous development, and it is advisable to obtain the views of at least one specialist contractor before undertaking any major slab raising or underpinning scheme.

3.16. Pavement overlays

3.16.1. Reasons for overlaying a concrete pavement

Some of the reasons and forms of overlaying a concrete pavement are listed in section 3.10. The basic forms of overlay are bituminous materials,

Table 3.4. Factors to be considered when designing an overlay

Surface condition of existing road	(*a*) overall good to fair (*b*) fair to poor (*c*) poor to very poor
Structural condition of the slab	(*a*) generally sound (*b*) considerable cracking (*c*) severe cracking
Relative vertical displacement	(*a*) stepping at joints and/or cracks (*b*) significant dynamic displacement by vehicles
Surface texture	(*a*) inadequate skid resistance in relation to traffic speed (*b*) poor surface water drainage

concrete or blocks. When selecting the type of overlay to employ several factors must be considered, as listed in Table 3.4, the final choice depending very much on the reasons for the overlay and the structural condition of the pavement.

3.16.2. Surface condition

Extensive surface scaling may result in a surface that has an unsatisfactory riding quality or appearance, both faults that can be rectified by resurfacing, using one of the three basic methods.

3.16.3. Structural condition of the slab

If the existing slabs are subject to excessive movements at joints, due to contraction and expansion, large vertical movements caused by lack of support or adequate load transfer, or slabs rocking, the performance of any surfacing will not be satisfactory in the long term. Such faults must be rectified before resurfacing is undertaken. The range of bituminous options, and factors which influence their choice are considered in Part II, and the forms of overlay considered here are limited to the use of either concrete or concrete blocks.

3.16.4. Concrete overlays

Concrete overlays have been used extensively overseas and have proved to be an effective method of restoring and strengthening concrete pavements. There is also long-term evidence of their success in the UK on airfield pavements.

The structural design of overlays relies essentially on an empirical method, using an equation developed originally by the Corps of Engineers in the USA.[3.23] The basic equation is

$$H_s^n = H_d^n - (CH_e^n)$$

where H_s is the thickness of the surfacing; H_d is the thickness of the slab that would be required if a new pavement were being built on the existing sub-grade; H_e is the thickness of the existing slab and n is a variable the value of which depends on the quality of the bond between the old slab and the overlay and is 1 for fully bonded overlays, 2 for unbonded slabs, 1·4 for partially bonded slabs. C is a factor which depends on the structural condition of the existing slab and modifies the overlay thickness to obtain the maximum benefit from it.

If the existing slab is in good condition, with only a few structural cracks, C is given a value of 1. At the other end of the scale, when the existing slab is badly broken and cracked, C is given a value of 0·35. It is the engineer's task to use his judgement and experience to evaluate C in a particular case, and between these two extremes. With a fully bonded slab system, the old slab and the overlay are integrated and behave as a single slab. To obtain the full bond the surface of the existing slab must be thoroughly cleaned to remove all traces of oil and rubber deposits, road lining materials and anything else that will prevent the overlay bonding. As long as the existing surface is sound, this is not a difficult operation and can be carried out with shot-blasting or flailing equipment used to clean floors, or by high-pressure water jetting, using equipment of the type shown in Fig. 3.29. As with thin bonded surfacing, already described in section 3.12, the surface of the old slab should be wetted, but without any free water on the surface at the time the surfacing is laid.

After preparation the surface is paved in the same way as normal paving, using slip-form pavers or rail mounted plant or by semi-manual methods, but omitting the separation/slip-membrane.

Joints and cracks in the existing slabs will reflect through the overlay, and therefore it is necessary to form joints immediately over those in the

Fig. 3.29. High pressure water blasting equipment

old slabs. If the existing slab contains longitudinal cracks, these must be stitched prior to casting the overlay (see section 3.14.4).

If the existing slab is badly cracked it can be overlaid with an unbonded, concrete overlay. In this situation the old slab will not contribute a great deal structurally and should be considered merely as a good sub-base. There is no need to prepare the old slab, *per se*, beyond sweeping off any loose debris. It must then be covered with a separating medium, which can be a continuous layer of plastic sheeting provided that the old slab is reasonably flat, the joints are not badly 'stepped', and the pavement overall meets the surface regularity for a sub-base.[3.4] If not, a thin regulating layer of fine asphalt can be used, this also acting as a separating membrane. The new slab is constructed in the normal way and, because the new and old slabs are separated, the joint spacing in the overlay can be entirely different from that of the old base slab.

With the partially bonded system, no positive action is taken to achieve bonding, but the old slab is cleaned to encourage some degree of bonding. This partial bond allows the old slab to make some contribution to the overall pavement strength. The joints in the overlay must be made to coincide with those of the old slab, in order to avoid reflective cracking.

There is a growing use of continuously reinforced concrete overlays for both bituminous and concrete roads carrying heavy traffic, as an economic means of creating roads with a low level of maintenance.[3.24]

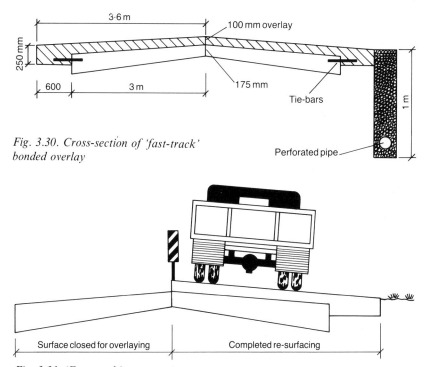

Fig. 3.30. Cross-section of 'fast-track' bonded overlay

Fig. 3.31. 'Fast-track' construction sequence

3.16.5. Fast-track construction

One excuse that has been used in the past for not using concrete overlays for either bituminous or concrete roads has been the belief that it will always result in long closure periods, an excuse that rarely stands up to close scrutiny. If necessary, towards the end of the overlay construction period, it is possible to minimize the delays due to curing by using concrete with a more rapid strength gain than normal. A considerable amount of work has been carried out in the USA using so-called 'fast-track' paving, allowing opening in 24 hours or less, after casting. An example of such a project in Iowa, using a thin-bonded, fast-track overlay, has been described by Calvert and Lane.[3.25] When the work was undertaken, the existing road was 50 years old, 6 m wide, and made with a tapered cross-section with an average thickness of 215 mm. During the work, the road was widened to 7·3 m, and provided with a bonded overlay 100 mm thick. Figure 3.30 shows a cross-section through the completed road and Fig. 3.31 indicates the construction sequence. The concrete contained 385 kg/m^3 of rapid hardening cement and 40 kg/m^3 of pulverized fuel ash. It was air-entrained and also incorporated a water reducing agent. This mix gave a cylinder strength of 24 N/mm^2 (32 N/mm^2 equivalent cube strength) at 24 hours. The use of fast-track construction is growing rapidly in the USA, and represents a major form of work in their maintenance and improvement works.

3.16.6. Concrete block overlays

Concrete blocks, laid in the standard way,[3.26] have been used to overlay both concrete and bituminous pavements. Originally block overlays were adopted purely for aesthetic reasons, but from work by Emery,[3.16] it is now known that they also give considerable structural enhancement.

Before overlaying a concrete pavement with blocks, any existing service chambers will have to be raised, and, possibly, kerbs. Joints and any medium or wide cracks should be covered with a metre wide strip of 250 μm gauge plastic, to prevent the loss of laying course sand. Block laying is then carried out in the normal way.[3.26,3.27]

Although this form of overlay has great potential for a wide range of work, it is doubtful whether it will ever provide a surface regularity of adequate quality for high-speed traffic. It has, however, been used very successfully for roads carrying heavy traffic travelling at speeds up to about 60–70 km/h.

3.16.7. Inadequate riding quality

Construction faults may result in a road with a surface regularity unacceptable to road users. As a general rule, the faster the traffic speed, the greater the need for a level surface. The basic problem may be either a local high area, a 'bump' or a depression. Depressions may be made good with a thin bonded topping, applied as described in section 3.12. The removal of bumps involves grinding off the high area with a purpose made 'bump-cutter', fitted with a cutting head of, either a gang of closely spaced saw blades on a single shaft, or some form of flailing device mounted towards the centre of a long wheel-based machine. Small high spots can be cut down with multi-headed scabblers, as long as they are operated with skill.

3.16.8. Inadequate surface texture

Surface texture is important in providing skid resistance for high speed traffic. In new concrete this is usually achieved by drawing a steel bristle broom across the slab. When this texture is worn away, it can be restored by transverse grooving, usually with a multi-bladed sawing machine having a working head width of at least 500 mm. The grooves should be narrow, about 3 mm and nominally 4 mm deep. In order to prevent the interaction of tyre and road surface from generating a single tone note, the groove spacing has to be irregular. The average groove spacing specified[3.4] is about 42 mm, varied, in a random manner, between 30 to 50 mm. Figure 3.32 shows a texturing machine.

There is no doubt that grooving does increase the noise level, both at the road side, and in a vehicle, but it has also been demonstrated that a good level of resistance to wet skidding cannot be achieved without incurring noise generation, no matter how the texture is created.[3.28]

Another form of machine, developed in Canada for grooving both concrete and asphalt, uses reflex-percussive equipment. This equipment

Fig. 3.32. Hardened grooving in progress

was included in a testing programme by the Federal Aviation Administration (FAA) in the USA, made to examine the improvement in the braking performance of aircraft resulting from different forms of grooving.[3.29] These tests showed a considerable improvement in resistance to skidding by a number of different forms of transverse grooving, and the unsymmetrical, vee-shaped grooving, formed by the percussive system was significantly cheaper than grooving by sawing. Unfortunately, the investigations by the FAA did not include noise measurement, presumably because noise generated by the rolling tyres would be insignificant when compared with aircraft engine noise.

3.17. Trench openings

Very successful, long lasting repairs can be achieved in concrete pavements, but they demand care and attention to detail.

3.17.1. Transverse trenches under unreinforced concrete roads

Where a trench crosses a road, the simplest and probably cheapest solution for the final reinstatement is the complete removal and replacement of the damaged slab between the joints on either side. If the trench crosses a joint, it will be necessary to break-out the slabs on either side, and rebuild both with a new joint in the same location as the original.

3.17.2. Transverse trenches under reinforced concrete roads

If the trench is some way from a transverse joint, two saw cuts, some 25 to 30 mm deep, are first cut parallel to the line of the trench. These cuts should be at least 1 metre apart and, if the trench has already been made, at least 300 mm back from the break-out lines. The concrete between the saw cuts is then broken out, but ensuring that the reinforcement is not broken. Once exposed, the reinforcement should be cut on a line approximately at the centre line of the trench, and the steel bent back to give access for the trench excavation. The exposed faces of the concrete should be broken out to provide sensibly vertical faces beneath the saw cuts. Once the trench has been back filled, and the sub-base reinstated, side forms are then fixed and the sub-base covered with a plastic slip membrane. The concrete forming the bottom of the repair is then placed, and compacted with a poker vibrator, after which the reinforcement is bent back to its correct location and an additional overlapping mesh wired to it. The top course concrete is then placed, compacted with a beam vibrator, finished to level, textured and cured. The new concrete will form a practically invisible repair that will not settle after a few weeks in service.

3.17.3. Longitudinal trenches under concrete pavements

These are the most difficult to reinstate. If the trench is near the slab edge, the concrete nearest the inner edge of the trench will have to be sawn through to give a clean vertical face. Concrete beyond this saw cut is then broken out to give access to the trench line. Once the work associated with the trench is completed, it is back-filled and the sub-base is reformed, after which the vertical slab edge is drilled to receive tie-bars, as described in section 3.19. Once the tie-bars are installed a groove former is glued to the edge of the concrete, the formwork is set-up, the sub-base level is regulated, a membrane is installed and the slab is recast. A strip of this type should not be less than 1 metre wide, and because it is both narrow, and its contraction restrained by the main slab, it should be reinforced, even if the main slab is not. It will have to be textured to match the existing slab as far as is practicable, and cured until strong enough to be opened to traffic. A similar technique can be used if the trench is to one side of a longitudinal joint.

If the trench follows a line coincidental with half the slab width, it will probably be most economic to replace the whole of the slab between longitudinal joints. In this case, when the slab is broken-out, the longitudinal joint tie-bars are left in place for re-use when the slab is recast. Before reconstructing the slabs, a joint forming strip should be glued to the vertical edge(s) of the retained edge(s).

3.18. Joint sealing

With a well-designed and constructed concrete road the amount of maintenance will be slight, but it is essential to monitor the performance of the joint seals, ideally by inspection annually. If a sealant fails, it can lead to damage to the slab, its sub-base, and the sub-grade. The different forms of resulting faults have been described earlier, but any of these will be much dearer to rectify than the cost of maintaining sealants.

The ideal time for joint resealing is, theoretically, when the slabs are in the maximum state of contraction, i.e. during winter. However, joints cannot be sealed when the grooves are wet, because the moisture will prevent bonding. Also, liquid sealants, or their primers, should not be applied if the slab temperature is below 5°C. Resealing is therefore mainly limited to the autumn and spring periods. To obtain the maximum life from the sealant, thorough cleaning and groove preparation is essential, and methods of doing this are now outlined.

3.18.1. Cleaning of sealing grooves

Before the old sealant is removed, it warrants examination in an attempt to ascertain the cause of its failure. It may have broken from the groove wall, be split, or be full of sand and small fragments of stone. If the sealant has split or broken from the groove walls, it could mean that the groove is too narrow in relation to the joint movement. Alternatively, the peeling may be the result of inadequate cleaning of the groove prior to its sealing. Splitting may indicate that the sealant was bonded to the base of the sealing groove, or that a hot-applied material had been overheated and as a result lost much of its elasticity. Detritus penetration indicates the use of a too soft sealant for the particular road.

Before any joint can be resealed the old sealing material has to be removed, initially by ripping out the bulk with the point of a pick. Alternatively, if the groove width will permit, it can be both cleaned and widened by sawing. The grooves should be re-inspected after the initial cleaning, looking for any arris spalling that may have occurred too extensively to be dealt with by joint widening, in which case the arrises will have to be reformed. This may be done by using either the thin-bonded cementitious repair technique, section 3.13, or, if the lengths of spalling are very short, by making good with synthetic resin mortar. The final sealing groove widths and depths should be those shown in Table 3.5, but in no case should they be wider than 40 mm for transverse grooves, or 30 mm for longitudinal joints. If the initial inspection showed that sealants had failed by detachment from the walls, or by splitting, and that the sealing grooves were narrower than those shown in Table 3.5, consideration should be given to opening the groove to the maximum appropriate width. Next, if the walls of the groove have not been cleaned by re-sawing, they must be cleaned, either by blasting with abrasive grit, or with high-pressure water. Equipment is available that automatically directs grit on to the walls, rather than to the base of a groove, and leaves them with a sandpaper like texture. Finally, residual dust and grit are blown away using an oil free air-line with a minimum pressure of 7 bars (100 lb/in^2). If the joint has been cleaned with high-pressure water, the groove walls must be allowed to dry.

3.18.2. Preparation of the cleaned sealing groove

The base of the groove must be covered to prevent the sealant bonding to it. If the base is such that the sealant width (mm):sealant depth − 5 mm ratio is between 1:1 and 1:2, it is only necessary to place a self-adhesive, bond breaking tape along the base of the groove. If it is too great in relation to its width, it must be caulked with either a closed cell foamed plastic ribbon or a single strand paper rope. Additionally, if a hot-applied sealant is to be used, any plastic ribbon must be checked to ensure that it will not dissolve at the sealant application temperature. Whatever the

Table 3.5. Dimensions of joint sealants

Joint spacing: m	Minimum width: mm	Minimum depth of seal: m		Depth below surface: mm
		Cold poured	Hot applied	
Transverse				
Contraction				
15 or less	13	13	13	5 ± 2
15–20	20	15	20	5 ± 2
20–25	25	20	25	5 ± 2
Greater than 25	30	20	25	7 ± 2
Expansion	30	20	25	7 ± 2
Warping	10	10	13	5 ± 2
Longitudinal	10	10	13	0–5
Gullies etc.	20	15	20	0–3

caulking material, it must be a tight fit in the groove, to make sure that it stays at the correct level while the sealant is placed, and will not let any sealant by-pass it. It is pushed down to level most easily, by using a hand-held flanged wheel run along the top of the groove, but alternatively, it can be pushed into place with the aid of a strip of wood.

If the groove is too narrow, it must be sawn or ground to the minimum depth required to give a sealant width: depth ratio of at least 1:1. The ends of the sealing grooves will need to be caulked to prevent fluid sealant leakage. The walls of the groove are then primed by brush or spray application, as recommended by the supplier. Primers are often supplied as two part packs, which must be thoroughly mixed in accordance with the manufacturer's instructions.

There are both minimum and maximum times after priming, within which the sealant must be applied. These times vary with the primer formulation and with the ambient temperature, and again the manufacturer's instructions must be followed.

3.18.3. Preparation and application of hot applied sealants

Hot applied sealants are produced in two basic forms for road use — pitch/PVC to ASTM D3406[3.30] or ASTM D3569[3.31] and rubberized bitumen to BS 2499[3.32] — each of which have to be heated to allow them to be applied. To avoid degradation of the rubber or PVC, heating must be done with care and in accordance with the manufacturers' instructions. The range, between the application, and the maximum heating temperature, to avoid materials degradation is small, typically 135° to 150°C. This means that it is essential to carry out melting in a thermostatically controlled container, usually also used for application, that heats uniformly, avoiding 'hot spots'. The sealant must be applied, within a few hours of being melted, into dry sealing grooves. Application is either through a hand held lance, or a spout, connected to the melter-applicator. Both are fitted with a cut-off valve, so that the person doing the sealing has complete control of material flow. The temperature of the concrete forming the groove should not be less than 5°C, otherwise the sealant will chill rapidly, resulting in poor adhesion. Heating the concrete, to allow working in cold weather, or as a means of drying the concrete, is not recommended for two reasons: (a) applied heat will soon be lost into the body of the concrete, and (b) as it cools internal water will be drawn towards the groove surface.

3.18.4. Mixing and application of cold poured sealants

Cold poured sealants are either polysulphide or polyurethane based to BS 5212[3.33] or silicone based to BS 5889,[3.34] and are supplied in two-part or three-part packs. Mixing full packs of each of the components supplied is essential, in order to realize the sealant's full potential. A slow-speed, mechanically powered paddle-mixer should be used, mixing one full batch at any one time. Once mixed the sealant is poured, usually directly from the mixing can, bent to form a pouring spout.

Where local repairs to sealants are required, cold materials are most practical as they need very little specialist application equipment.

3.18.5. Sealing cracks

Where it is necessary to seal cracks they must first be widened to at least 13 mm, either by sawing or with a crack cutter. This is necesssary to allow practical pouring of the sealant, and to avoid subsequent over-strain. Once cut, the groove over the crack is cleaned out with compressed air, primed, and sealed in the same way as a joint.

3.18.6. General comments

All the sealing materials listed are available in oil-resistant grades, which are recommended for sealing joints in any pavement where there is a risk of significant oil or fuel spillage.

Silicone based sealants, to BS 5889,[3.34] which are cold applied have a relatively low order of strain capacity and their use must be limited to tied joints, or cracks where movement is very restricted.

3.19. Full depth reconstruction

Methods of doing this, where the slab has to be broken into to dig a trench, were described in section 3.17.

Where a full depth reconstruction is necessary to repair deep spalling, a different technique is required, as a working joint has to be created as part of the repair. Another example is where full depth reconstruction is needed to rectify wide transverse cracking in a reinforced slab, which indicates a locked joint near the crack, a lack of reinforcement, or a lack of reinforcement overlap. Whatever the reason, the crack will need to be made into a joint. As stated earlier any cracking in an unreinforced slab is best rectified by rebuilding the defective slab.

3.19.1. Rectifying a deep spalled joint

Spalling may be apparent on one or both sides of the joint, but in any case is serious. If the road is fairly new it indicates the most likely problem to be poor dowel alignment, a fault that can now be detected from the road surface.[3.11] If the road is several years old, it could be due to expansion of the dowel bars as they rust, which indicates inadequate sealant mainte- nance. In any case, the concrete on either side of the joint will have to be removed, and the joint reconstructed. Two ways of dealing with this are detailed below.

3.19.2. Complete joint construction

First, a saw cut is made to a depth of 25–30 mm back 1 m from, and parallel to, the original joint line. The concrete is broken-out between the joint and the cut, taking care not to damage the reinforcement which, when found, must be bent back to allow access to the bottom part of the slab. Breaking-out must be done carefully, and to form sensibly vertical faces below the saw cuts. Once the old concrete has been broken out, the loose debris removed, and the sub-base made good, a new joint assembly is set up on a slip-membrane. The type of joint, contraction or expansion, whichever was needed originally, should be used again. The dowels must be correctly aligned and firmly supported and sheathed, as described in the

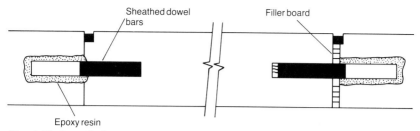

Fig. 3.33. Dowelled expansion/contraction joint as part of full depth repair

Department of Transport Specification.[3.4] If only one lane is to be repaired, the joint must also line up with the joint in the adjoining lane. The existing tie-bars are bent back, into where the slab is to be recast. The slab is then rebuilt, compacting the bottom course with internal vibrators, after which, the reinforcement is bent back to its original location, then the top concrete is placed and compacted with a beam, finished to level, textured, and cured. Before the repair is opened to traffic the joint will need to be sealed. This is an ideal situation for the use of a preformed sealant as this can be installed with less delay than for poured materials, but the groove will need to be sawn to ensure a uniform groove width.

3.19.3. Replacing failed dowel bars

Where dowel bars are found to be badly misaligned, or corroded through, new ones will have to be installed. The slab on one side of the existing joint is broken-out, by first making a saw cut, 25–30 mm deep, and about 1 m back from the joint line. The concrete is broken-out and the reinforcement retained, as described earlier. The exposed dowel bars are cut-off, flush with the vertical face. Horizontal holes, large enough to receive 20–25 mm diameter bars, are then drilled at mid-slab depth and at 300 mm centres, but clear of the old dowel locations. These holes should be 200 mm deep to receive 400 mm long mild steel dowel bars. The holes are blown clean and then part filled with an epoxy resin mortar, followed by grease-free dowel bars. The dowel bars must be supported in their correct alignment until the mortar has set, after which the slab is recast in the usual way. As shown in Fig. 3.33 both expansion and contraction joints can be rebuilt in this way.

3.19.4. Installing tie-bars

If a slab has been broken-out it may be necessary to install tie-bars along longitudinal joints between new and old slabs, or to provide a tie across a transverse construction joint.

Tie-bars are installed in a similar manner to that used for dowel bars, but as no movement is intended there is no need to worry about alignment. Tie-bars should be 20 mm in diameter, or for slabs greater than 225 mm deep, 25 mm diameter, of high yield deformed steel. The bars, 400 mm long and at 600 mm centres, are installed at mid-slab depth. Figure 3.34 shows a typical section through such a joint.

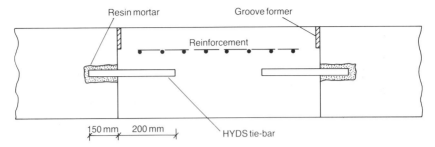

Fig. 3.34. Tied longitudinal repair

3.20. Summary

The following few words are brief reminders of points made previously, and considered essential for any highway maintenance engineer, who has roads with concrete running surfaces in his care. This part of the book outlines the causes of problems that may be found with a concrete pavement, but it is not meant to imply that all, or even any of these faults, are common in concrete roads. Because of the nature of the faults, mainly due to construction errors, it is not possible to forecast every type of problem that may occur, but it is hoped that the information given, combined with useful information in the various references, will enable a qualified highway engineer to rectify any fault that he may find. It is wrong to claim that concrete roads will not require maintenance, but if the road has been correctly designed and built, maintenance will be of a low order. Annual inspections of joint sealants are recommended, and if this is not possible, inspection intervals should not exceed three years. During these inspections the general condition of the joints should also be examined, as this will give a good clue to the future behaviour of the road. There is no doubt that the most vulnerable part of any concrete pavement is its joints, and these demand the greatest attention both in construction and in maintenance.

PART II. BITUMINOUS PAVEMENTS
3.21. Historical use of flexible construction

The historical development of roads can be traced for several thousand years, dating back to examples of ancient constructions in Crete, China and Egypt, which offer evidence of man's need to reduce the difficulty of travel, particularly when transporting heavy burdens. A form of asphaltic construction appears to have been used in the processional road at Aibur Shabu in Babylon dated 600 BC shown in Fig. 3.35.[3.35] In Crete, the riding surface of basalt flagstones was founded on layers of clay and stones set in plaster, and many roads to this day utilize the routes formed by Roman military engineers using multi-layer construction of stones graduated in size from large broken stones at the base to gravel and sand surfacing layers.

The advantages of constructing with angular interlocking hard materials were established at an early stage, and in Britain this technique

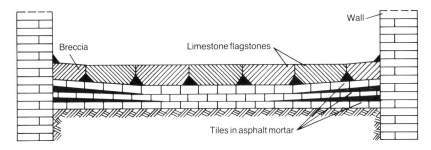

Fig. 3.35. Use of asphalt mortar in processional road at Aibur Shabu, Babylon, about 600 BC

is further associated with McAdam who convinced the Government that expenditure on roads, formed with a granular stone surfacing some 250 mm thick, would improve journey times for coaches. At this stage, the construction did not include a binder, and relied entirely on interlock of the stone for its load carrying capacity.

The first example of a rolled asphalt pavement is believed to have been in America, in about 1870, where a binder produced from powdered natural rock asphalt was used. Such materials, which were imported, proved to be expensive, and the search for, and improvement of, cheaper alternatives commenced.

Continued research and development, aimed at clarifying and advancing design knowledge, and improving both materials and laying techniques, has resulted in a range of materials for road construction covered by standard specifications. Advice contained in documents such as Road Note 29[3.36] enables engineers to match the anticipated traffic loading with the thickness of construction, and the strength of the sub-base material, to give a desired life in terms of the number of standard axle passes that the road can sustain. Similar procedures enable the maintenance engineer to modify or replace existing construction, aided by information gained from carriageway surveys and monitoring routines, as detailed in Chapter 8.

Great Britain is one of the few countries in the world where the whole of the public road system, of some 340 000 km, has some form of all weather surfacing. This represents a maintenance task amounting to approximately two billion square metres of surfacing of varying age, material and condition. The range of materials and techniques available requires the maintenance engineer to develop knowledge and experience in the performance and cost of alternatives for a variety of situations. The following are definitions and materials most commonly encountered. Further information can be obtained from the respective British Standards cited below.

3.22. Definitions used in highway works

The following is a list of definitions commonly used in highway works.[3.37, 3.38]

Sub-grade: upper part of the soil, natural or constructed, which supports the loads transmitted by the overlaying road structure.

Sub-grade improvement layer (capping layer): layer of granular or treated material at the top of the sub-grade to provide improved foundation for the pavement.

Pavement: road structure above the sub-grade.

Rigid pavement: pavement in which the main structural element is a high strength concrete slab that also provides the wearing surface.

Continuously reinforced concrete pavement: rigid pavement or rigid composite pavement in which the high-strength concrete slab is reinforced and has no construction or expansion joints.

Rigid composite pavement: pavement in which the main structural element is a high strength concrete slab over which a bituminous surface is applied.

Flexible composite pavement: pavement in which the roadbase is cement bound.

Flexible pavement: pavement in which the roadbase is non-cement bound.

Road formation: surface of sub-grade in its final shape after completion of earthworks.

Sub-base: one or more layers of material placed immediately above the formation.

Roadbase: one or more layers of material placed above the sub-base that constitutes the main structural element of a flexible or a composite pavement.

Basecourse: course forming part of the surfacing immediately below the wearing course.

Wearing course: part of the surfacing, the surface of which is in contact with the traffic.

Surfacing: that part of the pavement above the roadbase.

Regulating course: course of variable thickness applied to a road surface to adjust the shape in preparation for an overlaying course of regular thickness.

Tack coat: thin film of binder to improve the adhesion between two courses.

Bitumen: viscous liquid or solid consisting essentially of hydrocarbons and their derivatives, which is soluble in trichloroethylene and is substantially non-volatile and softens gradually when heated. It is black or brown and possesses water proofing and adhesive properties. It is obtained by refinery processes from petroleum and is also found as a natural deposit or as a component of naturally occurring asphalt in which it is associated with mineral matter.

Cut-back bitumen: bitumen whose viscosity has been reduced by blending with a suitable 'volatile' diluent.

Bitumen emulsion: dispersion of bitumen in water with an emulsifying agent.

Anionic bitumen emulsion: bitumen emulsion in which the emulsifying agent coats the droplets of bitumen with a negatively charged organic ion.

Cationic bitumen emulsion: bitumen emulsion in which the emulsifying agent coats the droplets of bitumen with a positively charged organic ion.

Aggregate: crushed rock, gravel, sand and slag which, when held together by a binding agent, forms the substantial part of such materials as concrete, asphalt and coated macadam.

Filler: fine non-plastic mineral matter used to stiffen bituminous binders and bituminous mixtures and to assist in filling voids in the mixtures.

Binder: bituminous or tar material that has adhesive properties.

Modified binder: bituminous binder, the properties of which have been modified by the incorporation of an additive.

Rolled asphalt: mixture of aggregate and bituminous binder used as a dense wearing course, basecourse and roadbase.

Design-mix asphalt: wearing course of rolled asphalt in which the bituminous binder content of the mixture is determined by specified mechanical tests.

Coated macadam: graded aggregate that has been coated with bitumen and/or a road tar in which a major part of the strength is derived from interlocking of the aggregates.

Pervious macadam: coated macadam in which the aggregate is graded to facilitate rapid drainage of surface water.

Mastic asphalt: asphalt in which mineral matter is suitably graded to form an impermeable solid at normal temperatures, but sufficiently fluid for laying, usually by hand float, when heated.

Slurry seal: mixture of binder, fine aggregate and mineral filler with water added to produce a material of slurry consistency.

Surface dressing: layer, applied as a wearing surface, that consists of chippings lightly rolled into a film of bitumen, bitumen emulsion, cut-back bitumen, road tar, or the like.

Rut: groove or depression formed in a surface layer of a road by the action of traffic.

Fretting: loss of particles of aggregate from a wearing surface associated with deteriorating cohesion in a material.

Stripping: displacement of bituminous binder from the surface of aggregate, usually by the action of water.

Fatting up: development of a smooth texture on a wearing surface due to excess bituminous binder.

Bleeding: exudation of bituminous binder to form an exposed film on the wearing surface.

3.23. Basic materials

3.23.1. Aggregates

For satisfactory performance, the following properties of aggregates need to be considered

(*a*) mechanical strength
(*b*) surface texture
(*c*) particle shape

(*d*) resistance to polishing and skid resistance
(*e*) specific gravity
(*f*) water absorption
(*g*) chemical stability of aggregates
(*h*) particle size distribution
(*i*) resistance to abrasion
(*j*) resistance to frost
(*k*) affinity to bitumen.

Details of the tests necessary to determine the acceptability of aggregates are given in BS 812.[3.39]

3.23.2. Bitumen

Penetration grade bitumens for highway use are specified in terms of penetration (hardness) from 35 pen (hardest) to 300 pen (softest) and softening point, and must have a minimum permittivity value of 2·63. Required properties are as shown in Table 3.6 and further detailed in BS 3690: Part 1.[3.40] Cut-back bitumens are specified in terms of viscosity, as shown in Table 3.7, and are also detailed in BS 3690: Part 1.[3.40]

3.23.3. Filler

Material passing a 75 μm sieve, which, when added to a mix, must be limestone or Portland cement and have a bulk density in toluene of not less than 0·5 g/ml and not more than 0·9 g/ml. The required properties of the filler are detailed in BS 812: Part 1[3.39] and BS 594: Part 1: 1985[3.38] and BS 4987: Part 1: 1988.[3.41]

3.24. Stages of maintenance

Maintenance of roads using bituminous materials falls into three main activities.

(*a*) surface dressing treatments, using a thin coating of small sized stone, which is retained in place by bitumen sprayed on to the existing surface

(*b*) resurfacing, which may be subdivided into the removal of the existing surfacing and replacement by a similar treatment, and superimposition of a further thickness of bituminous material (overlay) on the existing surface or addition of bituminous surfacing to an existing concrete road

(*c*) reconstruction, which entails more costly removal of the full construction depth and the substitution of a newly designed alternative construction thickness, which may be entirely bituminous, concrete overlaid with bituminous surfacing or concrete throughout.

Each activity requires a process of redesign.

3.25. Pavement design

Modern pavement design, which consists of layered construction, each varying in composition, is shown in Fig. 3.36. The thickness of each layer

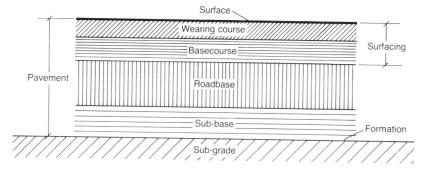

Fig. 3.36. The structure of a flexible road

will vary according to estimates of the traffic loading, the strength of the underlying soil and the chosen construction materials. A design method for new construction is given in the Transport and Road Research Laboratory (TRRL) publication LR 1132[3.42] and the tables and charts therein are also used in the estimation of residual life and overlay thickness required for maintenance operations. Structural design has been, and still is, based partly on empirical evaluation of the measured performance of full-scale experimental sections of road, but advances in theoretical design, based on multi-layer linear elastic models, have made predictive analytical designs more accurate in dealing with the long term performance of roads.

Therefore, the designs in LR 1132 have combined these approaches, and will give substantially greater performance than those based on Road Note 29.

3.25.1. Design life

Design life is now defined as 'that surface condition when rutting in the wheel path exceeds 10 mm, or when cracking is evident'. The design charts, detailing thicknesses of construction, are based on the assumption that there is an 85% probability that roads will last 20 years (without the need for strengthening overlays) before that condition is reached.

3.25.2. Traffic loading

Traffic loading is considered in Road Note 29 as the cumulative number of equivalent standard 80 kN axles. Since 1979 a rotating census of average daily flows of commercial vehicles has been carried out on 170 sites on three days per month, for each month of the year, to arrive at the annual average daily flow (AADF). Work carried out in the UK and USA has shown that pavement damage is approximately proportional to the fourth or fifth power of applied axle load, therefore, a 12 tonne axle is about five times more damaging than an 8 tonne axle. In structural design terms cars do not contribute to the failure of road pavements.

Clearly, the estimates of traffic growth are an important factor in assessing the design life requirements of the road.

Table 3.6. Properties of penetration grade bitumens

Property	Test method	Technically identical with	Grade									
			15 pen	25 pen	35 pen	40 pen HD	50 pen	70 pen	100 pen	200 pen	300 pen	450 pen
Penetration at 25°C	BS 2000, Part 49	ASTM D 5-73, IP 49/86	15 ± 5	25 ± 5	35 ± 7	40 ± 10	50 ± 10	70 ± 10	100 ± 20	200 ± 30	300 ± 45	450 ± 65
Softening point: °C Minimum Maximum	BS 2000, Part 58	IP 58/86	63 76	57 69	52 64	58 68	47 58	44 54	41 51	33 42	30 39	25 34
Loss on heating for 5 h at 163°C (a) loss by mass (maximum): % (b) drop in penetration (maximum): %	BS 2000, Part 45	IP 45/58(86)	0·1 20	0·2 20	0·2 20	0·2 20	0·2 20	0·2 20	0·5 20	0·5 20	1·0 25	1·0 25
Solubility in trichloroethylene (minimum): % by mass	BS 2000, Part 47	IP 47/85	99·5	99·5	99·5	99·5	99·5	99·5	99·5	99·5	99·5	99·5
Permittivity at 25°C and 1592 Hz (minimum)	BS 2000, Part 357	IP 357/83(86)			2·630	2·630	2·630	2·630	2·630			

Table 3.7. Properties of cut-back bitumens

Property	Test method	Technically identical with	Grade		
			50 s	100 s	200 s
Viscosity (STV*) at 40°C, 10 mm cup	BS 2000, Part 72	IP 72/86	50 ± 10	100 ± 20	200 ± 40
Distillation					
(a) Distillate to 255°C (% by volume maximum) 360°C (% by volume)	BS 2000, Part 27	ASTM D 402 73(82) IP 27/74(88)	1 8–14	1 6–12	1 4–10
(b) Penetration at 25°C of residue from distillation to 360°C	BS 2000, Part 49	ASTM D 5-73 IP 49/86	100–350	100–350	100–350
Solubility in trichloroethylene (% by mass minimum)	BS 2000, Part 47	IP 47/85	99·5	99·5	99·5

* Standard tar viscometer.

3.25.3. Summary of design trends and concepts in LR 1132

The road pavement design should ensure that there is minimal deformation in the sub-grade at the end of the design life. The strength and stiffness of the sub-grade affects the stress levels in the road pavement layers. The California Bearing Ratio (CBR value) test is a practical method of assessing sub-grade stiffness and strength.[3.43] Adequate drainage during construction and throughout the design life of the pavement is essential.

Where a CBR value of less than 5% is found, a suitable capping layer should be provided as a platform on which the subsequent road pavement layers can be constructed with minimum disruption from wet weather. As the capping layer is a platform on which to construct the pavement there is no need to increase its thickness relative to higher traffic loads.

Any material within 450 mm of the road surface must not be susceptible to frost, to eliminate frost heave. The fatigue life of hot rolled asphalt (HRA) roadbase at a given level of tensile strain is about twice that of dense bitumen macadam (DBM) roadbase because of the higher binder content. Therefore, designs have evolved in which the lower roadbase is HRA, with the remaining thickness of roadbase and base course in DBM, followed by an HRA wearing course.

Change in the nominal penetration of DBM roadbase, from say 100 pen to 50 pen, has little affect on fatigue, deformation or resistance, but at 20°C nearly doubles the stiffness modulus. Also, if additional filler is added, the resulting material, heavy duty macadam (HDM), has increased stiffness, and the engineer may utilize such materials either to reduce the overall pavement thickness or increase the life expectancy.

3.25.4. Design method

The design method generally used entails

(a)   determining mixed commercial vehicles in each direction
(b)   assuming rate of growth of traffic (graphs are given for various rates)
(c)   deciding on design life (normally 20 years followed by overlay)
(d)   obtaining number of cumulative commercial vehicles in nearside lane (from graphs)
(e)   converting to equivalent standard axles
(f)   determining or estimating CBR of sub-grade
(g)   determining thickness of sub-base (from graph)
(h)   selecting material for roadbase and obtaining thickness from appropriate graph together with thickness of surfacing
(i)   selecting basecourse and wearing course materials.

3.25.5. Overlay of an existing surface

Overlay of an existing surface is a means of extending the life of the pavement, if carried out before major deterioration has taken place. It is also necessary to survey the site and ensure that any proposed changes in level do not create drainage or threshold problems, since the level of kerbs and footways are usually affected, and any structures above the carriageway may be critical for height clearance. The reasons for overlaying are (*a*) to improve the structural strength of the pavement, necessary because of deterioration and/or increase in traffic loading

(*b*) loss of riding quality

(*c*) loss of an adequate skidding resistance.

Overlays are designed in a similar manner to new construction previously detailed, where additional strength is required. However, the important difference is that the design is based on an estimate of the residual strength in the existing pavement. One method of arriving at this value is by deflectograph survey, discussed in Chapter 8. This produces high speed data, which can be adjusted and related directly to the overlay thickness required to produce a future life under the anticipated traffic intensity. The method is detailed in TRRL document LR 571.[3.44]

3.25.6. Perceived riding quality

The perceived riding quality of a road, by a driver, is a function of the number and amplitude of surface irregularities, vehicle suspension design, traffic speed and driver expectations. Equipment such as the high-speed road monitor developed by the TRRL can measure the condition of surfacing and recording data quickly. Most unsatisfactory conditions can be corrected by the removal and replacement of the wearing course. However, underlying problems such as rocking concrete slabs, faulty expansion or contraction joints, and other pavement failure problems, need to be investigated and corrected by methods detailed in Part I.

3.25.7. Design of mix

In the maintenance context, the majority of asphalt used will be drawn from the recipe mixes shown in Tables A, B and C in BS 594: Part 1: 1985.[3.38] As the name implies, recipe mixes have evolved as a result of many years of field experience and experimentation, which can now be relied upon to produce satisfactory results under most conditions and using a wide variety of materials. The alternative 'design method' offers another approach that is intended to produce materials to meet the very high intensities of traffic found on some roads, and to take advantage of developments in research in materials and design theory. It is likely that the tolerance of the recipe mixes makes them the preferred choice for maintenance works on the majority of roads.

3.26. Coated materials

The materials in common use in the UK, with a brief description of their properties and applications, are listed below. Common to all blacktop material is the nature of the binder, which is thermoplastic, normally bitumen, a mixture of bitumen and naturally occurring bitumen (Trinidad Lake Asphalt), or bitumen modified by an additive. By far the greatest proportion of materials laid conform to BS 594[3.38] or BS 4987.[3.41]

3.26.1. Hot rolled asphalt — BS 594: 1985 (HRA)

Hot rolled asphalt is a dense, durable material, hot mixed and laid, which is used as a roadbase, basecourse or wearing course. Bound with penetration grade bitumen, in the range 35–100 pen, with the coarse and fine aggregate fractions separated on the 2–38 mm sieve. The aggregate is gap graded for wearing courses and relies on the sand/filler/bitumen mortar for performance rather than aggregate interlock. It is mainly the fine aggregate portion that determines the Marshall stability, flow,[3.45] and workability characteristics of the mix. It is the standard material specified for motorways and major roads, and the wearing course usually has a roughened surface for skid resistance, produced by the application of coated chippings rolled into the surface.

3.26.2. Coated macadams — BS 4987: 1988 (CM)[3.41]

Coated macadams are a range of materials from dense bitumen macadams to open graded macadams, and including for the first time pervious macadam. The performance of all these materials depends primarily on aggregate interlock. Compaction by rolling, or in open graded macadam by initial rolling and post-compaction under traffic, is therefore critical. The binder is predominantly bitumen (but has also been a bitumen–tar blend or tar), which acts as a lubricating agent, assisting compaction and binding the mineral aggregate together.

The final void (air) content of the compacted material is dependent on

(a) the grading, from the highest percentage (25%) in the open textured mixtures to the lowest (5%) in dense mixtures
(b) the aggregate friction, which relates to the micro-texture of the aggregate surface and resists the aggregate particles bedding closely together.

A void content is necessary because, if the voids were completely filled with binder, the material would be unstable under trafficking. Proneness to rutting and flushing of the binder to the surface, particularly in high ambient temperatures would also be increased. The void size is dependent on the grading of the aggregate.

Coated macadams can be used on estate roads, footpaths, playgrounds and play areas, and on lower category roads (less than two million standard axles). Dense bitumen macadam basecourse and roadbase, however, being effectively continuously graded and combined with harder grade bitumen, is stiff, and is a high load carrying material, which usually forms the bulk of the blacktop pavement thickness in the highest traffic category roads.

Pervious macadams are a range of wearing course materials with a designed void content in the range 20–25%. They act as a drainage layer capable of discharging surface water to the edge of the carriageway, and must be laid on impermeable mixtures. Attention to the means of drainage below the level of the running surface is necessary.

3.26.3. Heavy duty macadams HDM and DBM 50[3.46] — Specification for Highway Works[3.47]

Heavy duty macadam is a development of DBM roadbase to BS 4987: 1988: Cl. 5.1, with 3% additional filler and 50 pen bitumen; DBM 50, as the name implies, is DBM roadbase material mixed with 50 pen bitumen. Both materials show an increase in elastic modulus over conventional DBM (by a factor of 2·2 and 1·7, respectively). This increase in stiffness, and thus load bearing capacity, can be utilized to reduce the pavement thickness or to increase its life expectancy compared with the same thickness of conventional material.

3.26.4. Mastic asphalt (MA) — BS 1447: 1988[3.48]

Mastic asphalt is a dense, voidless material consisting of a hard bitumen, or bitumen/Trinidad Lake Asphalt (TLA) binder in the range 12–20 pen mixed with limestone mineral matter. It is generally hand laid with wooden floats, and mixed on the laying site by remelting the mortar blocks, and adding coarse aggregate. It is impermeable, and is used in special applications subject to very heavy traffic, for example, bus lay-bys, or where its resistance to deformation and fatigue, and waterproofing qualities, are particularly appropriate. Other uses include bridgedecks and multistorey car parks, where the improved performance justifies the extra cost.

3.26.5. Grouted macadam (GM)

Grouted macadam is a two-stage process, consisting of a predominantly single sized macadam, bound with a relatively hard binder (100–200 pen), and with a designed void content in the range 20–25%. After cooling to ambient temperature, a cementitious grout, consisting of cement/sand/water and polymer modifiers is vibrated into the remaining voids and is allowed to cure. It is used in areas where high resistance to point loading, and chemical and fuel spillage is required, e.g. container parks, docks, airport aprons, garage forecourts and has also been used experimentally in contraflow bus lanes, to resist the formation of wheeltrack rutting.

3.26.6. Dense tar surfacing (DTS) — BS 5273: 1985[3.49]

Dense tar surfacing is a dense, hot mixed wearing course material, bound with high viscosity tar, C46–C54, the coarse and fine aggregate fractions being separated on a 3·35 mm sieve. It has particular application where fuel spillage is a problem, such as motorway service areas and garage forecourts.

3.26.7. Modified binders and additives

Bitumen for the UK road market is manufactured to the requirements of BS 3690.[3.40] Consumption of bitumen was in 1987 some 63 million tonnes world wide (excluding communist countries for which statistics are not available). Of this total, over half, 33 million tonnes, was used in the US market and approximately 2·1–2·2 million tonnes in the UK. Modified bitumens currently form a very small percentage of these totals.

In recent years, a wide variety of modified bituminous materials has been developed, many marketed under invidual brand names. The maintenance engineer may understandably be baffled by choice, and by the claims of suppliers for materials, about which little is divulged, and for which experience is limited. Most approach the problem with care and are prepared to assist the development process by conducting well supervised and recorded trials. Help is at hand in this area from the County Surveyors Society, whose Maintenance Standards and Techniques Group have collected information nationwide on many of the available materials.

Some of the modifiers used with bitumen and their claimed properties are listed below.

Tar: blended with bitumen to increase resistance to fuel/oil spillage and improve weathering characteristics.

Refined Trinidad Lake Asphalt (TLA): blended with bitumen and kept in stirred tanks, because the naturally occurring TLA has a mineral content of approximately 37%. Improves weathering characteristics by evolving a sandpaper surface — and some evidence suggests greater strain values.

Gilsonite: a very hard, naturally occurring, mined bitumen that when added to refinery bitumen (5–10% addition) reduces permanent deformation in heavily trafficked pavements.

Carbon black: an addition of up to 20% of the total mix can improve asphalt durability and reduce the onset of rutting and deformation.

Sulphur: elemental sulphur substitutes for the bitumen and is fluid at the mixing and laying temperatures, but sets as crystalline sulphur at ambient temperatures. In the UK, mixes with 35% by weight of the bitumen have been laid. It increases the Marshall stability (by approximately 50%, and improves fatigue resistance and resistance to fuel spillage. It is widely used in the USA where sulphur is cheaper than bitumen, and can be used as a substitute for bitumen entirely. If mixed at too high a temperature there is a risk of hydrogen sulphide gas being given off, which is highly toxic, and becomes a health risk to the public and operatives.

Ethylene vinyl acetate (EVA): a copolymer derived from crude oil. A 5% addition to the bitumen content is commonly used and the modified binder is usually pre-blended. There is an increase in resistance to permanent deformation and if blended with higher grade bitumen, improvement in workability compared with 50 pen is achieved. Hence its usage in poor weather conditions, in effect to extend the laying season. S-type and F-type are available.

Polyethylene and polypropylene: these thermoplastic materials are derived by polymerizing olefins obtained from waste in various manufacturing processes. Blending of these thermoplastic polymers requires sophisticated equipment and is carried out in the absence of air. The optimum ratio is 93 parts bitumen to 7 parts polymer. Advantages include improved cohesion and flexibility, and resistance to deformation, and rutting.

'Natural' rubber (Department of Transport Specification for Highway Works Cl. 931 — Road Note 36):[3.50] usually incorporated with bitumen as either ground rubber powder, crumb or as latex. It is also used in surface dressing, where latex is easily incorporated with bituminous

emulsions. Generally, it increases viscosity and the elasticity of the binder, and aggregate adhesion, and in surface dressing, reduces bleeding of the binder to the surface. It is normally a 5% addition to the binder content.

Styrene–butadiene rubber–synthetic latex (SBR): a copolymer of hard and soft monomers in an aqueous emulsion. The ratio of styrene/butadiene is variable according to the end properties required. It increases viscosity at high temperatures, lowers viscosity at low temperatures, increases the adhesion to the aggregate and enhances the elasticity and resistance to deformation, especially at high ambient temperatures. It is generally a 3–7% addition to the binder content of the mix.

Styrene–butadiene–styrene (SBS): a block copolymer with the molecules in a linear or star configuration. It increases the softening point of a blended binder, but requires compatible bitumen for satisfactory blending. Increases in elasticity, aggregate retention, and resistance to deformation are gained. It is generally a 7% addition to the binder content.

Manganese catalyst: Chemcrete — an oil based liquid soap, containing manganese salts, which act as a catalyst when mixed with bitumen, causing controlled oxidation of the elements of the bitumen. Ketones are formed, cross-linking within the bitumen. There are improvements in Marshall stability with time, and the workability, adhesion and resistance to ageing are also enhanced. Generally, 1·5–2·0 of the active catalyst (by mass of bitumen) is added to the binder content.

Epoxy resin-modified asphalt: a two-component chemical reaction system added to bitumen, which greatly increases resistance to deformation, dynamic stiffness, and reduces fuel and oil damage. As it is a time-dependent reaction, care has to be taken to ensure that the material is mixed, transported, laid and compacted prior to the chemical reaction being completed.

Other bitumen modifiers, such as methacrylates, are being researched and it is likely that the number of modifiers will grow as a result of the US Strategic Highway Research Programme (SHRP) initiative. Many of these materials are commercial developments limited to the initiating company, and performance safeguards are normally incorporated in contract negotiations. A mix modifier, as opposed to a binder modifier, is the incorporation of 25 mm long polypropylene or polyester fibres. Small percentage (0·25%–0·75% by weight) additions are claimed to increase resistance to rutting, deformation, and reflection cracking. With all modified preblended binders, it is essential to control storage conditions, and the handling of the binders in the manufacturing plant, to avoid problems, such as hardening and variations in percentage composition. Specialist contractors are required for satisfactory results.

3.27. Deterioration of pavements

Pavements deteriorate with age and use, and the engineer needs to identify the type of deterioration and, if possible, its cause in order to establish a priority of response in the highway maintenance programme. The following are common types of deterioration.

3.27.1. Ageing and weathering

Bitumen and tar age from the moment that they are incorporated into a mix. This is caused by oxidation, which hardens the binder. In road mixes, as a rule of thumb, bitumen below a penetration of 20 is at the end of its life. Loss of binder efficiency, and brittleness, prevent the material from containing the stresses imposed by traffic, leading to the development of cracks. This process is most obvious in the wearing course, where the surface receives most air and sunlight. The condition can be assessed during inspection by noting changes in the colour of the bituminous binder, from the initial black to a light grey. Chippings will be more prominently exposed and many will have been plucked out. If handled, pieces of the surfacing will probably disintegrate, and individual stones can be dislodged due to loss of adhesive properties in the binder.

3.27.2. Potholes

Potholes are relatively small holes in the road surface, due to a loss of material. The cause may be material failure or faulty workmanship or the use of inappropriate material in, for instance, trench reinstatements. Unless attended to promptly, traffic action will widen and deepen the holes, allowing damaging water ingress and increased accident risk. Potholes may also be a symptom of underlying structural failure. These all too common faults in road surfacing present hazards, particularly to two-wheeled vehicles, and can damage all classes of vehicles. The highway authority has a duty under Section 41 of the Highway Act 1980[3.51] to take action to repair such faults.

3.27.3. Rutting

Rutting describes the formation of depressions or tracks in the pavement surface caused by wheel loads and high temperatures, combined with the character and design of the carriageway surfacing. Rutting is especially apparent in areas of high stress, such as

- (a)   the approaches to traffic lights
- (b)   channelized locations such as bus lanes
- (c)   the slow lanes of trunk roads which carry the majority of commercial vehicles.

The greater the loads imposed on the pavement, the slower the loading rate, and the higher the temperature, the greater will be the rutting tendency. Ruts of over 100 mm depth have been seen in Arabia at the stop line of traffic lights, caused by grossly overloaded commercial vehicles combined with pavement temperatures above 75°C, which far exceeds the softening point of the binder.

Studies, carried out in the UK, indicate that the majority of rutting occurs during a few days of the year, when pavement temperatures exceed 45°C. In the summer of 1976, which precipitated much of the design mix HRA laid since, pavement temperatures were recorded in the range 55°C–60°C. This is at the top end of the range of softening point for the 50 pen binder most commonly used in HRA wearing course, and above the softening point of 100 pen binder used in DBM wearing course. The rutting caused by one day at 60°C can be the same as that for one year at 14°C, and as the ruts develop, the deterioration accelerates because vehicles tend to be locked into the ruts in the wheel tracks. Therefore, in very hot climates, rolled asphalts, which depend on the mortar strength, are rarely used and asphaltic concrete with aggregate interlock for stability is favoured. However, the latter can be brittle in colder conditions and is thus more prone to cracking. British specifications recognize the problem and offer a range of hardness for bitumen from which a material can be chosen to suit known weather patterns and local experience.

3.27.4. Pushing

Pushing is related to rutting and deformation, again occurring in areas of high stress. It can cause the material to flow and fold up on itself. This condition may indicate that the binder is too soft, leading to plastic flow under traffic, or, more rarely, can be due to fuel/oil spillage, which has softened the material locally. Pushing is often confined to the wearing course, but the nature of the deformation needs to be investigated using coring techniques.

3.27.5. Deformation

The term 'deformation' is often wrongly used as an alternative to rutting, but it is a term that should apply to a more general distortion, which can be due to a variety of causes. It can be caused by the same processes as rutting, but can also, for example, be due to frost heave. In frost-susceptible sub-bases, frost heave deformation can be spectacular, and the author has seen frost heave deformation on a newly constructed carriageway which left the road in a sine wave condition longitudinally, varying from peak to trough by 300 mm. In this instance, the road returned to its 'as constructed' level after thawing.

Settlement behind bridge abutments, due to post-compaction, can also appear in the surface as deformation running transversely across the carriageway.

If a pavement is stressed beyond its load bearing capacity locally, or if the load bearing characteristics of the sub-grade vary, parts or the whole pavement can deform differentially. If laying machinery is allowed to work on a foundation, which is unable to bear the loads imposed by the laying process, damaging deformation will occur. If the delivery vehicles are seen to cause rutting and deformation of the sub-grade prior to the blacktop layer being placed, action must be taken either to improve the compaction, or replace the sub-grade material before proceeding with blacktop.

3.27.6. Fretting

Caused by either ageing of the binder with consequent lack of adhesion or on newly laid surfaces due to insufficient compaction or poorly formed longitudinal joints. Failure at the joints also occurs in old pavements, and is more common in DBM type materials, which rely upon aggregate interlock for satisfatory performance, compaction being crucial. In any machine laid material, compaction at the centre of the laying 'rip' is always greater than at the edges, due to the rolling pattern. Great care must therefore be exercised to ensure the matching of one longitudinal point with another, and to check that the roller is not 'riding' on the cold material. DBM wearing course, because of its compaction requirement, is not an easy material to lay successfully and requires good workmanship and supervision. All joints in bituminous surfacing should be cut back vertically and painted with bitumen, otherwise fretting at the joint can occur. DBM wearing course is also sensitive to the binder content, and the characteristics of the aggregate used. A 'dry' mix will be more prone to fretting at critical stress locations. Thin areas, of less than twice the nominal size of the aggregate, will also be prone to fretting. Fretting may also occur following 'stripping' due to water penetration. In this respect, some aggregates are more difficult to coat with binder than others, because absorbed retained moisture affects the bitumen bond. This can be countered by the addition of hydrated lime or an anti-stripping agent to the binder.

Thermal expansion and contraction where reflective cracking occurs leads to the breakdown of the 'face' of the joint, and the aggregate becomes dislodged by traffic action.

3.27.7. Cracking

The most common form of cracking is reflective cracking, which may occur when cement bound materials are overlaid with a blacktop pavement. The form of cracking is commonly transverse, but in older pavements, can be coupled with longitudinal cracking. Surface cracking on a fully flexible construction is rare in the UK. However, where the load bearing capacity of the pavement has been substantially exceeded, a form of cracking, which appears as interconnected, irregular and segmental, will occur but this has no connection with reflective cracking.

It was once thought that reflective cracking started in the base layer and worked up through the pavement to the wearing course, but recent evidence of blacktop material laid over lean mix concrete, has turned this theory upside down. It is now believed that the cracks are initiated in the wearing course and work downwards, and that the lean mix concrete base cracks as soon as the first layer of blacktop is laid on it.

Such cracking over cement bound material occurs generally in a regular pattern, and appears as a clear break in the surfacing, which opens and closes according to temperature changes. This movement can later be inhibited by detritus filling the crack, thus causing additional stress and breakdown of the edges of the crack, which are also subjected to damage by traffic. Sometimes two parallel cracks appear, indicative of a poor contraction joint in the concrete beneath, and this often leads to the bituminous material between the cracks breaking down and being dislodged.

Longitudinal cracks in a composite construction are usually the result of the lean mix being laid with a slip form paver in two widths, creating a reflective crack in the surfacing over the joint between the two bays.

All cracks allow the potentially damaging ingress of surface water, and should be sealed as soon as possible by thoroughly cleaning out any detritus and loose material, using compressed air, drying, and then sealing with bitumen.

3.27.8. Polishing

Polishing of a surface is a potential hazard especially in wet conditions, since it will cause loss of skid resistance and increase the risk of accidents. All aggregates polish under traffic, but the rate of polishing varies. The Polished Stone Value (PSV) is an indication of the resistance to polishing; as a comparative value against a standard aggregate, the higher the number achieved in a standard test the greater the resistance to polishing (BS 812).[3.39] Aggregate with a high PSV (62 +) is at a premium and is generally used for coated chippings in HRA wearing course. A minimum PSV requirement is not specified in BS 594 or BS 4987 for aggregate incorporated in the mix, but a value is generally specified by the purchaser, especially for wearing corners, in order to exclude aggregate with a low resistance to polishing, such as limestones and gravels. Rough, angular fine aggregate will impart a greater resistance to polishing and better skid resistance than smooth rounded particles.

3.27.9. Plucking

Plucking is the loss of aggregate under trafficking, most commonly the loss of coated chippings from a chipped asphalt surface in high stress areas, such as roundabouts, but it can also be extensive if chippings are not properly embedded in the asphalt. There will always be some loss of chippings in a surface with a texture depth requirement averaging 1·5 mm, and that fact is recognized in BS 594: Cl. 6.3.2; Note 2. If, however, adverse weather, particularly wind, causes rapid surface chilling, an adequate chip embedment can be difficult to achieve and any 'proud' chippings will be rapidly plucked out by traffic. This same situation can occur with surface dressing for the same reasons.

3.27.10. Embedment

Embedment is the loss of surface texture when chippings in HRA are applied and compacted into a wearing course that is

- (a)   too hot
- (b)   too rich in binder
- (c)   a combination of these factors
- (d)   of low stability.

Embedment of chips can occur in surface dressing due to too thick a binder layer, from opening to traffic too soon, or where estimation of the existing surface hardness results in the choice of inappropriate size of chipping. In HRA, compliance with a specified texture is normal, and excessive embedment will mean that this value will not be consistently achieved. Similarly, after surface dressing, the surface will appear fatty and lack texture. In both instances the skid resistance will be lowered, perhaps dangerously. In the case of HRA, the matrix may wear away under traffic, being softer than the chippings, but this would be a lengthy process, and should not be relied on.

3.28. Temporary road surfaces

Temporary road surfaces are inevitable during the course of the more extensive types of maintenance. During such periods, the condition of the carriageway, if still in use, must be safe. The following extract from a Department of Transport letter underlines some of the aspects requiring attention from the maintenance engineer.

(a) When road surfaces are removed or re-shaped by planing operations before being re-surfaced, the pattern of grooves left on the temporary surface and the presence of gratings and covers standing proud of the surface often constitute additional accident hazards to which riders of motor cycles and bicycles are particularly exposed.

(b) Highway Authorities are under a duty of care to ensure that when works are carried out the Highway is left in a condition which is not dangerous to road users. In relation to the preparation of carriageways for resurfacing it is important to plan the operations and supervise their execution so that the planed surface is left with a degree of regularity that is not only suitable for the application of the new surfacing, but is also reasonably safe for use by all types of traffic during the period of exposure.

(c) The economic management of highway maintenance will often necessitate preparation of long lengths of pavement ahead of the resurfacing work, with periods of inaction between these operations. Such periods give the public an impression of unnecessary delay and a lack of concern for the safety of two-wheel traffic in particular.

(d) Give particular attention to the programming and contractual arrangements for planing and resurfacing works so as to reduce to a minimum the periods that elapse between these operations, and to take all reasonable steps to reduce hazards in the periods when the planed lengths are used as temporary running surfaces. This should include the display of signs to Figure 8.71 in Chapter 8 of the Traffic Signs Manual[3.52] on each approach to the planed area.

3.29. Repair types and methods

The following repair procedures identify the range of response to a number of problems, ranging from immediate requirements to the large scale planned expenditure involved in reconstruction of the pavement. In overall terms these repairs consume about 30% (metropolitan district) and 40% (county) of the respective maintenance budgets.

3.29.1. Potholes (bitumen macadam to BS 4987)

(a) Remove all mud, dust, leaves and loose material.
(b) Cut hole to a regular shape with all sides vertical or undercut.
(c) Remove debris and any collected water.
(d) Paint the interior surfaces with a thick coat of bitumen emulsion, hot bitumen or cold thixotropic bitumen.

(e) Slightly overfill the hole with coated macadam to BS 4987.

(f) Fully compact the material in layers not exceeding 75 mm using plate rammer or vibrating roller.

(g) Seal all surface joints with bitumen approximately 50 mm wide. A number of proprietary 'instant' premixed materials are also available, usually designed to resist deformation. Whichever material is used, the importance of preparation of the hole and compaction of the filling material is stressed, and for these specialized preparations, adherence to the manufacturer's instructions is necessary.

3.29.2. Potholes (using anionic or cationic road emulsion)

(a) Remove all mud, dust, leaves and loose material.

(b) Cut hole to a regular shape with all sides vertical or undercut.

(c) Remove debris and any collected water.

(d) In dry conditions wet the sides of the hole.

(e) Apply emulsion class A1-60, A1-55 or K1-60 to all surfaces.

(f) Slightly overfill the hole with clean aggregate (28 mm to BS 63: Part 2[3.53] or two-thirds the depth of the hole, whichever is the lesser) and ram or roll.

(g) Pour in sufficient emulsion to coat all stones.

(h) Cover area with clean 10 or 6 mm chippings and again ram or roll.

Such methods are receiving trial consideration (by mechanized process).

3.29.3. Patching

Patching may be defined as the replacement of defective flexible material, hand laid to any depth not less than the wearing course thickness to effect a permanent restoration of the stability and/or riding quality of the pavement. Excluded from the work of patching are

(a) the filling of depressions and cracks not involving removal of existing pavement surfacing

(b) the sealing of pavement surfacing by the application of dry or precoated aggregate and/or binder unless this is an essential component of the patching method

(c) the replacement or repair of the pavement base, sub-base or sub-grade

(d) the use of concrete

(e) the use of mechanical spreader and spreader boxes.

The above definition also excludes emergency repairs needed for safety rather than longevity. Elsewhere in the book, mention has been made of the need to develop meaningful unit cost data. The above definition taken from ref. 3.54 and sequenced operations in Table 3.8 are offered as a means of identifying more closely this work category and permitting a more sensible financial basis than currently exists in this area.

3.29.4. Planing

Planing is the mechanical removal of the existing surface so that the new surfacing can be laid to the original finished level, but it does not mean that

Table 3.8. Specification and sequence of operations for patching

Element	Operation	Specification
1. Preparation	Break up Excavate and remove Cleanse Dispose of Cleanse	Defective areas of surfacing to limits marked out, using specified breaker equipment Pavement to limits marked out and to stepped widths and depths specified, to form cavity, using specified breaker equipment, and hand tools as necessary, to final dimensions Cavity, using hand tools All excavated material Adjacent pavement area
2. Cavity treatment	Apply	For all cold and warm laid materials: specified cold emulsion at the given covering capacity to base and sides of cavity For all hot laid materials: filled bitumen or equivalent proprietary compound to sides, and cold emulsion to base of cavity
3. Basecourse application	Fill	Where specified by management: cavity to basecourse level, allowing for compaction, to specified thickness and compaction, with basecourse material from either: transport vehicle or materials adjacent to patch site using specified hand tools
4. Basecourse compaction	Compact Check	Basecourse material using specified compaction equipment as appropriate, using hand tools to complete where necessary Level of compacted basecourse surfaces using specified measuring equipment. If the level of the compacted basecourse surface is lower than specified by an amount equal to or greater than the maximum aggregate size of the basecourse material, a further layer of basecourse material should be laid, compacted and checked. If the level of the compacted basecourse surface is such that the resulting depth of the wearing course will be less than 11/2 times the maximum aggregate size of the wearing course material, the entire basecourse should be removed over the area concerned, and replaced with new material, compacted and checked. In all other cases the basecourse level should not be altered. The differences in level arising from any inaccuracies should be accommodated in the thickness of the wearing surfaces
5. Wearing course application		As for element 3, using wearing course material to final pavement level

Element	Operation	Description
6. Wearing course compaction	Sweep Compact Check	Pavement surface adjacent to patch Wearing course material using specified compaction equipment as appropriate, using hand tools to complete where necessary. See elements 7 and 9 for compaction of initial area and surface treatment materials Level of compacted wearing course using specified measuring equipment. If on checking level of the wearing course after compaction any area is below or more than 6 mm above the level of the surrounding pavement, the full depth of the wearing course material should be removed in the areas concerned, and replaced by new material, compacted and checked. If so delegated, the re-use of material removed from the patch site under this clause, and the corresponding clause in element 4 shall be at the discretion of the chargehand
7. Initial sealing	Apply Compact	All open textured surfacing materials Pre-coated sealing grit to wearing course to specified covering capacity using specified hand tools Decisions as to the necessity to compact this material, and if to be compacted, whether carried out as part of element 6 or as a separate compaction operation, are to be made by management This operation can be completed separately in respect of each patch or carried out on the same day in respect of a number of patches, at the discretion of the chargehand in accordance with site circumstances
8. Final sealing		All open textured surfacing materials The final permanent and early sealing of patches is an essential component of the process. The seal should extend not less than 100 mm from the edges of the patch. It is not, however, specified here in detail, since it is frequently carried out, for organization, economic and equipment reasons, as a subsequent and separate operation, often by a different gang, and the techniques of the sealing of patches are common to other aspects of pavement maintenance not covered by this method. This may require future consideration as a separate preferred method
9. Surface treatment	Apply Compact	To hot and cold asphalts (or equivalents) only, and where specified by management Dry or coated aggregate, as specified by management, to wearing course, to specified covering capacity, using specified hand tools Decisions as to the necessity to compact this material, and if to be compacted, whether carried out as part of element 6 or as a separate compaction operation, are to be made by management
10. Pavement cleansing	Cleanse Dispose of	Surface of patch and adjacent pavement area, using hand tools specified Detritus. See note to element 7

the existing profile be followed exactly, with the same amount removed everywhere. There should be an improvement in surface regularity and profile after planing, achieved by removing more on high spots and less on low spots. Since the Heath Robinson machines, which applied naked flame to the surface to heat it prior to scraping off the existing material, through to machines that applied infra-red heat, planing has become, almost exclusively, a cold process. Cold planers have drums laced with hardened steel picks that can be adjusted in shape, number and pattern, according to the material being planed or the finish required. They vary in drum width from 0·5 m to almost 4 m, and achieve high rates of progress, removing depths, in one pass, of up to 150 mm dependent on the material encountered. Blacktop or concrete materials can be removed and the majority of machines now produced are self loading, via conveyor, into lorries, thus enabling material to be removed as rapidly as it is milled. Automatic sensing devices operating from kerb lines, or existing surfacing, allow precise control of the finished profile. Small planing drum attachments can be fitted to tractors or shovels to deal with reinstatement works, and specialist drums can also plane to pre-set profiles.

3.30. Skid resistance — anti-skid surfacing (Specification for Highway Works Cl. 924)

The skid resistance of a road surface is a function of the friction generated between the tyre and road interface. Thus, the greatest friction and therefore resistance to skidding would be provided by a slick tyre (i.e. a tyre with no tread) on a completely smooth road surface, in dry conditions. In wet conditions this combination would be lethal. Therefore, skid resistance is a compromise between tyre tread design, to provide rapid removal of water from the tyre print, and the road surface, which should also ensure rapid escape of surface water.

On high speed roads (85 percentile over 90 kph) the skid resistance is obtained by specifying a minimum texture depth of 1·5 mm/1·03 MTM (Mini-texture meter), which is a measure of the roughness of the surface after coated chippings have been embedded into the rolled asphalt wearing course. The coated chippings also have a minimum PSV specified, which is a measure of the stone's resistance to polishing under traffic. Furthermore the bitumen has a minimum Permittivity Index of 2·36, which is a measure of the ability of the binder to weather and expose the aggregate surface. How relevant bitumen permittivity is in the current requirements for texture depth is questionable as the tyre/road surface, which effectively is the tyre/chip interface, is the predominant factor in skid resistance.

The texture depth aids rapid dispersal of surface water to prevent aquaplaning at high speed. It is to be noted that skid resistance values are not constant, and normally will drop in the summer and rise in the winter. This is caused by the cycle of embedment of the coated chippings into the surface due to higher ambient temperatures (even in the UK pavement temperatures can exceed the softening point of 50 pen bitumen, the most commonly used binder in rolled asphalt wearing course), thus leading to

loss of texture, which may be restored by the wear of the matrix under traffic, and weathering in the winter.

On urban and lower speed roads, the predominant influence on skid resistance is the micro-texture and resistance of the aggregate to polishing. Skid resistance values (SFC) are obtained from SCRIM surveys (see Chapter 8). If identical surface materials are used on different sites, SFC values are inversely related to the volume of traffic, under similar environments. Since the resistance to polishing of the aggregate is so critical to the skidding resistance of the surface, research has been done to find improved natural or processed materials. Amongst the best produced so far is calcined bauxite, which, when combined with an epoxy binder, produces a highly effective long life treatment. Cost inhibits the widespread use of this material, but when justified by savings in potential accidents, it can provide demonstrable cost benefits. Used for many years in high risk locations, the advantages are beginning to be appreciated even for lesser risk sites. The calcined bauxite is spread on to the binder without compaction, and surplus aggregate is removed by vacuum sweeper prior to trafficking. The aggregate size is approximately 2·0–3·0 mm with a PSV value of 75.

Details of research and practical experience are fully documented[3.55] for the pioneer use of this treatment in the London area over the past 20 years.

3.31. Surface dressing

Present financial constraints on road maintenance are believed to be leading to greater use of short-term measures such as surface dressing. A high proportion, approaching half, of some country routine maintenance budgets are being expended on this form of treatment, and overall a figure of some £180 million was being spent annually on this item, according to a survey in 1985 by the County Surveyors Society. Added to the general concern of achieving a satisfactory return on investment and greater knowledge of the performance of particular materials, there is a growing opinion, based on trends in the National Road Maintenance Condition Survey (NRMCS), that palliative measures are masking the underlying, and serious deterioration of many roads, which will lead to a large increase in the eventual structural repair costs.

3.31.1. Economics of surface dressing

Research work carried out by Giles[3.56] and Sabey[3.57] at TRRL identified relationships between the PSV of aggregates used in the surfacing of roads, modified by traffic flow (commercial vehicles per lane per day) and a factor for junctions, and accident risk. A paper prepared by Culham and Richardson,[3.58] comparing the costs of various materials and including tyre wear and delays, concluded

> Generally the results of this economic appraisal conform to expectations, in that with higher traffic flows and accident risk ratings, the performance of the high sfc treatments is superior to the performance of granites and with the highest traffic flows and risk ratings, the performance of epoxy/bauxite is markedly better than that of other treatments.

Two conclusions stand out as being particularly robust

(*a*) the use of granite is justified in only low flow/low risk situations
(*b*) epoxy/bauxite is a justified choice in all high flow and many high risk situations.

These conclusions lead one to suspect that epoxy/bauxite — and, at lower flows, gritstone — are economically justified choices as surface dressing treatments in more cases than is perhaps generally realized.

3.31.2. *Surface dressing in use*

Surface dressing is a common technique used in road maintenance

(*a*)   to improve the surface texture and resistance to wet road skidding
(*b*)   to seal the surface against water penetration
(*c*)   to arrest disintegration of the existing road surface.

The materials used comprise a bituminous adhesive coat followed by the spreading of stone chippings, carefully chosen for strength, colour, shape and size, which is regulated according to the hardness of the underlying surface. Full details of design for surface dressing are given in Road Note 39 (2nd edition).[3.59]

It is a rapid process, which, when carried out by a competent contractor in suitable weather conditions, gives a cheap, effective result. It can be carried out more than once, but care has to be taken when repeating the operation, because a build up of binder can cause fatting up, and bleeding of excess binder in hot weather. Such faults are especially apparent in the vehicle tracks, and, if developed, removal of the old surface dressings by planing is the remedy. Properly employed, however, surface dressing is a cost effective process which, when carried out at say 3–5 year intervals, extends the life of a surface. Usually it is carried out on a surface that is still sound, but beginning to show signs of ageing. Often there is a planned cycle of maintenance, for instance, after an open textured macadam or DBM surface has been laid for say 3 + years, surface dressing will be considered. High performance surface dressings are now available with polymer modification for use on heavily trafficked trunk roads.

Chippings may be coated lightly, or uncoated, and are spread by hand, for small areas, or machine, ensuring that the whole surface has a dense layer of chippings. It is important that excess chippings are finally swept away after rolling and later after several days trafficking. Bitumen emulsions are chosen from anionic emulsion classes A1-60 or A1-55 and cationic emulsion classes K1-60 and K1-70, full details being given in BS 434: Part 2: 1984.[3.60] The most popular emulsion is cationic K1-70. Compaction is carried out by rubber tyred rollers, immediately after spreading chippings, and later by the action of traffic. There is a serious risk of damage, both to the surface dressing and to the windscreens of vehicles if traffic is allowed to pass over the newly completed dressing at unrestricted speeds after laying, or if removal of surplus chippings is not carried out effectively. Another approach to surface dressing is the 'rational approach' described by Elborn *et al.*[3.61] and based on early research by Hanson of

New Zealand. In this method, the behaviour of chippings after trafficking is considered, and incorporated as a design feature. In addition to size, the 'average least dimension' of the aggregate is allowed for as a factor affecting the effective loss of surface texture with time and loading (embedment). Also in use for specialized applications are developments in binders, such as foamspray, and polymer modified thermoplastic bitumens. Epoxy resin binders have also been used extensively for difficult sites, usually in association with premium aggregates, such as calcined bauxite (see section 3.30).

Many recent developments in surface dressing methods have been under active consideration at trial sites, including

(a) pad coat treatment, which is used on variable road surfaces to counteract changes in embedment. The initial application is of 6 mm surface dressing followed after an extended interval (1–3 years) by a second similar application
(b) a racked in technique, in which an initial dressing of 10 or 12 mm chippings is spread to approximately 90% coverage, followed by a further coating of 6 mm chippings
(c) a process similar to racking in but with a second application of binder between chipping applications, which is referred to as the 'double dressing' technique.

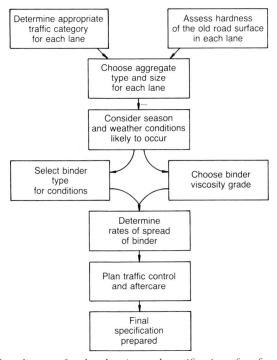

Fig. 3.37. Flow diagram for the planning and specification of surface dressings

3.31.3. Preparation for surface dressing

The following procedure for preparing for surface dressing is based on that recommended in ref. 3.62.

(a) Check the condition of the existing surface. Minor cracking and limited variations in level can be corrected or accommodated in the process, but there is no gain in strength, and if the carriageway is in distress from traffic loading, more drastic repair methods are needed. The stages of surface dressing preparation are shown as a flow diagram in Fig. 3.37.

(b) Ensure that equipment is serviceable, and calibrated.

(c) Check that materials are ordered in accordance with the specification.

(d) Where premium systems are to be used, check that contractor and supervisory staff are experienced in the laying of such materials.

(e) Programme the works to take advantage of weather conditions suited to the process, and taking necessary traffic arrangements into account.

(f) Ensure that effective steps are taken to minimize the effects of opening to traffic in terms of damage to the surfacing (possible need for speed restriction) and danger to road users (thorough and repeated sweeping and speed restriction).

(g) Carry out subsequent checks on the condition of the surfacing, especially where previously untried materials have been used.

Useful data (from TRRL reports) are given in Tables 3.9–3.16.[3.63]

Table 3.9. Surface dressing — rates of application of chippings (by size)

Nominal size of chippings: mm	Rate of application: kg/m^2
14	13 ± 2
10	10 ± 1
6	7 ± 1
3	6 ± 1

Table 3.10. Surface dressing — target rates of application for lane traffic categories 4 and 5 (cold emulsion)

Types of surface	Lane traffic category			
	4		5	
	Nominal size of chippings: mm	Emulsion rate: l/m^2	Nominal size of chippings: mm	Emulsion rate: l/m^2
Very hard	Double dressing recommended			
Hard	6	1·5	6	1·6
Normal	10	1·5	6	1·5
Soft	14	1·5	10	1·5
Very soft	14	1·4	10	1·4

Table 3.11. Surface dressing — target rates of application for lane traffic categories 2, 3, 4 and 5 (K1-70 emulsion applied hot)

Types of surface	Lane traffic category							
	2		3		4		5	
	Nominal size of chippings: mm	Emulsion rate: l/m²	Nominal size of chippings: mm	Emulsion rate: l/m²	Nominal size of chippings: mm	Emulsion rate: l/m²	Nominal size of chippings: mm	Emulsion rate: l/m²
Very hard	Not recommended		6	1·3	6	1·5	6	1·6
Hard	14	1·5+	10	1·3	6	1·3	6	1·4
Normal	14	1·4+	10	1·3	10	1·3	6	1·3
Soft	20	1·3	14	1·2	14	1·3	10	1·3
Very soft	Not suitable for surface dressing		20	1·2	14	1·2	10	1·2

Table 3.12. Surface dressing — target rates of application of K1-70 emulsion for impervious hard shoulders

Types of chippings	Nominal size of chippings: mm	Emulsion rate: l/m²
Crushed rock and slag aggregate	10	1·6
	6	1·4
Crushed gravel	10	1·8
	6	1·6

Table 3.13. Surface dressing — lane traffic categories

Category	Approximate number of commercial vehicles carried per day in the lane under consideration
1	2000–4000
2	1000–2000
3	200–1000
4	20–200
5	< 20

Table 3.14. Surface dressing — site definitions

Site	Definition
A1 (very difficult)	Approach to traffic signals on roads with a speed limit > 40 miles/h (64 km/h) Approaches to traffic signals, pedestrian crossings and similar hazards on main urban roads Approach to major junctions on roads carrying > 250 commercial vehicles per lane per day
A2 (difficult)	Roundabouts and their approaches Bends with radius < 150 m on roads with a speed limit > 40 miles/h (64 km/h) Gradients of 5% or steeper, longer than 100 m Generally straight sections of and large radius curves on B
B (average)	Motorways Trunk and principal roads Other roads carrying > 250 commercial vehicles per lane per day
C (easy)	Generally straight sections of lightly trafficked roads Other roads where wet accidents are unlikely to be a problem

Table 3.15. Surface dressing — road surface hardness categories

Hardness category	Penetration at 30°C mm	Classification of surface
Very hard	0–2	Surfaces such as concrete or exceptionally lean bituminous mixtures with dry stony surfaces into which there will be negligible penetration of chippings under very heavy traffic
Hard	2–5	Surfaces containing some hard bituminous mortar into which chippings will penetrate only slightly under heavy traffic
Normal	5–8	Surfaces into which chippings will penetrate moderately under heavy and medium traffic
Very soft	> 12	Surfaces into which even the largest chippings will be submerged under heavy traffic. Such surfaces are usually rich in binder

3.31.4. Common types of failure

Common types of failure are shown in Table 3.17. Judgement of the maintenance engineer is needed when deciding at what stage repair and replacement takes place, most concern being with regard to the potential for skidding accidents. An indication of life expectancy is shown in Table 3.18 (item 5).

3.32. Slurry seal (ASTM D 3910[3.64] and BS 434: Parts 1 and 2[3.60] Specification for Highway Works Cl 918)[3.47]

There has been a marked revival of interest in the use of slurry seal in the past few years, particularly in Europe. In Spain, for example, well over $10 \times 10^6 \, m^2$ of slurry seal are laid annually, even on motorways. In the

Table 3.16. Surface dressing — recommended nominal size of chippings in millimetres

Type of surface	Lane traffic category (approximate number of commercial vehicles currently carried per day in the lane under consideration)				
	1 (2000–4000)	2 (1000–2000)	3 (200–1000)	4 (20–200)	5 (< 20)
Very hard	10	10	6	6	6
Hard	14	14	10	6	6
Normal	20	14	10	10	6
Soft	*	20	14	14	10
Very soft	*	*	20	14	10

Table 3.17. Surface dressing — common types of failure

Fault	Cause	Remedy
1. Loss of chippings at an early stage	Maybe slow break in emulsion or poor wetting (cut-back bitumen)	Increase binder content — use pre-coated chippings
2. Loss of chippings during first winter	Lack of embedment or binder too brittle	Check surface hardness, choice of binder and weather
3. Bleeding of binder during first hot summer	Wrong binder viscosity for the temperature range	Revise specification
4. Fatting up	Excessive use of binder, binder/chipping ratio increased due to crushing of aggregate or dust absorption, chipping embedment	Plane off and resurface

UK, the total has risen to 8 × 10⁶ m² per annum. The process consists of a wearing course graded aggregate, of 10 mm, 6 mm or 3 mm nominal size, which is mixed in situ in a specially designed truck-mounted pugmill. It is blended with bituminous emulsion (sometimes with the addition of a polymer modifier for additional performance), adhesion agents, water and cement, or hydrated lime. The resulting mix is fed to a spreader box, mounted on the back of the unit. The residual bitumen content, depending on grading and requirement, can vary from 6·5–16·0% by weight of dry aggregate. Batches can be up to 2 tonnes/mix and thus at a thickness of 3–10 mm, large areas can be surfaced daily. The water in the mix evaporates and the emulsion sets on 'breaking', the timing of which can be adjusted by the mineral filler content and chemical agents. The setting time can vary from 15 minutes to 12 hours, depending on weather conditions. The process does not normally require compaction, and can be laid in more than one layer. If rolling is required it is normally carried out with a multi-tyred smooth tread roller.

3.33. Resurfacing and overlays

Resurfacing is carried out for one or more of the following reasons.

(a) To restore the ride quality of the pavement.

(b) To restore the skid resistance of the wearing course.

(c) To achieve an impermeable surface to prevent water ingress to the existing pavement.

(d) To renew the wearing course when the existing surfacing has oxidized and embrittlement of the binder has caused fretting, and

Table 3.18. Summary of construction performance data for the UK (based on a questionnaire to highway authorities reported at the IHT Workshop, Leamington Spa, 1983)

Element	Performance (life in years)*
1. Road bases	At least 20
2. Concrete wearing courses	Average 25 for all road classes
3. Hot rolled asphalt wearing courses	Average 16 for classified roads, longer for unclassified
4. Dense macadam and macadam surfaces	Average 11–12 for classified roads, longer for unclassified
5. Surface dressing (using either cut-back bitumen, bitumen emulsion or tar bitumen binder)	5–6 principal roads (up to 8 with 'hot chip' process) 6–7 classified roads 8–9 unclassified roads

*Durations are based on broad experience nationally but, in view of the escalation in the weight and numbers of commercial vehicles, may be optimistic. With the relatively long life expectations involved, newer materials require field trials of long duration in order to prove their advantages and durability.

loss of cohesion of the aggregate, and thus to prolong the life of the existing pavement.

(e) If settlement or subsidence has taken place, to restore the longitudinal profile, and reduce the dynamic load on the pavement.

In all the foregoing circumstances resurfacing is defined in the strict sense of replacing or superimposing the wearing course only, with a minor proportion of basecourse repairs. Where a basecourse is used over the majority of the area to be resurfaced, it is a strengthening overlay (see section 3.34). If an existing wearing course is planed off and relaid, the new wearing course will not contribute significantly to the overall pavement strength. However, if the existing wearing course can be overlaid, there will be a contribution to the pavement strength due to this increase in the overall thickness of the bituminous layers. In all resurfacing operations, the aim should be to lay an even layer of wearing course, and irregularities of profile should first be corrected by regulating the existing surface. The regulating can be done, either with wearing course, or with basecourse material, dependent on the depth needed. The more even this existing pavement is, the more successful the resurfacing, in that compaction, texture and regularity will be improved. Also the more even the profile, the less stress the overall pavement is subjected to, since research shows that commercial vehicles can impose loads many times greater than their nominal axle loadings, due to 'bottoming out', on an uneven surface.

Considerable damage may thus be caused by the rerouting of traffic on to minor roads, without first ensuring an adequate structural strength and ride quality, usually by overlaying. When specifying the material to use for resurfacing or overlays, account has to be taken of the volume, speed and type of current and projected traffic, the soundness of the existing pavement, the availability of resources and the cost effectiveness of the proposed works. The last factor is of great importance, and consideration should be given to upgrading the specification of the resurfacing, thereby increasing the residual life of the pavement.

3.33.1. Compliance of materials with specification

During the course of roadworks, the routine testing of materials delivered can often cause concern due to apparent divergence from specified limits. Unfortunately, many test results are available only after considerable placing has been done, and in road surfacing operations may even apply to layers already covered. Obviously efforts should be made to obtain results quickly, but decisions are still likely to be needed once the work is in progress and can involve the choice of drastic action, such as removal, or perhaps a grudging acceptance, possibly eased by offers of extended maintenance periods. On larger jobs, one further approach has in the past been researched by the TRRL.[3.65] The system proposed entailed a statistical appraisal of the results and compared actual results with a notional 'standard job'. Among the conclusions was the proposal that inferior material should be paid for at a reduced scale rather than rejected. Such an approach would seem to offer a 'value for money' alternative to costly wastage of material.

3.33.2. Transport and laying of materials
(BS 594: Part 2: 1985)

The nature of highway maintenance allows the majority of work to be carried out in compliance with the above standard. A summary of the recommendations is as follows.

(*a*)   Delivery vehicles shall be insulated and sheeted to avoid excessive temperature drop in materials, and the rate of delivery co-ordinated with works progress. Contamination of the materials by diesel oil or dusts is to be avoided.

(*b*)   Prior to laying, all surfaces shall be clean, free from mud and slurry and shaped to proper profiles.

Permitted deviations of surfaces shall be

(*a*) $+10$ mm and -30 mm for sub-base to receive rolled asphalt road-base

(*b*) ±15 mm for roadbase to receive rolled asphalt basecourse

(*c*) ±6 mm for basecourse to receive rolled asphalt wearing course on motorways, trunk roads or principal roads

(*d*) ±10 mm for basecourse to receive rolled asphalt wearing course in other locations.

Longitudinal tolerance for resurfacing of existing prepared surface is not to exceed 13 mm under 3 m straightedge if two course resurfacing, or 10 mm for single wearing course. The above shaping shall be done either by the application of regulating courses to low areas or by cold planing of high areas.

Where a tack coat is required, it shall be bitumen emulsion complying with class A1-40 or K1-40 of BS 434: Part 1[3.60] applied at a uniform rate of spread of 0·35 l/m^2 to 0·55 l/m^2.

Laying shall, where practicable, be by self propelled paving machine, and shall be suspended in adverse weather, e.g. wet weather causing free standing water on the surface, or frozen or ice or snow covered surfaces, or when the temperature falls to 0°C.

Many maintenance operations involve small areas of repair which may be laid by hand. For such works the material should be spread in a loose uniform layer and the areas used for receiving deliveries should be hard and clean. Undue delay in final placing should be avoided otherwise cooling of the material will adversely affect compaction.

Compaction of all bituminous surfaces is vital if adequate strength and durability are to be achieved. Equipment comprises at least an 8 tonne roller, or its equivalent vibrating roller, for small and hand laid areas, and at least two such rollers for machine laid surfacing using one paver.

Skidding resistance is improved by the use of coated chippings of selected aggregate. On high speed roads, such as motorways, an average texture depth of 1·5 mm/1·03 (MTM) is required. The methods used to determine average values include the sand patch test (BS 598: Part 3)[3.45] and calibrated MTMs.

3.33.3. Tests on materials

The important aspects of testing bituminous materials for use in roads are detailed in BS 598: Part 3: 1985, preliminary testing of constituents and sampling methods being described in BS 812[3.39] (aggregates) and BS 3690[3.40] Part 1 (binder). Parts of BS 2000[3.66] cover standard tests on the bitumen: Part 49 covers penetration at 25°C and Part 58 covers softening point (ring and ball). In addition to a design method for determining mix proportions, BS 598: Part 3 offers useful guidance on

(a) measurement of the rate of spread of coated chippings
(b) determination of texture depth
(c) measurement of core densities
(d) compaction roller performance
(e) measurement of the temperature of rolled asphalt
(f) the determination of air voids in a specimen

3.34. Reconstruction

Reconstruction is the replacement of the whole road pavement, including the sub-base, to enhance its load bearing capacity. This may mean either excavation of the existing sub-grade to increase the overall depth of the pavement, or increasing the performance of the sub-grade, by lime or cement stabilization, or geotextile grid.

Reconstruction should take place only at the end of the service life of a pavement and when such procedures as strengthening overlays are not viable. It becomes necessary when traffic loading has exceeded the load bearing capacity of the pavement, causing unacceptable strain and other constraints, such as kerb faces, bridge headroom clearances and static loads on underbridges, preclude strengthening overlays. If traffic volumes and types have been grossly underestimated, the design life of a new pavement can be exceeded well within the current design life of 40 years, even though a strengthening overlay is envisaged mid-life with that design life for flexible pavements. To minimize the whole life cost of the road, optimum maintenance procedures are required to get the maximum life/cost benefits, and these must be carefully tailored to the actual process of deterioration.

3.35. Repave (Specification for Highway Works Cl. 926, BS 594)[3.38]

If the area to be resurfaced is large enough, and of consistent specification, repaving may be considered. The process consists of planing off 20 mm of the existing surfacing, normally HRA wearing course, preheating, scarifying and reprofiling the planed area and then laying a new wearing course of HRA 20 mm thick.

The new combined wearing course is chipped and compacted as a conventional resurfacing. The technique calls for large scale machinery, and with the number of units involved, including planer, lorries to cart arrising, preheater, delivery lorries, repaver machine, chipper and rollers, comprises a long paving train. However, it is highly cost effective and very rapid. Production rates of 1·5–2 km per night have been achieved, causing minimum traffic disruption and including a vehicle lane taken out, relaid, and road marked with studs. All the cores taken from the combined surfacing have shown a perfect and indistinguishable bond between new and existing material.

3.36. Recycling

The re-use of blacktop surfacing materials in new overlays developed following the oil crises of the 1970s and as a result of cold planing advances. The concept of re-using resources is a sound and convincing one to engineers and the public alike, and in some countries, notably the USA, has gained widespread acceptance.

The main factors that control the extent of recycling are economic ones, involving the price of bitumen and the availability of quality aggregates, against the process costs of recycling. Some States in the USA have little indigenous aggregate resources, and/or are faced with long distances to transport aggregates. Some of these States therefore have mandatory requirements enforcing the use of recycled material. It is noticeable in the UK, where transport distances are small, and high quality aggregate abounds, that the decline in crude oil price and consequent drop in bitumen price has removed a lot of the impetus from this type of process.

3.37. Overbanding (BS 3690: Part 1[3.40] (3148 BS 2499[3.67])

Overbanding is a method of sealing minor surface cracks in the road pavement by pouring hot or cold bitumen compounds into a spreader box, which is drawn over the crack, filling it and leaving a film of bitumen 50–75 mm wide and 2–3 mm thick on the surface.

As in all sealing techniques involving poured bitumen compounds, care in application and correct choice of grade of material is essential for good performance. The surface should be clean and dry, free from dust and debris, and hot compressed air should be used to ensure cleanliness and adhesion. The film thickness should be even and not too thick, nor of excessive width, because overbanding, especially longitudinally, can pose traffic hazards to motorcyclists and cyclists. Indeed if band widths in excess of 100 mm have to be considered the wrong technique is being used. Also 'tram lining' overbands on double cracks longitudinally can be especially hazardous to two-wheeled traffic.

3.38. Bituminous overlays of cement-bound materials

The overlaying of concrete pavements and composite pavements (lean mix sub-base, bituminous overlay) presents special problems. Overlaying a rigid construction, in which thermal expansion and contraction is relieved by joints, with a thermoplastic material that is flexible and joint-less, and required to contain those thermal movements without repeating the same joint pattern, requires one of the courses of action shown below. There may also be vertical movement caused by water ingress washing out the fines in the sub-base, or settlement. Any rocking slabs should be stabilized prior to overlaying (see also Part I) using one of the following methods.

(a) Overlay the concrete with sufficient blacktop thickness to 'insulate' the concrete and reduce the range of temperatures causing expansion and contraction.

(b) In composite pavements the material over the transverse cracks can be planed out with a specially adapted cold planer, the joint in the lean mix being sealed, and then new basecourse material (HRA or DBM) compacted in layers to the existing pavement level. The whole carriageway is then overlaid with new wearing course.

(c) Overlay the concrete with a layer of bituminous material, modified to contain the strains imposed on the wearing course by the expansion/contraction, normally in bands over the existing cracks.

(d) Reduce the concrete pavement slab size by fragmentation, reseating the segments on the sub-base by compaction, in effect to create a semi-flexible sub-base, and then surface with bituminous overlay.

(e) By overlaying the concrete and inducing cracks in the overlay over the joints, and then filling the cracks with a flexible bituminous compound.

Solution (a) is a costly one, as an overlay of at least 150–200 mm is required. This in turn, apart from the expense of the overlay, presupposes that such a thickness of overlay can be accommodated in respect of levels, and that underbridges can support the additional dead load. Also at some stage in the life of the overlay, due to weathering (see section 3.27.1), some joints may repeat in the wearing course due to reduced strain resistance over time.

Method (b) has proved possible with advances in cold planing technology. A specially adapted drum mills out the existing material to a predetermined profile, treating only the cracked zone, and thus offering savings in the work required.

In method (c) SBS, SBR, EVA (F) modified materials all have enhanced strain resistance values when compared to non-modified binders. These materials can be utilized to reduce the thickness of overlays in some cases by more than 50% if properly designed and combined with stress absorbing membrane (SAM) utilized as an interlayer between the existing and new wearing surface.

Method (d) has progressed considerably in the past few years especially in the USA. At one stage a fairly crude procedure of smashing the concrete slab into smaller fragments was utilized, but this has now evolved into a technique of controlled fracturing of the slab producing fine hair cracks, the segments then being reseated on the sub-grade by rolling, normally with a multiwheel pneumatic tyred roller (PTR) or very heavy vehicle. The segments can be thought of as large agglomerates of aggregate, and the reduction of the slab to these segments clearly reduces the extent of the thermal expansion and contraction to be accommodated. The fragmented pavement is then overlaid conventionally to the thickness required for the anticipated traffic loading.

In method (e), conventional overlays of cement bound bases can be carried out, repeating the transverse joint pattern in the wearing course by saw cutting, and filling the formed joint with poured bitumen or modified bitumen compounds. The problem with this technique can be that a secondary crack can appear if the joint alignment is not exact.

For special applications such as bridge decks incorporating movement joints coupled with imposed dynamic loads and rotational forces, a buried joint, 0·3–1 m plus wide, is laid to the full depth of the bituminous layers, modified by rubber or SBR to accommodate the high strain values, without reflective cracking. The pavement between the joints is laid in conventional materials. The joint can also be overlaid with an elastomer modified (SBR, SBS) wearing course.

3.39. Cost effectiveness and cost comparisons

The relative costs of materials and maintenance techniques are always difficult to establish because they are so dependent on volume and location.

Coupled with the initial costs of materials and techniques is the cost effectiveness of the different processes compared to their life expectancy. The concept of whole life costing in pavement design for new roads is having a commensurate impact on maintenance procedures.

General comparative figures for maintenance techniques are hard to come by, but some evidence exists for the following conclusions.

Where site conditions permit, the longest duration and most cost effective method is to overlay existing pavements. This is hardly surprising since overlays, dependent on thickness, can add to the load bearing capacity of the pavement, and thus prolong the life of the whole pavement. They also offer the opportunity to improve the ride quality and thus reduce the dynamic loads caused by previously deteriorating surface regularity. The ageing of the pavement and oxidation deterioration is reduced by the superimposition of the new surfacing, and improved skid

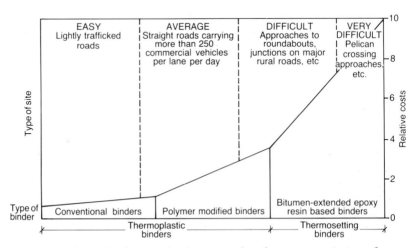

Fig. 3.38. Relationship between binder type and performance requirement for surface dressings

resistance can be introduced. Thus, it is the only technique that can effectively restore most of the desirable qualities of the original pavement. Other maintenance techniques can usually only provide one or two of the benefits available with an overlay. Table 3.18 shows a summary of experience with various materials in the UK.

In a recent survey carried out in the USA, which has by far the largest stock of maintained roads of any country in the world (the annual production of bituminous materials is greater than the rest of the world put together), the following life expectancy was given for the various maintenance procedures.

(a) Using new material

overlays	13 years
chipseal (surface dressing)	5 years
slurry seal	5 years
pothole patching	3 years

Cost effectiveness (ranked on a scale 1–10 with 10 being most effective)

overlays	9
surface dressing	7
slurry seal	5
pothole patching	5

(b) Using recycled material

overlay	12 years
hot in place	11 years
cold in place	9 years

Cost effectiveness

overlay	8
hot in place	6
cold in place	5

It must be borne in mind, however, that asphaltic concrete is the predominant material (which is prone to cracking and embrittlement) in the USA, and thus techniques like surface dressing are likely to be more successful there than in the UK.

Utilizing a numeric factor format for ranking, the relative costs in the UK for the maintenance procedures outlined in this chapter are as follows.

Planing (40 mm)	1–2 per m²
Surface dressing	1–3 per m²
Slurry seal	1–3 per m²
Resurfacing (25–40 mm)	5–6·5 per m²
Strengthening overlays (100 mm)	11·5–13·5 per m²
Repaving (plane out + 20 mm)	4·5–6 per m²
Grouted macadam (40 mm)	10·5–12·5 per m²
Resin anti-skid	15–18 per m²
Patching (urban — excavate + 100 mm HRA)	27–33 per m²

All the figures are for machine lay volume contracts, except patching, which is for volume hand lay. An indication of the usage of different binders and relative costs is shown in Fig. 3.38 for surface dressing treatments.

3.40. Future development

It is a truism that the pace of change is ever increasing, and this is certainly true of bituminous materials and processes. A look into the future, however, can suggest areas where development needs to take place.

Computer advances should mean that analysis of road pavement behaviour will provide more accurate predictive information and this should lead to more reliable designs and an increase in the cost effectiveness of new and reconstructed pavements.

Bitumen has been described as black magic, with little known about the complex interaction of chemical components relative to performance, and the performance when coating aggregate in thin films varying from 10–100 μm. The interest in, and advantages of, modified binders to enhance performance will increase and indeed BS 3690: Part 4[3.40] will contain test procedures to analyse these binders. However, as a counter to this trend, one would expect that bitumens of specific chemical composition will be developed for enhanced performance, tailored to end needs.

These improved binders should provide a better performance and life expectancy from pervious macadams and lead to their more widespread adoption on motorways and high speed roads, where their qualities of better skid resistance, less spray and quieter tyre generated noise can be exploited.

Great strides have been made in the recognition of the importance of compaction and the means of providing it. Vibrating rollers, common in Europe and the USA in the 1970s, are now used in the UK, and the means of compaction coupled with methods of measuring and monitoring it (nuclear density meters and Percentage Refusal Density — BS 598: Part 1044[3.68]) will ensure better life expectancies from bituminous materials.

The one area that needs development is in the laying of the material. Apart from enhanced mechanical performance, paving machines are very similar to their forerunners of the 1930s. The high speed profilometer, coupled with improved satellite and computer surveying techniques, should lead to computerized level control, certainly for motorways and high speed trunk roads. Thus, for overlays or reconstructions on major roads, if existing level data and required new finished level data could be provided to a microcomputer on the paving machine, the new road level could be laid automatically with improved ride quality, to the advantage of both road users and pavement life. Temperature probes in the paving machine could be linked to the compaction equipment, so that the compactive effort, controlled by on-board nuclear density meters, would be automatically regulated. Hydraulically extending screeds, augers and ultrasonic sensors controlling the 'head' of material in front of the screed (highly important to the quality of the finished surface) are developed technologies, which are either already introduced, or in the process of introduction.

Greater automation of the paving train will lead to higher costs in capital investment, but will be more than repaid by high performance in output, quality and longevity of the pavement. It will also limit the level of skills necessary for operatives in the paving train, and thus limit the difficulties in recruitment and training. However, it may lead to a two-tier level of sophistication in equipment and performance between major roads and the rest of the road system.

As a result of proposed legislative changes in 1992 it is likely that the commercial vehicle weight will go up from 38 tonnes, thus increasing the vehicle damage factor. To offset this potentially damaging effect on the UK's road stock a more widespread use of high stiffness, greater load spreading capacity materials, such as HDM, will be necessary.

The last imponderable is the degree of standardization of European national standards after 1992. It will be interesting to see the cross-fertilization of ideas, techniques and materials, that the breakdown of barriers and the increased internationalism of companies and centres of learning will bring. It is to be hoped that some degree of rationalization will reduce the number of mixes contained in the current British Standards, and allow the continuation of the trend towards smaller nominal sized aggregates, leading to better compaction.

Acknowledgements

The help of the following organizations in the preparation of Part II is acknowledged: British Standards Institution, American Society for Testing and Materials, BACMI Ltd, Transport and Road Research Laboratory, Institute of Highways and Transportation, Blaw Knox Ltd and Shell Bitumen UK.

References

3.1. *Road Vehicles (Construction and Use) Regulations 1986.* Her Majesty's Stationery Office, London.

3.2. AUDIT COMMISSION. *The management of highway maintenance.* Report, 1988.

3.3. MILDENHALL H.S. and NORTHCOTT G.D.S. *A manual for the maintenance and repair of concrete roads.* Her Majesty's Stationery Office, London, 1986, 80.

3.4. DEPARTMENT OF TRANSPORT *et al. Specification for highway works. Part 3.* Her Majesty's Stationery Office, London, 1986.

3.5. BURT A.R. M4 motorway, a composite pavement. Surface cracking. *J. Inst. Highw. Transpn,* 1987, December, 16–19.

3.6. TRANSPORT AND ROAD RESEARCH LABORATORY. *A guide to the structural design of pavements for new roads.* Her Majesty's Stationery Office, London, 1970, Road Note 29, 3rd edn.

3.7   DEPARTMENT OF TRANSPORT *et al. Structural design of new road pavements.* Departmental Standard HD 14/87, Her Majesty's Stationery Office, London, 1987.

3.8. WESTERGAARD, H.M. Stress in concrete pavements computed by theoretical analysis. *Public Rds, Wash.,* 1926, **2**, item 2, 25–35.

3.9. DEPARTMENT OF TRANSPORT *et al. Notes for the guidance on the Specification for highway works. Part 3.* NG 1000, Her Majesty's Stationery Office, London, 1986.

3.10. DEPARTMENT OF TRANSPORT *et al. A guide to concrete road construction.* Her Majesty's Stationery Office, London, 1978.

3.11. FRANKLIN R.E. and WINNETT M.A. The location of dowel bars in concrete pavements. *Highways, Wash.,* 1988, **56**, 42–43.

3.12. WELLER D.E. *A review of the low-speed skidding resistance of a number of concrete roads containing various aggregates.* TRRL, Crowthorne, 1970, LR 335.

3.13. BRITISH STANDARDS INSTITUTION. *Specification for chlorene rubber compounds.* BS 2752: 1982 (1987). BSI, London.

3.14. AMERICAN SOCIETY OF TESTING MATERIALS. *Specification for preformed polychloroprene elastomeric joint seals.* D2628-81, ASTM, Washington, DC, 1981.

3.15. NEVILLE A.M. *Properties of concrete.* Pitman, London, 1983, 3rd edn.

3.16. EMERY J.A. The use of concrete blocks for aircraft pavements. *Proc. Inst. Civ. Engrs,* Part 1, 1988, **80**, 451–464.

3.17. NATIONAL CO-OPERATIVE HIGHWAY RESEARCH PROGRAM. *Synthesis of highway practice — 45.* Transportation Research Board, National Research Council, Washington, DC, 1977, 1–13.

3.18. LILLEY A.A. *Further trials of early trafficking of bonded cement mortar and concrete toppings.* Cement and Concrete Association, Slough, 1973, Publication 42.482.

3.19. BRITISH STANDARDS INSTITUTION. *Specification for aggregates from natural sources.* British Standard 882: 1973. BSI, London.

3.20. EL-JAZAIRI B. Rapid repair of concrete pavements. *Concrete,* 1982, **16**, September, 12–15.

3.21. THOMPSON E. and LILLEY A.A. Distribution of cement in floor screeds. *Nat. Bldr Lond.,* 1982, **163**, April, 64–67.

3.22. DEPARTMENT OF TRANSPORT *et al. Vacuum grouting of concrete road slabs.* Advice Note HA6/80, Her Majesty's Stationery Office, London, 1980.

3.23. US ARMY CORPS OF ENGINEERS. Rigid airfield pavements. *Engineering and design manual.* EM 1110-45-303, 1967.

3.24. BLANSHARD, S. Overlaying the M18 with concrete. *J. Inst. Highw. Transpn,* 1988, February, 29–35.

3.25. CALVERT G. and LANE J. *Thin bonded overlay with fast track concrete.* Iowa Department of Transport, Ames, Construction Report FHWA No. DTFH 71-86-502-1A-22.

3.26. LILLEY A.A. and COLLINS J. *Laying concrete block paving.* Cement and Concrete Association, Slough, Publication 46.022, 1976.

3.27. KNAPTON J. Pavement rehabilitation using concrete blocks. *Proc. 3rd Int. Conf. Concr. Blocks, Rome,* 1988, 209–216.

3.28. SALT G.F. Skid-resistant road surfacings and tyre noise. *Proc. Inst. Civ. Engrs,* Part 1, 1979, **66**, 115–125.

3.29. AGRAWAL S.K. and DAIUTOLO H. *The braking performance of an aircraft tire on grooved Portland cement concrete surfaces.* US Department of Transportation, Federal Aviation Administration, Washington, DC, Interim report FAA-RD-80-78, 1981.

3.30. AMERICAN SOCIETY OF TESTING MATERIALS. *Specification for joint sealants, hot poured, for concrete and asphalt pavements.* ASTM, Philadelphia, 1985, Standard D3406-85.

3.31. AMERICAN SOCIETY OF TESTING MATERIALS. *Specification for joint sealants, hot poured, elastomeric, jet-fuel-resistant type for Portland cement concrete pavements.* ASTM, Philadelphia, 1985, Standard D3569-85.

3.32. BRITISH STANDARDS INSTITUTION. *Specification of hot applied sealants for concrete pavements.* BS 2499: 1973. BSI, London.

3.33. BRITISH STANDARDS INSTITUTION. *Specification for cold applied joint sealants for concrete pavements.* BS 5212: 1975. BSI, London.

3.34. BRITISH STANDARDS INSTITUTION. *Specification for silicone based building sealants.* BS 5889: 1980. BSI, London.

3.35. SCHREIBER H. *The history of roads.* Barrie, London.

3.36. TRANSPORT AND ROAD RESEARCH LABORATORY. *Road note 29,* 3rd edn. Her Majesty's Stationery Office, London, 1970.

3.37. BRITISH STANDARDS INSTITUTION. *Glossary of highway engineering terms.* BS 6100: 1985. BSI, London.

3.38. BRITISH STANDARDS INSTITUTION. *Specification for constituent material and asphalt mixes.* BS 594: Part 1: 1985. BSI, London.

3.39. BRITISH STANDARDS INSTITUTION. *Testing aggregates.* BS 812: Parts 1–4: 1975–76.

3.40. BRITISH STANDARDS INSTITUTION. *Bitumens for building and civil engineering.* BS 3690: Parts 1–3. BSI, London.

3.41. BRITISH STANDARDS INSTITUTION. *Specification for coated macadam for roads and other paved areas.* BS 4987: Part 1: 1988. BSI, London.

3.42. TRANSPORT AND ROAD RESEARCH LABORATORY. *The structural design of bituminous roads.* LR 1132. Her Majesty's Stationery Office, London.

3.43. BRITISH STANDARDS INSTITUTION. *Methods of test for soils for civil engineering purposes.* BS 1377: 1975. BSI, London.

3.44. TRANSPORT AND ROAD RESEARCH LABORATORY. *Pavement deflection measurements and their application to structural maintenance and overlay design.* LR 571. Her Majesty's Stationery Office, London.

3.45. BRITISH STANDARDS INSTITUTION. *Methods of design and testing of rolled asphalt and bituminous mixes.* BS 598: Part 3: 1985. BSI, London.

3.46. TRANSPORT AND ROAD RESEARCH LABORATORY. *Improved roadbase macadams: road trials and design considerations.* Research Report No. 132. Her Majesty's Stationery Office, London.

3.47. DEPARTMENT OF TRANSPORT. *Specification for highway works.* CI 930. Her Majesty's Stationery Office, London.

3.48. BRITISH STANDARDS INSTITUTION. *Specification for mastic asphalt for roads and footways.* BS 1447: 1973. BSI, London.

3.49. BRITISH STANDARDS INSTITUTION. *Specification for dense tar surfacing for roads and other paved areas.* BS 5273: 1985. BSI, London.

3.50. TRANSPORT AND ROAD RESEARCH LABORATORY. Road note 36, 2nd edn. Her Majesty's Stationery Office, London, 1968.

3.51. *The Highway Act, 1980.* Her Majesty's Stationery Office, London.

3.52. *The traffic signs manual,* ch. 8. Her Majesty's Stationery Office, London.

3.53. BRITISH STANDARDS INSTITUTION. *Specification for single sized roadstone and chippings.* BS 63: Part 2: 1971. BSI, London.

3.54. DEPARTMENT OF THE ENVIRONMENT. *Preferred methods of construction. Part 1: Patching.* Her Majesty's Stationery Office, London, 1973.

3.55. HATHERLY L.W. and LAMB D.R. Accident prevention in London by road surface improvements. *Proc. 6th Int. Wld Highw. Conf., Montreal,* 1970; YOUNG A.E. The potential for accident reduction by improving urban skid resistance levels. Queen Mary College, University of London, 1985.

3.56. GILES C.G. The skidding resistance of roads and the requirements of modern traffic. *Proc. Instn. Civ. Engrs,* 1957, **6**, 216–249.

3.57. SABEY B.E. The road surface and safety of vehicles. *Symposium on vehicle and road design for safety.* Institution of Mechanical Engineers, London, 1968.

3.58. CULHAM P.G. and RICHARDSON P.W. *An economical appraisal of surface dressing treatments*. Department of Transport, London.

3.59. DEPARTMENT OF TRANSPORT. *Road note 39*, 2nd edn. Her Majesty's Stationery Office, London.

3.60. BRITISH STANDARDS INSTITUTION. *Bitumen road emulsions*. BS 434: Part 2: 1984. BSI, London.

3.61. ELBORN M.J. *et al. Aspects of surface dressing technology*. Hampshire County Council, B. Boulton Holdings and Mobil Oil Co.

3.62. SOUTHERN D. *Premium surface dressing system*. SIPC.

3.63. TRANSPORT AND ROAD RESEARCH LABORATORY. *A guide of road surface dressing practice*. LR 627. Her Majesty's Stationery Office, London.

3.64. AMERICAN SOCIETY FOR TESTING MATERIALS. ASTM D 3910.

3.65. BRITISH STANDARDS INSTITUTION. *Methods of design and testing of rolled asphalt and bituminous mixes*. BS 598: Part 3: 1985. BSI, London.

3.66. BRITISH STANDARDS INSTITUTION. *Penetration of bituminous materials*. BS 2000: Part 49; *Softening point of bitumen (ring and ball)*: Part 59. BSI, London.

3.67. BRITISH STANDARDS INSTITUTION. *Specification for hot applied joint sealants for concrete pavements*. BS 2499: 1973. BSI, London.

3.68. BRITISH STANDARDS INSTITUTION. *Methods of sampling and testing*. BS 598: Part 104. BSI, London.

Bibliography

Bituminous materials in road construction. Her Majesty's Stationery Office, London, 1962.

Chemcrete RR54.

Construction Industry International, 1988, May.

Highways and Transportation.

INSTITUTE OF HIGHWAYS AND TRANSPORTATION. *9th annual workshop*.

Roads and Bridges, 1988, May.

Specification for highway works. Her Majesty's Stationery Office, London, 1986.

4

Footways

Walking is a significant means of transport accounting for one-fifth of journeys to and from work, consisting of nearly half of all shopping trips, one-third of social and personal business trips (to banks, dentists, benefit offices, etc) about two-thirds of children's journeys to school, and one-third of recreational and other journeys.[4.1]

Nearly half the population of Great Britain experiences problems with cracked and uneven footways in their neighbourhood. Out of all the consumer surveys conducted at the National Consumer Council, this is one of the highest problem levels ever recorded.[4.2]

Footways are a neglected part of our infrastructure (Fig. 4.1), which have not received due attention for a variety of reasons

(a) objective and purpose ill-defined
(b) design and maintenance parameters unclear
(c) little apparent financial or political return for attention.

Considered against the asset value of an overall highway network, the relative importance of footways will vary. In the London Boroughs, Metropolitan Districts and other urban areas, the relative value will be high, while in rural areas this will be low. In Sheffield, the asset value of footways is estimated to be £130 million (22% of the total highway worth).

Figure 4.2 has been prepared from the National Road Maintenance Condition Survey,[4.3] which was corrected by adding winter maintenance and lighting energy to deduce the total highway maintenance spent, such that the information is compatible with that given by Hatherly in 1978[4.4] and the Audit Commission in 1987.[4.5]

The environmental and sociological value of good footways, and particularly a high standard of maintenance, is becoming understood as society changes and becomes less tolerant of its unacceptable surroundings, and this is emphasized by increasing litigation following personal injury accidents incurred by pedestrians.

4.1. Development of footways

Following the demise of the Romans the present development of footways can be traced back to Anglo-Saxon days. At that time, towns were few and transport between them and the many villages was predominantly on foot, with the pedestrian generally having a clear way. The increased

Fig. 4.1. A neglected footway

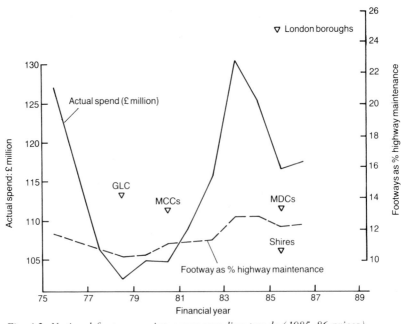

Fig. 4.2. National footway maintenance spending trends (1985–86 prices)

Table 4.1. Approximate dates of footway development

Date	Feature	Reference
1765	Paved footways and raised kerb stones in Westminster	4.6
1811	No 'sidewalks' in Paris	4.6
1840	Walking surfaces nearly all well flagstoned and broad kerb stones in Sheffield	4.7
1850 (see Fig. 4.3)	Footways 10 ft–15 ft (3 m–4·5 m) wide with 2 in (50 mm) crossfall and kerb not greater than 9 in (225 mm)	4.8
1860	Increased use of 'York' stone from Yorkshire and north Lancashire between $1\frac{1}{2}$ in (38 mm) and 4 in (100 mm) thick up to 5 ft 6 in (1·65 m) square	4.9
1868	22 904 yds (20 613 m) of asphalt footway constructed in Sheffield	
1900	Precast concrete flagstones become available	
1925	Increased use of tarmacadam	
1929	First standard for the manufacture of precast concrete flagstones produced by the Institution of Engineers	
1945 +	Increased use of precast concrete flagstones in residential areas	
1950	Hand mixing of tarmacadam on a heated plate still occurring on some sites	
1950 +	Removal of stone flagstones in urban areas and replacement with bituminous macadam normal	
1965	Damage to footways by vehicle overrunning becoming a problem	
1967	Pedestrianization of urban ureas using precast concrete flagstones	
1980	Small element precast concrete flagstones first used in Birmingham	

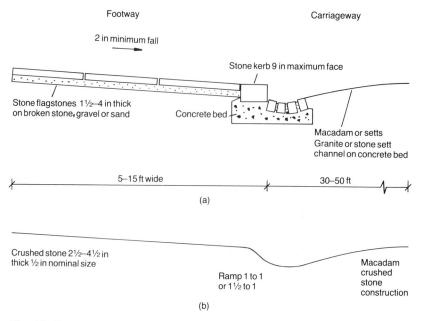

Fig. 4.3. *Footway construction about 1850: (a) urban; (b) rural*

Table 4.2. *Objectives of a footway*

1. To provide a safe walking path for pedestrians segregated from traffic
2. Free from
   (*a*) obstructions
   (*b*) depressions
   (*c*) trips
   (*d*) standing water
   (*e*) loose surfaces
3. Laid to plane and even gradients
4. Self cleansing fabric of construction
5. Surface should be well lit
6. Surface should be non-slip in wet and dry weather
7. There should be no gaps which will trap small wheels, canes or shoe heels
8. Sudden changes in gradient should be avoided
9. Compatible with immediate surroundings to enhance the environment
10. Design and maintenance standards should permit its easy unhindered use by all pedestrians from the fit and able to those with serious mobility and other difficulties
11. Should be capable of resisting the loading from foreseeable vehicle overrunning
12. The need for maintenance should be minimized consistent with achieving lowest whole life cycle costs
13. Should be easily reinstated if disturbed
14. Delineation should be obvious to both pedestrians and motorists

Table 4.3. Footway design standards

1. Surfacing materials — to enhance the environment, resist local point loads and achieve minimum whole life cycle costs

2. Construction — to be capable of accepting overrunning from commercial vehicles or physically prevent access of vehicles and achieve minimum whole life cycle costs

3. Widths

minimum	2·0 m
at bus stops	3·0 m
adjacent to shops	4·5 m

4. Gradients — while related to site topography, the following are preferred

longitudinal minimum	1 in 100
crossfall maximum	1 in 40
minimum	1 in 80
ramps preferred	1 in 20
maximum	1 in 15

5. Crossings — dropped crossings to be provided at all radius points. At controlled crossing points, a textured and colour differentiated surface should be used

6. Channel — at all crossing points a channel block should be used in conjunction with a bullnosed centre stone kerb. The vertical rise at the kerb should not be greater than 10 mm

7. Bollards — to be not less than 1 m high and have colour differentiation banding on top one-third. Placed immediately behind a 300 mm wide kerb

8. Surface texture — not greater than 3 mm

9. Skidding resistance — coefficient of friction $> 0·5$

10. Drainage — positive system to be provided capable of accepting rainfall at a rate of 50 mm/h. Gratings to be flush with surface, non-slip, have openings not greater than 20 mm
    and set perpendicular to the line of pedestrian flow

11. Lighting

Crime risk category	Surface luminosity (lux)	
	Average	Minimum
High	10·0	5·0
Average — low	6·0	2·5
Very low	3·5	1·0

12. Street furniture — all sign poles and lighting columns should be sited at the back of the footway

Table 4.4. Footway routine maintenance standards

Defect	LAA code	10 years
1. Trip or hole	Maximum 20 mm	10 mm
2. Horizontal gap	Maximum 20 mm	10 mm
3. Depressions > 25 mm under 0·5 m straightedge	None	20 mm
4. Rocking flagstones	None	None
5. Loose surface	None	None
6. Standing water	None	None

7. Statutory Undertakers Reinstatements — the objective in heavily used pedestrianized and shopping areas is that the reinstatement should form the final surface without further work being necessary. In other areas where a temporary reinstatement is acceptable, final repair should be completed within 14 days of the Undertaker leaving the site

use of wheeled carts and horses from about 1550 progressively deposed the pedestrian from the highway. About 1700, particularly in towns, a segregation began between carriageways and footways. At that time the construction of both carriageways and footways consisted of broken stone although it appears at this early date that the footway was raised above the carriageway (see Table 4.1).

4.2. Objective and purpose of footways

An examination of various publications[4.10–4.14] indicates that the objective and purpose of a footway is unclear and a wide range of capability must be allowed for, including the 10 million people who may be considered to have some mobility handicap.[4.15] Taking account of this, objectives against which a footway may be designed and maintained are suggested in Table 4.2.

This can be seen to represent a considerable challenge to both the designer and maintainer and requires that the problems of the two groups are considered together and not separately, as has too often been the case.

Typical design standards are set out in Table 4.3. The routine maintenance standards shown in Table 4.4 are based on the Local Authority Association (LAA) Code of Good Practice; also shown is what may be regarded as a 10 year objective.

4.3. Legal aspects

Members of the public have a right to pass and repass along the highway; this is an ancient common law right, the existence of which is an essential characteristic of the highway.

A feature of this is that the highway shall not be obstructed and this extends to both the user and the Highway Authority. There are various duties placed on the Highway Authority; one of the more important is that highways shall be maintained. Unless allowed by a specific piece of legislation the Highway Authority has no powers to obstruct or alter the fabric of the highway.

The more important legislation, parts of which relate to footways (see Table 4.5), is

(a) Highways Act 1980.
(b) Road Traffic Act 1974.
(c) Control of Pollution Act 1974.
(d) Traffic Regulations Act 1984.
(e) Town and Country Planning Act 1971.
(f) Public Utilities Streetworks Act 1950.

The Public Utilities Streetworks Act 1950 governs the conduct of both the Highway Authority and Statutory Undertakers when planning to work in, or working on, the highway. A feature of this is the need for the various parties to serve notice on each other of proposed works and the ability of the Highway Authority to prevent, for a period of 12 months, the excavation of a newly laid highway.

Section 156 Highways Act 1980, however, specifically relates to the carriageway, consequently it is not possible to protect the footway. The major loophole for the undertaker is to claim an 'emergency' with consequential need to access his apparatus. The present position is unsatisfactory and leads to considerable frustration on all sides. Equally there is an absence of case law to help clarify this situation and it is hoped that

Table 4.5. Legislation affecting footways

Feature	Act	Section
Right to pass and repass	Common law	
Duty to maintain	a	41
User can complain about maintenance	a	56
Different standards acceptable	a	58
Need to provide a footway	a	66
Offence to drive on footway	a	72
Obstruction		
building materials	a	175
scaffold	a	169
rubble	a	171
hoarding	a	172
skip	a	139
Cleaning the highway	c	22
Duty to remove snow	a	150
Power to provide		
footway lighting	a	66
safety features	a	28
traffic islands	a	68
subways	a	69
footbridges	a	70
lighting of highway	a	97
Control of traffic, e.g. parking	d	1
Pedestrian precincts — establishment of	d	2
	e	212

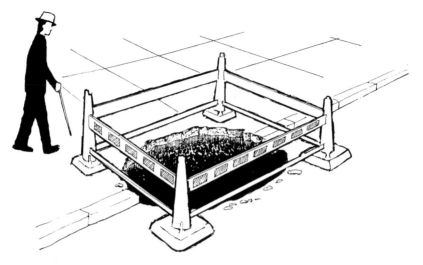

Fig. 4.4. Guarding of excavations

future legislation following the Horne Report[4.16] will provide clearer guidelines.

Guarding of excavations within the highway is covered by section 175A of the Highways Act 1980 and section 8 of the Public Utilities Streetworks Act 1950, and is also dealt with by Chapter 8 of the *Traffic signs manual*.[4.17] The precautions taken are usually inadequate and there is a clear need for improvement. Figure 4.4 shows what should be regarded as a minimum standard for the protection of all excavations.[4.18]

4.4. Management system

The proper management of any maintenance operation requires that information from various sources is available to establish need and monitor performance. Performance can best be monitored using a database approach due to the variety and volume of information to be processed and presented. The list in Table 4.6 should be regarded as a *minimum* from which the system can be established to suit local needs.

From this information it will be possible to define maintenance need, treatment option economics, the effectiveness of the maintenance operation, standards of service provided, and trends and issues that need examination to ensure that the service delivery is acceptable to the consumer. Only by accepting the need for greater consumer satisfaction will progress be made. Inadequate funding against undefined need and ill-defined objectives and standards should not be allowed to continue.

4.5. Standards, inspection and rating

4.5.1. Management system

A maintenance management system can be described as shown in Fig. 4.5.

To demonstrate need requires the definition of a set of standards, or policies, against which the need for remedial action can be measured. In this manner a fully rational budget can be prepared. This is termed intervention-led maintenance.

This framework contrasts with the more normal budget-led system where funding has been determined on an historical basis with no clear starting point. In many cases maintenance is essentially responsive to ad hoc inspection and complaint. This is termed breakdown-led maintenance.

The analogy of running a car is convenient here in that reliability can only be attained by proper servicing as it is too late when breakdown occurs.

In highway maintenance, for the foreseeable future at least, there will be an element of both breakdown and intervention within the system. Good service delivery and economics require that the amount of breakdown maintenance is minimized to no more than one-third of the available budget.

4.5.2. Inventory

The information required for a basic inventory of what is to be maintained is set out in section 4.4.

4.5.3. Defects

Before attempting to understand standards and policies it is necessary to define what is meant by defects and how they can be described and categorized. A helpful starting point is provided by MARCH (Maintenance Assessment Rating and Costing of Highways),[4.19] which sets out

1. Inventory of assets comprising
    location
    length, width
    pedestrian flows
    construction
    condition
2. Funding records
3. Cost trends for specific operations
4. Materials used records
5. Accident records
    location
    defect
    injuries
    personal details
6. Complaints
    type
    cause
    time to repair
7. Periodic consumer survey
    surface acceptability
    maintenance thresholds

Table 4.6. Minimum management information

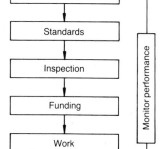

Fig. 4.5. Maintenance system diagram

Table 4.7. MARCH footway defects

---

1. Minor footway deterioration occurs only on footways constructed in flexible materials
    - (*a*)   fine crazing $\leqslant 2$ mm wide
    - (*b*)   loss of aggregate caused by 'drying out' of the binder

---

2. Major flexible footway deterioration comprises
    - (*a*)   cracking of surface > 2 mm wide
    - (*b*)   coarse crazing > 2 mm wide
    - (*c*)   scabbing or fretting of stone from surface
    - (*d*)   depressions > 25 mm deep
    - (*e*)   areas > 1 m^2 of standing water > 6 mm deep
    - (*f*)   trips > 13 mm formed behind kerb, manhole covers, etc. are treated in the same manner as for projections and sharp edges on flagstoned footways.

---

3. Major rigid footway deterioration comprises
    - (*a*)   projections and sharp edges > 13 mm < 20 mm high (> 20 mm should be dealt with urgently)
    - (*b*)   cracks or gaps between flagstones > 20 mm wide provided the gap is > 6 mm deep
    - (*c*)   rocking flagstones
    - (*d*)   depressions > 25 mm deep
    - (*e*)   areas > 1 m^2 of standing water > 6 mm deep

---

defects under two major headings that relate to the severity of those defects, namely 'major' and 'minor'. MARCH also differentiates between flexible and rigid construction. The MARCH defects defined are as shown in Table 4.7.

4.5.4. Maintenance standards or policies

Standards and policies were first proposed in 1970 and are set out separately for footways and kerbs in varying degrees of detail in the Marshall Report,[4.20] the LAA Code of Good Practice 1983[4.21] and in Department of Transport Code of Practice 1984.[4.22] Examples of these can best be seen in the LAA Code (Table 4.8).

4.5.5. Maintenance of footways[4.23]

The object of maintaining footways is to provide a reasonably safe path for pedestrians by day and by night.

In shopping areas and town centres, footways should be maintained with an even surface free from loose material and standing water. In other areas, the minimum maintenance standard should be to keep them safe and free from standing water.

The following conditions will usually require the instigation of repairs

- (*a*)   dangerously rocking flagstones
- (*b*)   projections greater than 20 mm high (including manhole frames and boxes)

(c) cracks or gaps between flagstones greater than 20 mm wide and more than 6 mm deep

(d) isolated potholes

(e) depressions and bumps more than 25 mm deep or high in a length of less than 0·5 m.

The degree of response will be related to the intensity of use and the degree of danger.

4.5.6. Maintenance of kerbs[4.24]

The object of maintaining kerbs is to protect pedestrians, to provide water channels, to lead surface water into gullies and to define and support the edge of the carriageway, e.g. to prevent overriding where other means are unsuitable. New kerbing should be provided where these facilities do not exist and where a need for them has been established. The warning levels are for existing kerbing.

Defective kerbing may take any of the following forms:

(a) longitudinal cracking

(b) broken

Table 4.8. Footway warning levels (LAA Code 1983)

Group to which applicable	Limitation or severity	Percentage of area	Treatment*
Busy urban (flexible)	Coarse cracking of the surface Coarse crazing Depressions > 25 mm deep Trips > 13 mm < 20 mm	30	Restore surface
Busy urban (rigid)	Trips > 13 mm > 20 mm Cracks and gaps > 20 mm wide and > 6 mm deep Rocking flagstones which are not dangerous Depressions > 25 mm deep	30	Restore surface
Less used urban and busy rural (flexible)	As for busy urban (flexible)	40	Restore surface
Less used urban and busy rural (rigid)	As for busy urban (rigid)	40	Restore surface
Little used rural	When potentially dangerous		Patch and restore surface

* The choice of surface treatment will depend on the failure mode, type of construction and importance of the footway. Generally, lesser used footways would only require surface treatment and heavily used ones reconstruction of the surface.

Table 4.9. Kerbing warning levels (LAA Code 1983)

Defect	Group to which applicable	Limitation or severity	Percentage of length	Treatment
Inadequate kerb upstand	*Urban* All	Total loss of upstand	10	Restore upstand
	Protected footway, i.e. with kerbside verge	Upstand 30 mm or less	100	Restore upstand
	Unprotected footway, i.e. no kerbside verge	Upstand 75 mm or less	100	Restore upstand
	No footway	Upstand 30 mm or less	100	Restore upstand
	Rural All	Total loss of upstand	20	Restore upstand
	Busy protected footway	Upstand 30 mm or less	100	Restore upstand
	Busy unprotected footway	Upstand 75 mm or less	100	Restore upstand
	Little used footway or no footway	Upstand 30 mm or less	100	Restore upstand
Kerb deterioration	*Urban* With busy footway	Where defective	10	Replace kerb
	Other sites		20	Replace kerb
Need for kerbing	*Urban* Unprotected footway	Overriding footway Carriageway drainage discharging across footway Surface water not reaching gullies Edge deterioration of carriageway	20	Provide kerb
	Rural Unprotected busy footway	As for urban unprotected footway	30	Provide kerb
	Unprotected little used footway	As for urban unprotected footway	—	Provide kerb as required to need

(c) spalled
(d) badly aligned
(e) badly tilted, i.e. more than 1 in 12
(f) generally disintegrated
(g) sunken channel blocks or setts.

Apart from urgent repairs undertaken for safety reasons, defective kerbs should be replaced in an annual programme, generally in association with other carriageway or footway works, but based on the warning levels cited in Table 4.9.

A more recent publication[4.25] can be seen as an alternative approach, related to an absolute, rather than a relative standard, which relates to consumer aspirations and may be indicative of future trends.

Table 4.10. Routine inspection frequency — footways

	Location	Frequency
1.	Very heavily used footways, major shopping areas and pedestrian precincts	2 weekly
2.	Heavily used footways, small shopping areas, central commercial, and schools/community centres	Monthly
3.	Frequently used urban residential and village streets	3 monthly
4.	Little used urban residential and rural areas	Annually

Table 4.11. Footways routine maintenance warning levels and objectives*

Defect	Location							
	1		2		3		4	
	IL	RP	IL	RP	IL	RP	IL	RP
Trip: mm	13/20 10	1 2	> 20 13/20 13	1 2 3	> 20 13/20	1 3	> 20 13/20	2 3
Rocking flagstones	All	1	All	2	All	3	All	3
Loose kerb	All	2	All	2	All	3	All	3
Missing kerb	All	2	All	2	All	2	All	3
Puddle	> 1 m² > 6 mm			2	> 1 m² > 10 mm			3
Horizontal gap	10 mm			2	20 mm			3

* IL: intervention level.
RP: response period to repair defect.
Category 1 within 24 hours; category 2 within 2 weeks; category 3 within 3 months.

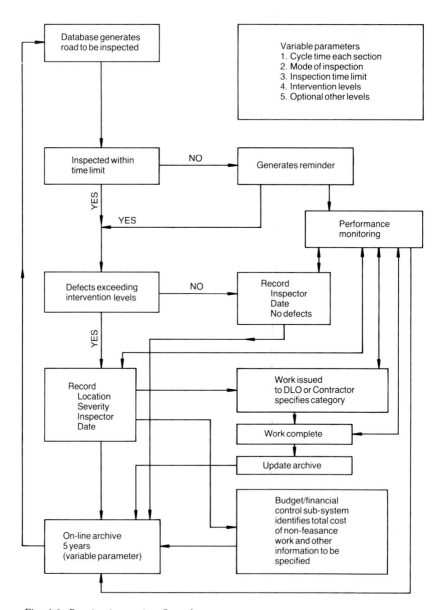

Fig. 4.6. Routine inspection flow chart

4.5.7. Inspections and rating

To be systematic requires a programmed inspection on a preset frequency, which may be related to the nature of the inspection and the anticipated work type. Two types of work are considered.

(a) *routine* — sometimes called a safety or non-feasance inspection as it relates to work of a limited character required to maintain safe passage

(b) *programmed* — relates to more extensive work usually associated with renewal of the asset or as a minimum to prevent further deterioration.

Routine maintenance inspection may be approached in the following way. From the original inventory, which in an urban area will most conveniently be in the form of a street list or gazetteer, the required inspection frequency is established (typical frequencies are shown in Table 4.10). These inspections assess condition against the warning levels set out in Table 4.11 and in many areas will need to be carried out on foot. The

AUTHORITY NAME		ROUTINE FOOTWAY INSPECTION

STREET_____ AREA _____ INSP _____
FROM _____ DATE _____
TO

LOCATION	CONS	TRIP			ROCKING FLAGSTONES	MISSING/LOOSE KERB	PUDDLE	HORIZONTAL GAP	Quantity		Date	COMMENTS
	TYPE	13/20	20/50	>50					Reqd	Done		

TYPES		CC	C/WAY CONCRETE	K	KERB STONE	ENTERED
FF	FOOTWAY FLAGSTONES	CT	C/WAY TARMAC	E	EDGE STONE	ACTIONED
FT	FOOTWAY TARMAC	DI	C/WAY IRONWARE	G	GULLIES	
FI	FOOTWAY IRONWARE	CR	C/WAY RNSTMENT	SU	STAT U-TAKERS	COMPLETED
FR	FOOTWAY RNSTMENT	V	VERGE	M	BARRIER/HAND-	FILED
FC	FOOTWAY CONCRETE				RAIL/SIGN/LAMP	

Fig. 4.7. Routine inspection sheet

severity of the defect and its location will determine the differing timescale within which the repair must be carried out.

In many Authorities the inspection record is kept on a card, which can also be used as a work instruction. Above a total length of about 500 km of highway, however, this becomes less practical and economies can be achieved using a database. A flow chart for such a system is set out in Fig. 4.6. A database also has the advantage that records can be accessed and statistical data prepared for management purposes which is difficult with cards. A typical record format for inspection is shown in Fig. 4.7.

Having established from the *routine* inspection that at a particular location more extensive work is called for, it is necessary to evaluate this need into a rating such that a hierarchy of need can be defined for *programmed* maintenance. In this instance, a detailed inspection is carried out to establish the incidence of the defects. This can be done using several standard systems as follows.

4.5.8. Programmed maintenance

MARCH defects are those described in Table 4.7 and relate well to the urban environment. While it is possible to specify up to 10 footway groups, it is normal to use just four, and guidance is provided on a location or weighting factor to reflect the importance of the particular footway (see Table 4.12). The rating or relative need factor is then calculated by considering the percentage incidence of the defects set out in Table 4.7, and a traffic factor, which is usually taken as 1·0

$$\text{rating} = \frac{\text{percentage defect in section}}{\text{location weighting factor}} \times \text{traffic factor}$$

Table 4.12. MARCH footway location weighting factors[4.26]

Footway group	Description	Weighting factor
01	Very heavily used footways Town centre footways Major shopping centre Pedestrian precincts Footways near schools and large factories, etc.	0·28
02	Heavily used footways Small shopping parades Footways near schools and offices not covered by 01 Near community centres	0·47
03	Frequently used footways Main footways in residential areas Village streets	0·65
04	Little used footways Minor footways in residential and rural areas	0·94

Table 4.13. MARCH footway intervention levels[4.27]

Minor deterioration	Major deterioration		Resurface
Surface treatment	Reinstate	Resurface	Minor + Major
65–100%	10–50%	50–100%	> 65% + > 10%

For example, consider two bituminous footways: A with 85% fine crazing and in location group 02, and B with 65% surface cracking greater than 2 mm wide and in location group 03

$$\text{rating A} \ = \ \frac{85}{0\cdot47} \times 1\cdot0 \ = \ 180\cdot8$$

$$\text{rating B} \ = \ \frac{65}{0\cdot65} \times 1\cdot0 \ = \ 100$$

A calculation such as this is undertaken for each location and when displayed in descending rating order establishes the relative need for each site. As MARCH has a first-order costing facility, this system can produce a cumulative listing of programme cost, which can be equated to the budget to define the extent of the programme.

In addition to producing a rating, MARCH also offers guidance on the remedial work based on intervention levels for the various defects (see Table 4.13). The rating is calculated only when the intervention levels are exceeded.

Three programmes of work are suggested, as can be seen from Table 4.13, and it is for the maintenance engineer to define the actual treatment. Guidance on this is given in other sections.

Another well used assessment system is CHART (Computerized Highway Assessment of Ratings and Treatments),[4.28] which was originally designed by the Department of Transport in the early 1970s. It is primarily intended for the management of trunk roads and as such is not as useful for footway work as MARCH in that it is essentially a do something/do nothing option and results in only the minimum of work on other than the most heavily used footways. The CHART 5 Inspection Manual[4.29] describes a two-level assessment of footway deterioration, i.e. 'minor' and 'major'. However, footway deterioration data can only be entered as a single level assessment, i.e. defect present. The level of assessment chosen by the Department of Transport is 'major deterioration' for inclusion in any programme of work.[4.30] The description of deterioration is similar to that in Table 4.7, although considerably less precise.

4.5.9. A future assessment/evaluation system

A fundamental proposition of maintenance is that it should restore the value of the asset. This then implies that the rating system should include a parameter that involves some proxy for investment or rate of return concepts. It must also be understood that maintenance, especially in the urban environment and particularly of footways, cannot be reduced

DP IABI

	FOOTWAY MAINTENANCE – RATING FORM

STREET _____ SIDE:– ODD/EVEN/BOTH

FROM _____ BUDGET ESTIMATE

TO _____ £

DATE OF ASSESSMENT _____ BY _____

DESIGN BRIEF

Length ....

Width   ....

Area   .... m²

TRIP INCIDENCE PER 25 m (>20 mm)	1	2	3	4	5
	1	3	5	7	8

Graph: Condition cd (vertical axis, 0 to 10) versus Area:% (horizontal axis, 0 to 80). Curves labelled Major (1) and Minor (2).

1	CD	CONDITION:– CD = MAJOR or MINOR or TRIPS + 0·5 (MAJ or MIN) (Max 10) CD	
2		ADDITIONAL FACTORS:–	
	CP	i Complaints received:– 1–5 No 1 pt; > 10 No 2 pt.	
	PT	ii Petition, Pressure Group, Tenants Association:– 2pt.	
	PI	iii Personal Injury Accident:– 2pt.	
	RC	iv Are rechargeable works included? 0–15% 1pt; 16-30% 2 pts; > 30% 3pts.	
	CM	v Does the scheme complement other development ? – 1pt (Max 10) AF	
3	LW	LOCATION WEIGHTING:– i SHOPPING AREAS/PRECINCTS 3·37 ii OTHER HIGH PEDESTRIAN TRAFFIC SITES 2·12 iii PEDESTRIAN THROUGH ROUTES 1·54 iv MINOR ESTATE ROADS 1·00 LW	
4		RATING:– (cd + AF) × LOCATION WEIGHTING × $\dfrac{AREA}{COST}$ or $\dfrac{1}{WLC}$ × 1000 R	

Fig. 4.8. Footway maintenance — rating form

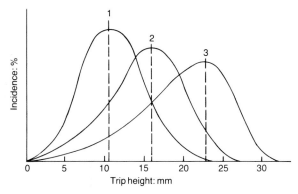

Fig. 4.9. Trip incidence

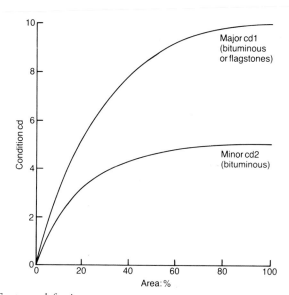

Fig. 4.10. Footway defectiveness

Table 4.14. Trip incidence

Trip incidence per 25 m	1	2	3	4	5
cd3	1	3	5	7	8

totally to a regime of condition based numerical evaluation. The policies of authorities and the aspirations of the elected Member must not be forgotten. To address these two aspects means that they must be allowed for in an evaluation system. A system is set out in Fig. 4.8, which takes into account the various aspects discussed so far.

Condition assessment is undertaken using the concepts of major and minor deterioration and the defects set out in Table 4.7 modified by the addition of a trip incidence. Trip incidence is intended to model the level of disturbance of a flagstoned footway, and to relate to a tolerable number of hazards in a unit length of a bituminous footway, both of which have a bearing on user acceptability.

Figure 4.9 shows three flagstoned footways at different states of user acceptance, which it is possible to assess by a detailed flagstone check. As this will be used on large flagstoned areas, particularly in pedestrian precincts, the use of area rather than incidence per unit length is more appropriate (see Fig. 4.10). It can, however, be modified for a typical 2 m footway if required and either system of units can be used.

For a standard 2 m wide footway or to represent trips caused by potholes, the relationship shown in Table 4.14 can be used for either bituminous or flagstoned surfaces. The value of cd, which has a numerical maximum of 10, to be carried forward to the rating form is either from consideration of major or minor deterioration separately or

$$cd = \text{trip incidence } (cd3) + \tfrac{1}{2}(\text{major } (cd1) \text{ or minor } (cd2))$$

Additional factors to be considered can be seen to relate to

(a)   local action — where an allowance is made for complaints, petitions and residents groups
(b)   the incidence of personal injury accidents
(c)   rechargeable works — any rechargeable work (e.g. from reinstatements) will effectively reduce the cost of the work to the Highway Authority and consequently enhance its cost benefit
(d)   complementary work — in urban areas where the Authority are redeveloping, there may be a desire for maintenance work to complement this refurbishment.

The location weightings can be seen to be identical to those used by MARCH.

In calculating the final rating, an allowance is made for an area/cost parameter to proxy the relative cost of differing solutions. For example, if there are two solutions to a problem, that which costs least will yield the greatest benefit. Alternatively, the reciprocal of whole life cost can be used. A multiplier of 1000 is used to provide a number of sensible proportion when comparing several hundred projects in a programme.

Separate programmes can be drawn up for various types of remedial work based on the intervention levels set out in Table 4.15. The relative need of each scheme against its competitor is demonstrated by the rating.

Table 4.15. Footway intervention levels

Programme	Defectiveness index*
Surface sealing/surface improvement	40–50
Resurface	50–65
Reconstruct	> 65

* Defectiveness index = 10 × cd.

Table 4.16. Typical footway constructions

Type	Wearing course	Base course*	Sub-base†	Relative cost
1. Bituminous A	15 mm	40 mm B	100 mm	1·0
2. Bituminous B	25 mm	60 mm B	150 mm	1·5
3. Mastic asphalt	30 mm	100 mm C	100 mm	5·0
4. Standard flagstone	50 mm	25 mm S	100 mm	2·0
5. Small element flagstone	70 mm	25 mm S	150 mm +	3·2
6. Natural stone flagstone	75 mm +	50 mm S	100 mm	8–10
7. Clay blockwork	65 mm	25 mm S	150 mm +	3·2
8. Concrete blockwork	65 mm	25 mm S	150 mm +	2·5
9. In situ concrete	100 mm	—	100 mm	1·6

* B: bituminous
  C: concrete
  S: sand.
† Type 1 crushed rock.
In some areas the base course thickness for a type 2 footway may be up to 100 mm.

*Table 4.17. Footway type evaluation**

Attribute	Footway type†								
	1	2	3	4	5	6	7	8	9
1. Low construction cost	5	4	2	4	3	1	3	4	4
2. Low maintenance cost	4	4	3	5	3	1	4	4	1
3. Low whole life cost	3	2	4	4	5	4	4	5	3
4. Variable colour and texture	1	1	3	4	5	3	5	4	2
5. Long life	1	1	3	4	5	5	5	5	4
6. Resistant to point loads	1	1	4	5	5	5	5	5	5
7. Resistant to overrunning	1	4	4	1	5	3	5	5	5
8. Reinstateable to original levels	1	3	4	5	5	4	5	5	5
9. Non-degradeable	1	1	3	5	5	4	5	5	3
10. Impermeable	2	3	5	3	3	5	4	4	4
11. Self cleansing	2	2	3	4	4	4	4	4	4
12. Retexturable	1	1	1	2	3	2	2	2	2
13. Non-slip	3	3	4	3	4	2	4	4	2
14. Can lay to shapes or falls	4	4	4	1	3	1	4	4	5
Totals	30	34	47	50	58	44	59	60	49

* Based on score: poor = 1 ↔ 5 = good.
† Footway types are as shown in Table 4.16.

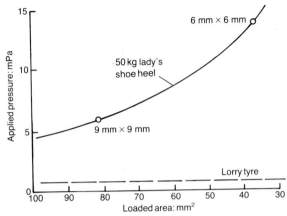

Fig. 4.11. Comparative footway loading

4.6. Types of footway and loading

Until vehicle overrun became a problem, from the mid-1960s, little thought was given to the structural design of footways, and construction followed fairly standard forms as shown in Table 4.16.

An evaluation of the various types of construction can be carried out by considering the various attributes that are desirable in a footway and rating them with a 1–5 score. This is shown in Table 4.17.

The main problem with footway design has been the evaluation of the likely loading, which can cause a local failure of the wearing course, a bearing capacity failure of the sub-grade or a combination of both. Pedestrian loads are low and will not overload the sub-grade. As dress fashions have changed over the years very high point loads can be developed under the heels of ladies' shoes. Figure 4.11 shows that a typical 50 kg lady with 6 mm square shoe heels will impart a stress of some 17 times that of a lorry tyre.

Vehicle overrun, however, causes considerably greater total loads which can lead to a bearing capacity failure of the sub-grade. The motor vehicle regulations[4.31] allow a maximum half axle load of 5590 kg on twin tyres, with the centres of the tyre contact area at least 300 mm apart and a maximum of 5250 kg on a single tyre. Overrunning of delivery vehicles with one side of the vehicle on the footway must therefore be allowed for in the footway construction.

Figure 4.11 shows the relative applied pressure on the wearing course of a footway. The pedestrian load is static; impact and rolling when walking can increase this by a factor of 2.

Following work started in 1984 at Newcastle University a method of balancing allowable stress in precast concrete flagstones with applied load has been published by Bull,[4.32–4.34] which is summarized below and described as the Newcastle Design Method.

With the introduction of pedestrianization in urban areas, it has become necessary to consider several important problems

(a) the material with which the pedestrian areas are surfaced
(b) the large number of heavy vehicles that frequently and illegally overrun footways
(c) the provision of adequate access and routes for delivery and emergency vehicles, so that the pedestrian surface is not damaged by those vehicles
(d) the effect of the public utilities and local authority routine maintenance activities.

The research involved a number of inter-related areas including a computer based analytical investigation, laboratory testing of single and multiple paving flagstones on various base material and site tests at four locations in the UK to produce a guide to design.

The starting points were the known properties of the paving flagstone, the size, the shape of the tyre contact area and the loading on the paving flagstone. Only square paving flagstones were considered as they are structurally more efficient than other rectangular shapes.

From this work, as shown in the following example, it is possible to calculate the required sub-base thickness to limit the actual tensile stress in the flagstone to less than an acceptable value, which is set out in BS 368[4.35] and shown in the second column of Table 4.18. This stress is reduced by various factors such that the sub-base and formation are not overstressed. In this way, while the flagstone will crack, this will be due to fatigue and, as its foundation is not overloaded, trips will not occur.

Example using the design charts (Figs 4.12–4.14)

Obtain the required sub-base thickness for a precast concrete flagstone footway expected to carry 32 000 standard axles in its design life, with a sub-base California bearing ratio (CBR) of 50% and a soil CBR of 15% using a paving flagstone size of 400 × 400 × 65 mm on a sand bedding layer of 25 mm.

Stage 1

(a) From Table 4.19, 32 000 repetitions gives a stress ratio of 0·6.
(b) The allowable flagstone tensile stress due to repeated loading (Table 4.18) is 0·6 × 4·78 = 2·868 MPa.
(c) Calculate the percentage reduction in observed stress (Table 4.18, third column) to achieve 2·868 MPa

$$100 - \frac{2 \cdot 868}{3 \cdot 72} \times 100 = 23\%$$

Table 4.18. *Maximum concrete stress due to an 80 kN standard axle load*

BS flagstone size: mm	Maximum allowable stress: MPa	Mimimum observed stress: MPa
600 × 600 × 63	4·79	7·75
450 × 450 × 70	4·8	4·42
400 × 400 × 65	4·78	3·72
300 × 300 × 60	4·79	2·95

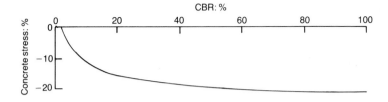

Fig. 4.12. Reduction in concrete paving flagstone stress related to soil CBR: Newcastle design method[4.39]

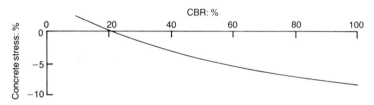

Fig. 4.13. Reduction in concrete paving flagstone stress related to sub-base CBR: Newcastle design method[4.39]

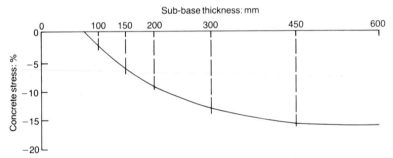

Fig. 4.14. Reduction in concrete paving flagstone stress related to sub-base thickness: Newcastle design method[4.39]

Table 4.19. Load repetitions to failure, related to stress ratio

Stress ratio	Repetitions
0·51	400 000
0·55	130 000
0·60	32 000
0·65	8 000
0·70	2 000
0·75	490
0·80	120
0·85	30

Stage 2

(*a*) For soil CBR = 15%, Fig. 4.12 gives an observed stress reduction of 14%.

(*b*) Deduct from required reduction (Stage 1(c)): 23 − 14 = 9%.

Stage 3

(*a*) For base CBR = 50%, Fig. 4.13 gives an observed stress reduction of 4%.

(*b*) Deduct from required reduction (Stage 2(b)): 9 − 4 = 5%.

Stage 4. For a required stress reduction of 5% from Fig. 4.13 a base thickness approaching 150 mm is required.

Sub-base thickness selected is 150 mm

4.7. Kerbs and edge restraint

A common requirement of all footway construction is the need for edge restraint, which is provided at the front by the kerb, and at the back of the footway by an edging (see Fig. 4.15). If the footway abuts either a building or a wall this edging can be dispensed with, but not otherwise. In addition to providing lateral restraint, which inhibits spread of the footway, kerbs and edgings prevent water ingress to the structure. In the case of an unrestrained flagstoned footway the flagstones float laterally, and unacceptably wide joints appear between adjacent units causing danger and allowing the ingress of water. As the kerb inhibits water flow into the carriageway foundations, so the back edging prevents water from getting into the sub-base of the footway. Water in the construction will decrease the bearing capacity of the sub-grade by up to 50% and increase the frost susceptibility of the construction in winter.

Various types of kerb will be found in differing locations throughout the country but these all perform the same fundamental functions, i.e.

(*a*) form a channel for the surface water
(*b*) form a raised barrier for the footway
(*c*) reduce number of vehicles mounting the footway

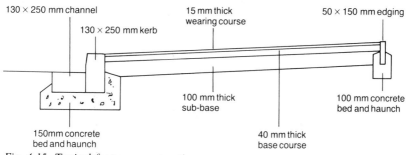

Fig. 4.15. Typical footway construction

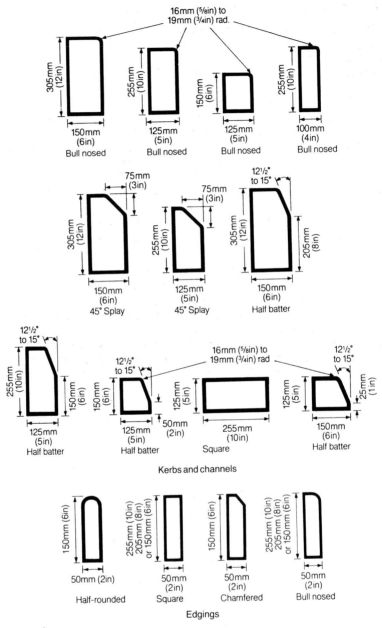

Fig. 4.16. Standard precast sections to BS 340

(*d*) form an edge restraint at the end of the carriageway and the front of the footway

(*e*) prevent ingress of water to the sub-base.

In the case of the special sections described later, kerbs can also be used as a positive anti-vehicle barrier and provide a novel and convenient drainage channel.

Kerbs can be formed of various materials some of which are as follows.

4.7.1. Precast concrete kerbs

Precast concrete kerbs, manufactured to BS 340 specification[4.37] are the most widely used and readily available. Kerbs and edgings are made to various cross-sections shown in Fig. 4.16. In addition a number of special colours and textures are available for use in environmentally sensitive areas. An example of this is a buff coloured bullnosed section which is available in a sand blasted finish and is a good substitute for natural stone. Kerbs are either straight, radiused or special and are available in either 915 mm or 610 mm lengths. There are four basic sections

(*a*) bullnosed — used generally in urban streets where footway protection is paramount

(*b*) half battered — the most usual general purpose section

(*c*) splayed — used where it is expected vehicles will leave the carriageway (e.g. in an emergency); they have also been used to good effect in narrow urban culs-de-sac where the adjacent footway has been designed to resist overrunning

(*d*) specials — comprise dropper and centre stones for drop crossings, and quadrants for islands and footway edgings, together with external and internal corners and outlet or weir kerbs.

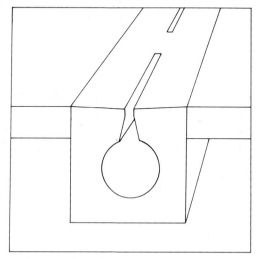

Fig. 4.17. Precast drainage channel

Additionally, and specifically for enhancing drainage, are channel blocks for gradients flatter than 1 in 150 and dished channels for footways. Several variants of slotted channel block are available for drainage in footways (Fig. 4.17).

A more recent development for drainage, which is being found to be beneficial in an increasing number of locations, is the Beany Block (Figs 4.18 and 4.19),[4.38] a patented system which has the advantage of not introducing weakness into the carriageway in the form of gullies. The system is comprehensive and is becoming increasingly popular.

Special barrier kerbs (Fig. 4.20) are available, which are designed to keep an errant vehicle on the carriageway in the case of an accident. Care should be taken in their use and thought given to the location, as an uncontrolled errant vehicle can itself be very dangerous.

Fig. 4.18 (right). Beany Block drainage system — part complete

Fig. 4.19 (below). Beany Block drainage system — installed

Fig. 4.20. Barrier kerb to protect footway

4.7.2. Natural stone kerbs

Natural stone kerbs are usually either granite or sandstone depending on location. They are typically 150 mm × 300 mm or 225 mm × 300 mm. Existing kerbs already laid are in random lengths from about 0·6 m–1·5 m and are dressed on two edges and both ends, the remaining two edges being rough finished. New natural stone kerbs are 10 times the cost of precast concrete and are now sawn finished. Their use is confined to prestigious locations. Existing stone kerbs are re-used subject to not having split on the bedding planes. The advantages and disadvantages of concrete and stone kerbs are presented in Table 4.20.

Table 4.20. Kerb types — advantages and disadvantages

Advantages	Disadvantages
Precast concrete	
Uniform size and shape	Less durable than stone
Lighter and easier to lay	Susceptible to frost
Cheaper than stone	Spall on impact
Available in many sections	
Readily available	
Natural stone	
Impact and abrasion resistant	Expensive
Long life	Not readily available
Low maintenance	Heavier and needs more
Good weather resistance	skill to lay

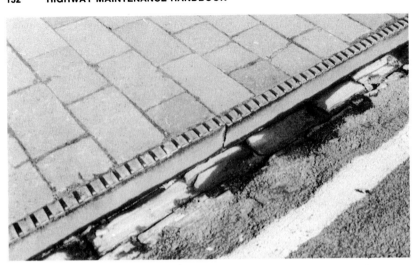

Fig. 4.21. Decorative cast iron kerb

4.7.3. Natural stone setts

Natural stone setts are used as an edge demarcation in various parts of the country. These are usually laid sloping and present a similar profile to splayed kerbs. They are used as decorative channel features in environmentally sensitive schemes. They are, however, not usually used at the front of a footway.

4.7.4. Clay bricks and concrete blocks

Clay bricks and concrete blocks are considered together here due to their common dimensions. As a consequence of the increased use of blockwork for pedestrian areas and footways there are a considerable number of special kerb, edging and channel sections available in both materials.

4.7.5. Other materials

In some areas examples can be found of various decorative materials (an example of a cast iron kerb is shown in Fig. 4.21).

4.7.6. Laying of kerbs

The laying of all forms of kerb is fairly similar and can be grouped into two categories (see Fig. 4.22).

    (*a*)   dry bed — the kerb is laid to line and level on a minimum 150 mm thick bed of semi-dry grade C7.5 concrete and backed with 100 mm of the same concrete

    (*b*)   wet bed — in this case the kerb race is cast, usually using steel formwork, as a separate operation and the kerbs are laid on a layer of bedding mortar between 10 mm and 40 mm thick; a 100 mm backing is used and applied later.

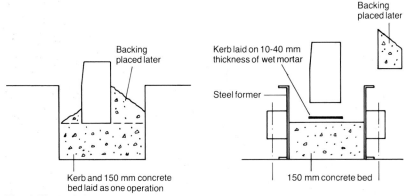

Fig. 4.22. Kerb laying

The advantage of the wet bed on a new construction, where a lift greater than the bed thickness is required, is careful control over concrete usage. Dry bed takes less setting up and is more normal for maintenance work, but is more wasteful of concrete.

Where replacement or removal and resetting is indicated (see Table 4.21) it may be necessary to remove more kerbs than those immediately affected to get an acceptable alignment. Additionally, where kerbs and edgings have sunk as a result of excavation, it may be necessary to provide a regulating patch on the channel or footway.

For a kerb to be replaced it is usually judged against the test of danger to pedestrians. Some authorities, however, accept the environment nuisance of spalling and damaged kerbs as being sufficient to warrant replacement.

Replacement involves the disturbance of the carriageway surface and when reinstatement is taking place care should be taken to ensure that

Table 4.21. Typical defects and maintenance of kerbs and edgings

Defect	Likely cause	Maintenance
Cracked	Accident damage	Possible replacement
Spalled	Accident Expansion Weather Old vibrated Manufacturing process	Probable replacement
Loose Sunk	Accident Excavation	Remove and reset
Tilted	Excavation Tree roots	Remove and reset Consider root pruning
Missing	Accident	Replace

Table 4.22. Tolerances for footway construction

Element	Tolerance:* mm
Wearing course	±6
Base course	±6
Sub-base	±10
Sub-grade	±20
Box or gully	+0–6

*Relates to the vertical departure from design levels.

Table 4.23. Compaction plant for footways

Type	Size	Minimum number of passes for compacted layer thickness*						
		Sub-base†		Base		Wearing course		
		100 mm	150 mm	60 mm	40 mm	15 mm	25 mm	40 mm
Vibrating plate	Mass/unit area under base kg/m²							
	1400–1800	8	N/S	6	4	2	3	5
	1800–2100	5	8	4	3	2	2	3
Vibrating roller	Mass/metre of roll: kg							
	700–1300	16	N/S	8	6	3	3	4
	1300–1800	6	8	‡	‡	‡	‡	‡

* The number of passes suggested is given as guidance for comparative compaction trials to validate plant performance.
† NS: not suitable.
‡ A vibrating roller of this size is not recommended for footway work.

there is a waterproof joint between the kerb and the bituminous surfacing. This is done by painting the joint with a 50 pen bitumen before laying the wearing course.

4.8. Footway surfacings

Regardless of the wearing course used on any footway there is a common theme that must run through the construction and maintenance operations, and this relates to tolerances (Table 4.22) and compaction. Many of the maintenance problems that are present today result from poor specification and compaction. The fact that the loading to which the structure is subjected has hitherto been ill defined is an inadequate reason for poor specification. In some ways, however, the generally low levels of loading make it more difficult to specify a footway successfully.

Compaction is the second major rule; while for Rankine[4.39] a roller of approximately 0·25 to 0·5 tonne may have been appropriate this is not the case today. On investigation many maintenance problems can be traced back to inadequate compaction. While Table 4.23 offers guidance on compaction plant the information given is not easily interpreted in site situations and not all sites have tables of manufacturer's performance information. A pragmatic solution is for highway authorities to devise a simple grouping of say four or five categories of roller, which will provide the required compactive effort. The specification of compaction is of equal importance to the specification for the wearing course.

Fig. 4.23. Blacktop footway

The sub-base should in all cases consist of Type 1 crushed rock,[4.40] although it may prove acceptable to use cold planings from carriageway maintenance works providing that there is a degree of consistency and a reasonable fines fraction. The use of Type 2 and other crushed rocks with a discernible clay fraction is not recommended due to possible problems of frost susceptibility, nor is the use of brick hardcore, due to the likelihood of foreign bodies and its tendency to degrade. The formation on which the sub-base sits should be consistent and dry; if there is any doubt, drainage should be provided.

In general a thickness of 100 mm is adequate for the sub-base, although a means of assessing the need for a greater thickness is described in section 4.6 for flagstones or can be deduced from Road Note 29[4.41] for bituminous construction.

4.8.1. Bituminous construction

Bituminous macadam (blacktop) construction (see Fig. 4.23) comprises a basecourse of open textured or dense bituminous basecourse to BS 4987 specification.[4.42] The latter is more expensive and unless the location is expected to be subjected to overrunning cannot be justified.

The wearing course is usually of fine cold asphalt, or 6 mm medium textured bituminous macadam to BS 4987 specification. Due to the light loading and relatively high amount of weathering the binder content should be about 0·5% higher than that which would be used for carriageway work; this will, however, necessitate an increase in fines. To neglect this requirement will lead to greater weathering and shorter life.

The progressive availability of a 6 mm dense bitumen wearing course is now leading to better performance, and a specification for this material, which is not covered by BS 4987, is given in Table 4.24. While the initial cost of a bituminous footway is relatively low its service life is less than other alternatives.

One of the major problems since the early 1970s has been the almost uncontrolled use of cutback or delayed set macadams, which have a

Table 4.24. Dense bituminous wearing course (6 mm) for footway

BS test sieve: mm	Percentage by mass passing	Aggregate	Bitumen: %
6·3	90–100	Crushed rocks 1–7	6 ± 0·5
3·35	65–80	Limestone	6 ± 0·5
1·18	30–50		
300 μm	10–25		
75 μm	2–6		

Type of binder	Aggregate temperature: °C		Binder temperature: °C	
	Minimum	Maximum	Minimum	Maximum
300 pen	65	100	95	130
200 pen	100	120	100	150

volatile flux oil added at the mixing stage. This volatile oil evaporates over a period; suppliers claim days but experience suggests longer. The general appearance of the laid surface quickly becomes anaemic and the relative longevity is poor. For other than emergency works, cutback or delayed set material should not be used. A low viscosity binder is recommended for footway works of either 200 or 300 pen.

In some areas the use of a single 40 mm or 50 mm thick wearing course of 10 mm dense bitumen wearing course is used as a combined wearing/base course. Economies are claimed and a solid dense surface results with proper compaction. One benefit of a single course layer is that it is possible to undertake inlaid reinstatements after statutory undertakers' activity.

Mastic asphalt, 30 mm thick, is used in urban areas where high quality work is required. It is laid hot, usually by a specialist contractor, on a 100 mm thick concrete base and has the advantage of acting as a waterproof layer, particularly where there are cellars under the footway.

Sand carpet rolled asphalt to BS 594 specification,[4.43] Table 5 (column 18), is also used in urban centre locations, generally unchipped, although its appearance can be improved by the light use of white chippings. The compacted thickness of this material is 30 mm and it is laid on a bituminous base course.

The use of tarmacadam is now almost non-existent due to its limited availability. In some countries tar is a prohibited material due to the relatively high content of carcinogenic materials. The use of an open textured macadam as a wearing course should not be permitted as the sealing grit required can lead to slippery and dangerous surfaces.

Laying of bituminous footways (Fig. 4.24) can be by mini-paver, although the majority are laid by hand. For good compaction the use of a twin-drum vibrating roller is to be preferred, and care should be taken to ensure compaction occurs adjacent to walls and buildings, in awkward corners and around street furniture. This can be accomplished using a vibrating plate or where required a hand rammer should be used. When laying by hand a lath 6 mm thick should be used along the top of the kerb to ensure a consistent finish at the kerb edge. This is used as a laying guide for the wearing course, ensuring the edges get adequate compaction, and is removed before rolling takes place.

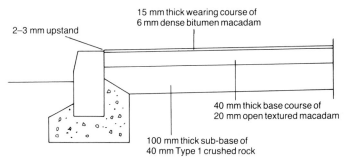

Fig. 4.24. Typical cross-section of a bituminous footway

Fig. 4.25. Standard paving flagstones

Table 4.25. Paving flagstones

Type*	Size: mm	Thickness: mm
1. Paving flagstones		
A	450 × 600	50 or 63
B	600 × 600	50 or 63
C	600 × 750	50 or 63
D	600 × 900	50 or 63
2. Small element paving flagstones		
E	450 × 450	70
F	400 × 400	65
G	300 × 300	60

*Types E, F and G are also available in 50 mm thickness for pedestrian only use.

Table 4.26. Grading of sand for laying flagstones and blocks

BS sieve	Percentage by mass passing	
	Laying course	Joint course
5·00 mm	90–100	95–100
2·36 mm	75–100	85–100
1·18 mm	55–90	75–100
600 μm	35–59	60–70
300 μm	8–30	12–40
150 μm	0–10	0–10

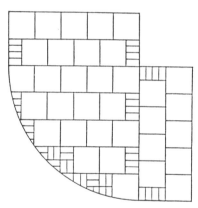

Fig. 4.26. (above). Small element
flagstones

Fig. 4.27 (left). Combined use of small
element flagstones and blockwork

4.8.2. Flagstoned construction (Fig. 4.25)

British Standard 368[4.35] governs the manufacture of precast concrete
flagstones, which are divided into two categories (Table 4.25). The two
categories are laid in a different manner on a common sub-base.

Paving flagstones. Paving flagstones are laid on a bed of sand to the
grading shown in Table 4.26. The sand is spread to a thickness of
30–50 mm and levelled, and the flagstones are laid and settled with a
pavior's maul. In some areas flagstones are laid tight jointed (touching)
but more normally a joint of 6 mm is left between adjacent flagstones,
which is filled by sweeping in a mixture of 4:1 sand/cement mixed dry. In
some areas this joint is filled with a wet mortar of similar mix. This has the
same effect in preventing the ingress of water to the bedding material.

Fig. 4.28. Laying sequence for small element flagstones: (a) lay and compact base, (b) screed and precompact sand bed, (c) lay small element dry, (d) compact with vibrating plate

An alternative to sand is to use a mixture of 20:1 sand/cement as a bed, the laying operation following the previous description. A further alternative is where the flagstones are laid on five spots of mortar, one in each corner and one in the centre. Flagstones laid in this way are only capable of supporting pedestrian traffic.

Small element flagstones. Small element flagstones are laid on a 25 mm pre-compacted bed of sand with a joint of 2–4 mm, and they are settled with a rubber-faced vibrating plate giving two passes before dry sharp sand is vibrated into the joints with the same plate, using a further three passes. The flagstones should ideally be half bonded as they rely for their stability on the mechanical interlock developed by the grains of jointing sand acting in shear. Joints greater than 6 mm should be avoided, as should wet mortared joints. Allowance should be made in the specification for topping up the sand joint fill and replating the surface after about three months of service. The cutting of small element flagstones (Fig. 4.26) should be avoided and instead details are arranged using blockwork as is shown in Figs 4.27 and 4.28.

Textured pavings, red in colour, have been designed to be used on the footway to impart information to the blind or poorly sighted at pedestrian crossings (see Fig. 4.29). The texture has three functions. Firstly, it helps blind people find the crossing. Secondly, in the case of a crossing having a pedestrian control, it helps blind people find the pole carrying the pedestrian push button, and, thirdly, it enables blind people while waiting to cross, to align themselves in the direction in which they should proceed when able.[4.44] The use of these pavings is governed by Department of Transport Advice Note TA 52/87,[4.45] which effectively means they are a traffic sign requiring a Traffic Regulation Order. As such they cannot be used indiscriminately.

Other forms of textured pavings are available for use as a tactile strip or an edge demarcation. These are usually a very exposed aggregate of buff or other neutral colour.

Fig. 4.29. Textured paving at controlled crossing

Fig. 4.30. Natural stone flagstone footway

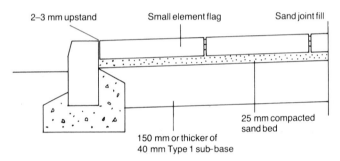

Fig. 4.31. Typical cross-section of a flagstoned footway

Natural stone flagstones (Fig. 4.30) require much more skill in laying due to their uneven thickness. They are traditionally laid on a bed of black ashes or sand and the joints between adjacent flagstones are buttered with 4:1 sand/cement mortar before laying to ensure a full joint (see Fig. 4.31). Newly sawn flagstones are available but are only used in prestigious locations due to their cost, a recent example being Parliament Square in Westminster.

4.8.3. Blockwork construction (Fig. 4.32)

Blockwork, both clay and concrete, is laid in the same manner as small element flagstones. Clay blocks cost about twice the price, for materials, as concrete but have an inherent texture and colour fastness not found in concrete. The final choice will depend on both aesthetic considerations and financial evaluation.

It is interesting to note that blocks are extensively used in The Netherlands where the CBRs are very low due to alluvial sands, particularly in reclaimed areas. Rather than attempt to attain the CBRs which would be looked for in the UK it is normal practice to relay the blocks on a seven to ten year cycle. In this case the blocks are lifted, the existing sand bed is screeded, and the blocks are relaid and vibrated into place. By doing this there is no materials cost after the initial laying other than a small amount of sand for regulating and it is therefore possible to justify a higher initial materials cost. A regular feature in The Netherlands is the use of the Woonerf, which is a joint use pedestrian and vehicle surface. While it is possible for vehicles to pass through a Woonerf the route is quite tortuous, to keep down speed, and the pedestrian has the right of way. Without exception, blockwork is used in these locations.

Brick paving can be found in many older urban locations, with either a smooth or textured surface, and is normally laid on lime mortar. As with normal walling the method of laying, type of mortar and particularly the drainage can affect the life of the footway. Currently, blocks are laid on a semi-dry 4:1 sand/cement mortar and settled with a lump hammer. Joints of between 6 mm and 10 mm are left and are filled with a run in grout or a semi-dry 4:1 mortar. This form of construction must not be trafficked for three to five days after laying. Brick paving laid in this manner currently tends to be used for smaller feature areas as the joint is very susceptible to damage from stiletto heels (see Figs 4.33–4.35).

4.8.4. In situ concrete

In situ concrete is laid either 100 mm or 150 mm thick on a waterproof membrane on the sub-base, with expansion joints at 6 m centres, or less, depending on the bay layout. Reinforcement is not usually used and recently the addition of chopped synthetic fibres, added to the mix, has increased the ability of the surface to resist impact loading. The surface of the concrete should preferably be either float or brush finished with a

Fig. 4.32. Blockwork footway

*Fig. 4.33. Brick paving —
smooth finish*

*Fig. 4.34. Brick paving —
textured finish*

*Fig. 4.35. Damaged joints
in brick paving*

floated arris, as a tamped finish can lead to tripping accidents and is less weather resistant.

4.9. Causes of deterioration

Progressive general deterioration can be due to a number of causes, either in isolation or combination; some are presented in Table 4.27.

Weathering usually has a much greater impact on flexible footways than on rigid ones. It is caused by repeated wetting and drying cycles and the progressive degradation of bitumen by the ultra-violet rays of the sun. This leads to a loss of aggregate which in turn acts as an abrasive on the surface (Fig. 4.36).

Wear from walking, which causes either polishing of the surface or rutting, is not a widespread condition, but can be seen in very heavily used pedestrian areas in urban shopping centres.

Disturbance by third parties is usually from the statutory undertakers, who, it is estimated in Sheffield, for example, affect about 2% of the area

Table 4.27. Causes of deterioration

1.	Weathering
2.	Wear from walking
3.	Disturbance by third parties
4.	Frost damage
5.	Overrunning and local impact
6.	Tree roots
7.	Weed growth
8.	Poor workmanship
9.	Inadequate specification
10.	Inadequate drainage

Fig. 4.36. Weathering of blacktop footways

Fig. 4.37. Disturbance by third parties

Fig. 4.38 (above). Frost damage to blacktop footway

Fig. 4.39 (right). Damage by overrunning

Fig. 4.40 (below). Damage by impact

Table 4.28. Prevention of overrunning

Active	Passive
Bollard	Parking control
Double kerb	Reinforced edge
Guardrail	
Tree planting	
Feature boxes	

of the footways annually. The settlement caused by this disturbance is invariably the result of the return of excavated materials affected by the weather and/or inadequate compaction (Fig. 4.37).

Frost damage occurs about once every ten years where the sub-base is frost susceptible and/or the water table is high. When water freezes it expands by about 8–10% by volume and this causes the surface to heave and burst. In many cases it will settle to its original level when freeze–thaw finishes. In very severe winters when repeated freeze–thaw cycles are experienced, serious damage can result to all footway construction. When damage is not severe the effects can be seen on a bituminous footway where a fine crack some 75 mm–150 mm behind the kerb occurs. On flagstoned footways frost damage may require the relaying of lengths of footway to replace them with an even surface. (Fig. 4.38.)

Fig. 4.41 (left). Damage by tree roots

Fig. 4.42 (below). Weed growth damage

Table 4.29. Footway deterioration and maintenance

Type of footway	Defect	Likely causes	Remedial works
Bituminous	Trip or pothole	Action of water and frost accelerates breakdown of wearing course	Fill cavity and patch
	Fretting or loss of aggregate	Loss of aggregate due to binder drying, lack of compaction	Seal surface
	Disintegration or crumbling	Binder failure, inadequate tack-coat or dirty basecourse when wearing course laid	Resurface
	Polishing	Heavy wear at concentrated usage points	Textured slurry seal or overlay
	Cracking general	Debonding from basecourse and differential thermal movement	Seal surface, patch as necessary
	Crack parallel to kerb	Frost heave in cold conditions, crack left when surface settles	Seal surface
	Surface deformation	Vehicle damage, subsidence due to water in sub-grade	Local or general reconstruction/ remove weed growth
		Upwards deformation caused by tree roots or weed growth	
	Edge spalling/crumbling	Inadequate excavation reinstatement	
		Lack of edge restraint. Weed growth	Provide edge restraint and patch
Paved	Trip	Water in sub-base causing loss of support, vehicle overrunning, frost	Relay
	Broken or cracked flagstone	Accident or overrunning, hard spot in bedding course, excess point load	Relay
	Polishing	Heavy wear at concentrated usage points	Retexture
	Rocking flagstones	Badly laid, water in bedding	Relay
	Rutting	Heavy wear at concentrated usage points	Relay
	Surface deformation	Vehicle damage, water in formation, tree roots, inadequate reinstatement, weed growth	Reconstruct/remove weed growth
	Joint widening	Lack of edge restraint	Provide edge restraint and relay
Rigid	Fine cracking	Faulty curing of flagstone at manufacturing stage	Possible patch/reconstruct
	Trip	Slab settled due to water in sub-base, poor sub-base compaction	Reconstruct
	Spalling	Surface deterioration and frost action	Possible patch/reconstruct
	Cracking	Excess point loading	Reconstruct
	Polishing	Heavy wear at concentrated usage points	Possible patch/reconstruct

Overrunning and local impact, in most cases associated with deliveries, causes loadings on the structure, which cannot be resisted by normal construction. Prevention can be categorized as either active or passive (see Table 4.28, Figs 4.39 and 4.40).

Tree roots, particularly in urban areas where forest trees have been planted, can cause heave of the footway of up to 200 mm–300 mm, which can at worst form an impassable step, or at best a serious trip caused by tensile cracking (Fig. 4.41).

Weed growth (see Fig. 4.42) is the result of inadequate attention at the construction or reconstruction stage and poor cyclic maintenance. An ideal weedkiller will be a mixture of chemicals to deal with both broad leaf perennials and annual grass type weeds. It should be applied both to the formation at the construction stage and the walking surface, the latter being most effective during April–September, and should form part of a three-year rolling programme (Fig. 4.43).

The ideal formulation will have the following attributes

(a) systemic — taken in through leaves
(b) translocating — travels through plant to kill root
(c) residual/persistent — active in soil for six to nine months

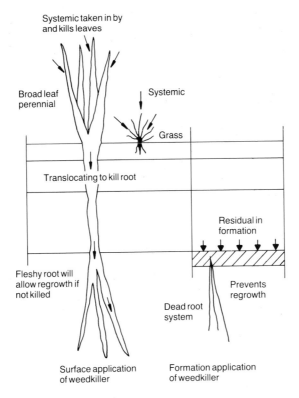

Fig. 4.43. Typical weedkiller application

Poor workmanship and inadequate specification can reasonably be considered together and can either singly or jointly have a significant deleterious effect on the longevity of the structure, some of the reasons being set out in Table 4.29.

Drainage is considered by many to be one of the three cardinal problems of a highway the other two being drainage and drainage! While this may seem a facile argument, poor drainage can be shown to have a most serious effect on any element of the highway.

From Table 4.29 the maintenance implications fall into treatments related to each construction type.

4.10. Remedial works

4.10.1. Bituminous footways

The objective of routine maintenance is to maintain safety and includes the filling of cavities and potholes, subsequent patching and small scale repair. The scope of work which must be undertaken to fill a pothole can be set out as follows.

(*a*)   Brush any loose material or water from the cavity.

(*b*)   Apply bituminous emulsion and wait for it to break (changes colour from brown to black as water evaporates).

(*c*)   Fill the cavity with fine bituminous material, ramming solid with a hand rammer or vibrating plate, and leaving it flush with the parent surface.

A temporarily filled pothole should not be left for more than three months before the area is patched to effect a permanent repair.

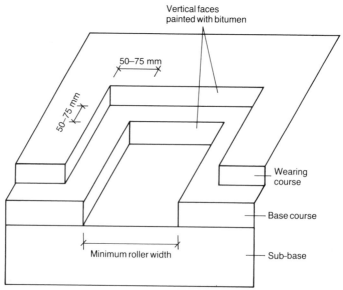

Fig. 4.44. Inlaid patching

With all inlaid patching the objective should be a plane level surface without any form of step or trip. The practicability of this will depend on the level of surface deterioration reached and whether there is a sufficient thickness of wearing course material, which can be planed off to form a regular rectangular cavity to receive the patch. Planing on a footway is becoming much more practicable with the advent of small milling attachments for small rubber tyred skid shovels of the 'bobcat' type. If this type of planer is available the sequence of operations is as follows.

(a) Plane rectangular areas and step in by 50–75 mm as shown in Fig. 4.44. The important consideration here is to ensure that the patch is of sufficient size to allow the roller to work properly. For example, it is pointless trying to carry out basecourse patching if the roller is greater than the width of the wearing course cavity.
(b) Remove any loose materials from the cavity.
(c) Apply bituminous emulsion to the base of the cavity.
(d) Paint the vertical edges of the cavity with 50 or 100 pen bitumen to effect seal.
(e) Fill the cavity with bituminous material.
(f) Compact.
(g) Repeat stages (c)–(e) if wearing course is used in addition to the basecourse.

The majority of patching on footways is overlay rather than inlay which involves similar work as follows.

(a) Brush off any loose materials.
(b) Apply emulsion.
(c) Lay fine wearing course material using a 6 mm edge lath to provide a regular and consistent edge.
(d) Compact.
(e) Seal the edge of the patch with 50 or 100 pen bitumen.

The most suitable material for this work is a 3 mm bituminous macadam, in accordance with the specifications set out in Table 4.30, which will result in a much more consistent job as it can be laid more thinly than fine cold asphalt, which has a 6 mm nominal aggregate size. The

Table 4.30. *Bitumen macadam (3 mm) wearing course for footways**

BS test sieve	Percentage by mass passing
6·3 mm	100
3·35 mm	75–100
1·18 mm	25–45
300 μm	8–22
150 μm	3–14
75 μm	2–8

*Aggregate shall be crushed rock. Binder content shall be 6% ± 0·5%. Binder shall be petroleum bitumen 300 pen. The mixing temperature of the aggregate shall be between 65°C and 100°C, and that of the binder between 90°C and 130°C.

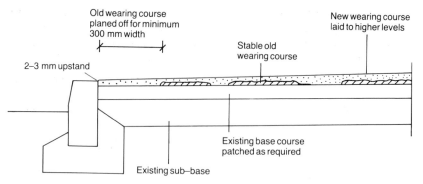

Fig. 4.45. Resurfacing of bituminous footways

guidance on compaction given in Table 4.23 should be used for this type of work.

The general principle with patching is to use the same material as the parent surface. For example, when working on a footway surfaced with either sand carpet rolled asphalt, or mastic asphalt, the respective material should be used. When working in these materials, the edges of the patches should be sawn vertically to ensure a clean sharp edge.

Resurfacing of a bituminous footway is difficult unless the existing surface has substantially worn away or can be removed, either wholly or in part, otherwise a step is created at the kerb. Care must also be taken to ensure that low air grates and damp proof courses in adjacent buildings are not affected.

With the small planer previously described it is possible to plane a 15–20 mm deep chase in the existing wearing course as shown in Fig. 4.45. As the general level of the footway will be lifted, particularly towards the back edge, covers and gratings will require raising. Any dry or suspect material should be removed before a bitumen emulsion is applied prior to laying the wearing course. Similarly, any suspect basecourse should be replaced.

The reconstruction of a bituminous footway involves the removal and replacement of all the existing wearing course and basecourse. Any areas of settlement should be investigated as this might indicate problems with adjacent drainage pipes as well as with vehicle overrunning. Any soft or wet spots in the sub-base should be removed, drainage provided and also new sub-base provided as necessary. The existing sub-base must be thoroughly rolled to the level tolerances shown in Table 4.22 prior to the application of a total weedkiller. Damage from tree roots may require a slight vertical re-alignment of the footway as an alternative to root pruning, since root pruning if incorrectly carried out may damage the tree, which can also become unstable and need removal. Footway reconstruction may require consideration of tree removal, with possible replanting of smaller more suitable species, if forest trees have been incorrectly used in the past.

Reinstatement following the activities of Statutory Undertakers' operations is a subject that has caused much debate over the years. The primary objectives are to restore the strength of the highway and to reinstate it to its original levels. This is accomplished by observance of the following.

(*a*) Formation should be replaced to the original CBR either in original or imported materials.

(*b*) Construction should be at least to the existing specification, and the layer thicknesses finished to existing levels.

This requires the replacement of at least 100 mm of Type 1 sub-base and 55 mm of bituminous material, the latter being placed in a single layer such that a permanent reinstatement can be undertaken either by inlay or overlay. The single most critical feature of the backfilling operation is adequate compaction and the common philosophy of, 'let it settle and top it up', is unacceptable.

Sealing of a cracked and porous surface can be undertaken by either surface dressing or slurry seal.

Surface dressing is a binder, either tar/bitumen, bitumen or more recently bitumen emulsion, applied to the surface at a rate of $0.8-1.0$ l/m^2 before chippings, usually 3 mm nominal size, are spread and rolled, excess chippings being removed after one week. In rural areas this is a viable treatment, but it is not so popular in urban areas due to its abrasive characteristics on children's knees.

Slurry seal is a bituminous emulsion extended with filler, laid cold with a squeegee; it can be open to traffic in about half an hour, depending on the prevailing weather conditions. Several proprietary brands are available in various colours; they are laid at a spread rate of 350 m^2/t and have similar performance characteristics. These, however, all have the disadvantage of following the profile of the existing surface, and will only mask minor level defects. They successfully seal a footway, but have the disadvantage of amplifying the visual impact of surface defects.

A recent development of slurry seal has been the availability of a polymer extended catalytic variety, which can have a variable setting time and be filled out by 3–5 mm aggregate. This is laid cold by squeegee and finished by slowly drawing a brush across the part set surface. The major advantage of a catalytic slurry seal is that it can be used in a single layer and will cover defects of up to 25 mm. It can be used to cover a whole surface, or as a patching material prior to a seal coat in normal slurry seal, and is considerably more versatile and easier to use than conventional patching materials, requiring no rolling and being about half the cost. A very large market is envisaged for this product, which is likely to change significantly bituminous footway maintenance practices (Fig. 4.46).

4.10.2. Flagstoned and block paved footways

Where flagstones and blocks have become dangerous it may be necessary to effect a temporary repair by removing the damaged elements and filling the cavities with a bituminous material or blockwork until permanent repairs can be made (see Fig. 4.47). Retexturing of flagstones and

Fig. 4.46. Repair with catalytic slurry seal: (a) original condition, (b) rudimentary patching, (c) laying slurry seal, (d) finishing surface, (e) finished job

Fig. 4.47. Temporary repair of flagstoned footway

paved areas, which have become slippery due to heavy concentrated pedestrian traffic, can be undertaken by three methods

(*a*) scabbling
(*b*) sand blasting
(*c*) shot blasting

Scabbling is slow and tends to crack concrete flagstones. It can be used successfully on natural stone flagstones, particularly when there is some form of surface growth. Sand blasting can be successful but results in a lot of fine particles, which have to be removed. Shot blasting with steel shot involves use of specialized machinery, which sucks up the debris and shot by vacuum. The steel shot is separated magnetically in the return loop for continuous re-use. This is a very successful process that tends to form a lightly exposed aggregate surface on the flagstone, giving a pleasing appearance.

Other forms of repair to cure trips, cracked flagstones and reinstatements, involve the process of relaying localized areas rather than widespread reconstruction. The problem of relaying has several facets, which are partly related to the bedding material. To relay a single flagstone, particularly a small element, can be difficult as the first problem is to remove the damaged element, which is likely to involve breaking it out with a high probability of unsettling adjacent flagstones. There is then the problem of relaying it on a bed, which is in a confined cavity with no possibility of lateral movement (Fig. 4.48(a)).

When local relaying is attempted a complete renewal of the bedding material should always take place. Alternatively, it may be necessary to consider relaying all flagstones which abut that which is damaged (Fig. 4.48(b)). Another alternative is to relay a full line of flagstones back to the edge restraint (Fig. 4.48(c)). When relaying small areas it is usual to lay on a 20:1 sand/cement mortar. In all cases, however, an experienced pavior is required to execute a good reinstatement.

Blockwork of either clay or concrete can easily be relaid following reinstatement work. It is unusual to need replacement blocks, which minimizes the cost of maintenance. The completion of a reinstatement in blockwork is set out in Fig. 4.49.

4.10.3. In situ concrete footways

Temporary repairs to make them safe are usually undertaken using bituminous material until permanent repairs can be carried out.

Where concrete has become spalled the normal method is to plane off or scabble the deteriorated section and reinstate with either an epoxy mortar or a fine concrete mix (2:2:1). The cavity formed should be at least 30 mm deep, the edges sawn, and a bonding agent used to assist adhesion. The surface should be covered and protected from traffic for at least three days.

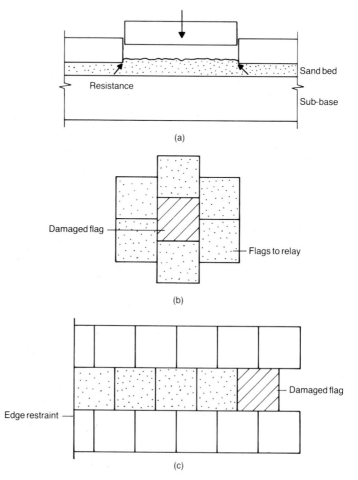

Fig. 4.48. Relaying flagstones: (a) confined bedding; (b) relay adjacent flagstones; (c) relay to edge restraint

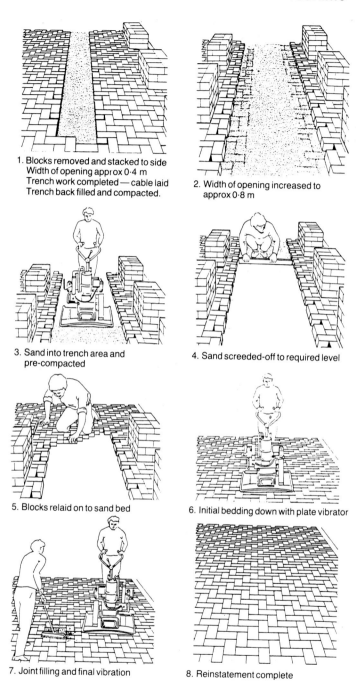

1. Blocks removed and stacked to side
   Width of opening approx 0·4 m
   Trench work completed — cable laid
   Trench back filled and compacted.

2. Width of opening increased to
   approx 0·8 m

3. Sand into trench area and
   pre-compacted

4. Sand screeded-off to required level

5. Blocks relaid on to sand bed

6. Initial bedding down with plate vibrator

7. Joint filling and final vibration

8. Reinstatement complete

Fig. 4.49. Reinstatement of blockwork (by courtesy of Interpave)

Permanent reinstatement, following statutory undertakers, involves the removal of the bituminous temporary filling. The sub-base should then be compacted and a waterproof membrane placed on its surface. The edges should be sawn and broken back to straight even lines and painted with an adhesion agent. Concrete mixed in 2:2:1 proportions is placed with a small surcharge, and vibrated into place, any surplus being removed. A float or brush finish can be used, finally spraying with a curing membrane. The surface should be covered and protected for at least three days.

Resurfacing of rigid footways is done in a similar manner to continuous patching but generally requires the lifting of kerbs. In this case it is likely to be cheaper to break out the existing slab and reconstruct. However, in some cases, it may be possible to provide a bituminous wearing course, and this will require the application of a tack coat after which the surface is laid in the normal way, covers and boxes being adjusted to suit.

4.11. Comparative economics

This section explores, in whole life cost terms, the economics of various forms of construction. All the figures relate to a particular contract, and

Table 4.31. Comparative economics — stages

1.	Validate specification, construction, workmanship, and maintenance profiles
2.	Calculate total construction and maintenance costs over 50 years
3.	Validate economics with discounted cashflow analysis
4.	Monitor performance, and incorporate into zero base budget

Table 4.32. Availability of information for whole life cost appraisal*

	Available	Confidence
Construction cost	Yes	High
Maintenance costs	Yes	High
User costs	No	—
Blacktop maintenance need	Yes	Good
Flagstoned maintenance need	Partly	Poor

* Cycle life
  Blacktop: maximum 25 years
  Flagstones: maximum up to ∞.

Table 4.33. Comparative constructions

Layer	Blacktop		Flagstoned	
Wearing course: mm	15	25*	50	70*
Base course: mm	40	60*	25	25*
Sub-base: mm	100	150*	100	150*

* Resistant to overrunning.

as the rates will vary from place to place, this section should be considered only as illustrative.

Whole life costing involves the consideration of construction and maintenance costs over the life of the structure annualized or discounted to a year 0 base and can be identified in four stages, as shown in Table 4.31. Some of the information required is readily available, with a high degree of confidence, other parts are not. The present position is summarized in Table 4.32. Both bituminous and flagstoned constructions are examined (see Table 4.33), and in each, two designs are considered; one which will resist overrunning and one which will not. In the case of the flagstoned construction, the 50 mm wearing course comprises standard 900 mm × 600 mm flagstones and the 70 mm option comprises 450 mm × 450 mm small elements.

Economic considerations are based on a 50 year period that equates to two life cycles for blacktop construction. As there is greater certainty about the maintenance assumptions associated with blacktop constructions, these are used to establish a limit case for life cycle costs against which flagstones can be compared. The concept of an annual relay allowance for flagstones is introduced, which can be compared against available data. It is at this point that problems occur, as few reliable data are available. Recognizing this problem, the comparison is based on equating the relay allowance for flagstones against the limit case established for blacktop.

The profile set out (see Fig. 4.50) will achieve a predictable standard of maintenance rather than the existing unsatisfactory breakdown system. The maintenance needs and cost associated with this profile are

years   0 and 25: new construction
years   9 and 34: slurry seal
years   17 and 42: slurry seal + 5% patching
years   25 and 50: renew blacktop (wearing course and base course — this is a continuous cycle with the sub-base never being renewed)

Costs for the two alternative constructions are shown in Table 4.34. The costs at year 0 are the new construction cost, and take no account of

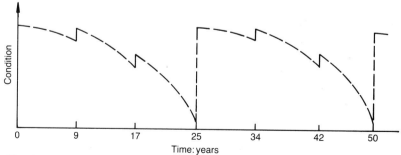

Fig. 4.50. Blacktop maintenance profile

Table 4.34. Cost comparisons for blacktop construction

Construction	Year							Total costs: £/m²	Annual costs: £/m² per year
	0	9	17	25	34	42	50		
15/40/100	6·19	1·20	1·35	5·94	1·20	1·35	5·94	23·17	0·463
25/60/150	9·20	1·20	1·35	9·61	1·20	1·35	9·61	33·52	0·670

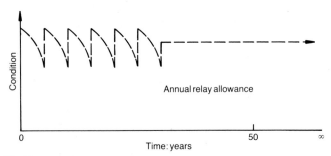

Fig. 4.51. Flagstoned maintenance profile

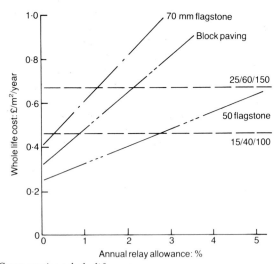

Fig. 4.52. Comparative whole life costs

Table 4.35. Cost comparisons between flagstoned construction and maintenance*

Construction	Cost: £/m²	
	New	Relay
50/25/100	12·15	7·76
70/25/150	19·94	20·69

* No allowance has been made for initial excavation in the construction costs.

excavation since this is a common factor to all options, as are kerbs and edgings; in this way it is possible to isolate the variable elements.

Flagstoned maintenance uses the concept of annual relay allowance, shown in Fig. 4.51, and the costs can be estimated by examining differing levels. The results are shown in Fig. 4.52. In the case of flagstoned constructions, the costs shown in Table 4.35 are used.

Figure 4.52 has been prepared by considering annual relay allowances varying between 0 and 5% such that the break-even point can easily be seen. A comparative time period of 50 years has been used and for ease of comparison the total cycle cost has been annualized by dividing it by this 50 year period.

A series of useful factors can be seen to result from this analysis, related to the broader aspects of zero based budgeting; an example is the annualized cost of maintenance, which can be deduced for both blacktop and flagstoned constructions.

Comparison of the normal lightweight blacktop and flagstoned construction shows that the costs equate at an annual relay allowance of 2·75%. Similarly, with the heavier construction, capable of resisting overrunning, this break-even point is at 1·3%. With block paving these levels of annual relay allowance for equal costs are 0·9% or 2·2%, respectively.

Looking at the practical maintenance situation, the various annual relay percentages are high and one would expect to relay less than 2·75% of normal flagstones per year, almost no small elements and even less block paving. A further and more significant factor, however, is that below 0·3% and 0·9% annual relay allowance, respectively, small element flagstone construction and blockwork construction, both of which are capable of resisting overrunning, are more economic than a normal lightweight blacktop construction.

While the mechanics of discounted cashflow (DCF) analysis are relatively straightforward, for it to be totally valid many more factors having a bearing on the economics must be considered. Some of these are set out in Table 4.36.

A likely proxy for user cost will be the quantified loss to society due to personal injury accidents suffered by pedestrians, for which there is very little information.

Table 4.36. Economic evaluation — other factors requiring consideration

1.	User costs
2.	Ability to reinstate after Statutory Undertakers
3.	Service life
4.	User reaction — is surface friendly
5.	Energy implications of 25 year replacement
6.	Ability to retexture to combat slipperiness
7.	Colour and texture
8.	Resistance to point loads
9.	Weed growth damage
10.	Self cleansing capability

Table 4.37. Future developments

1.	Improved information systems will allow a better case to be put for funding
2.	Objectives and standards of maintenance will become clearer
3.	Better understanding of consumer expectations
4.	Formal performance monitoring related to condition
5.	Legal minimum maintenance standards
6.	Heavier traffic resistant construction
7.	Emphasis on whole life costing
8.	Product development associated with harmonized EEC standards

There is little doubt that in strict economic terms a DCF analysis is valid, but there are many factors to evaluate before it is meaningful. It is emphasized that specification and laying practice are critical parameters as are the ruling tender prices used.

4.12. Future developments

To attempt to assess how future developments may affect footway maintenance is not easy as the whole area of highway maintenance is in competition with other spending programmes for funding. Once rational facts are put forward to justify the need to invest more, then footways must compete against other areas within highway maintenance. Table 4.37 is an attempt to look into the future.

Sources of further information

British Aggregate Construction Materials Industries, 156 Buckingham Palace Road, London, SW1W 9TR.

Manufacturers' catalogues.

National Paving and Kerb Association, 60 Charles Street, Leicester, LE1 1FB.

The Concrete Block Paving Association, 60 Charles Street, Leicester, LE1 1FB.

References

4.1.   NATIONAL CONSUMER COUNCIL. *What's wrong with walking?* Her Majesty's Stationery Office, London, 1987, 142.

4.2.   NATIONAL CONSUMER COUNCIL. *What's wrong with walking?* Her Majesty's Stationery Office, London, 1987, 4.

4.3.   STANDING COMMITTEE ON HIGHWAY MAINTENANCE. *National Road Maintenance Condition Survey 1986: report.* Department of Transport, London, 1986.

4.4.   HATHERLY L.W. Maintenance in urban areas. *J. Instn Highw. Engrs*, 1978, **25**, May, 5–10.

4.5.   AUDIT COMMISSION. *Analysis of the questionnaires on routine maintenance and surface dressing in London boroughs and metropolitan districts.* Audit Commission, London, 1987.

4.6.   DERRY T.K. and WILLIAMS T.I. *A short history of technology.* Clarendon, Oxford, 1960, 433, 434.

4.7.   HOLLAND G.C. *The vital statistics of Sheffield.* Tyas and Greaves, Sheffield, 1843, 93.

4.8.   RANKINE W.J.M. *A manual of civil engineering.* Griffin, London, 1880, 13th edn revised by W.J. Millar, 625.

4.9. FURNESS J.M. *Fifty years' municipal record 1843–1893*. Townsend, Sheffield, 1893, 152.

4.10. DEPARTMENT OF TRANSPORT. *Roads in urban areas*. Her Majesty's Stationery Office, London, 1966.

4.11. MARSHALL A.H. *Report of the Committee on Highway Maintenance*. Her Majesty's Stationery Office, London, 1970, 117.

4.12. MITCHELL J. *The Causey campaign*. Report by Working Party. Sheffield Branch of National Federation (UK) for the Blind, 1985, 2.

4.13. NATIONAL CONSUMER COUNCIL. *What's wrong with walking?* Her Majesty's Stationery Office, London, 1987, 3.

4.14. NATIONAL CONSUMER COUNCIL. *What's wrong with walking?* Her Majesty's Stationery Office, London, 1987, Appendix B.

4.15. INSTITUTION OF HIGHWAYS AND TRANSPORTATION. *Providing for people with a mobility handicap*. IHT, London, 1986.

4.16 DEPARTMENT OF TRANSPORT. Roads and the utilities. *Review of the Public Utilities Streetworks Act 1950*. Her Majesty's Stationery Office, London.

4.17. DEPARTMENT OF THE ENVIRONMENT. Traffic safety measures for road works. *Traffic signs manual*. Her Majesty's Stationery Office, London, 1973, 8.

4.18. INSTITUTION OF HIGHWAYS AND TRANSPORTATION. *Providing for people with a mobility handicap*. IHT, London, 1986.

4.19. MARCH 2. *Highway maintenance system — engineers' manual*. MARCH Group, 1983.

4.20. MARSHALL A.H. *Report of the Committee on Highway Maintenance*. Her Majesty's Stationery Office, London, 1970, 117.

4.21. LOCAL AUTHORITY ASSOCIATION. *Highway maintenance — a code of good practice*. Her Majesty's Stationery Office, London, 1983.

4.22. DEPARTMENT OF TRANSPORT. *Code of practice for routine maintenance*. DTp, London, 1984.

4.23. LOCAL AUTHORITY ASSOCIATION. *Highway maintenance — a code of good practice*. Her Majesty's Stationery Office, London, 1983, Section 3.3.

4.24. LOCAL AUTHORITY ASSOCIATION. *Highway maintenance — a code of good practice*. Her Majesty's Stationery Office, London, 1983, Section 5.3.

4.25. NATIONAL CONSUMER COUNCIL. *Pedestrians, an action guide to your neighbourhood problems*. NCC, London, 1987.

4.26. MARCH 2. *Highway maintenance system — engineers' manual*. MARCH Group, 1983, Appendix C.

4.27. MARCH 2. *Highway maintenance system — engineers' manual*. MARCH Group, 1983, Appendix C.

4.28. DEPARTMENT OF TRANSPORT. *CHART 5 — Illustrated site manual for inspectors*. London, 1986.

4.29. DEPARTMENT OF TRANSPORT. *CHART 5 — Illustrated site manual for inspectors*. London, 1986, Sections 15, 16.

4.30. TRANSPORT AND ROAD RESEARCH LABORATORY. *The CHART system of assessing structural needs of highways*. SR153UC TRRL, 1975, 22.

4.31. *Motor vehicles, construction and use*. Amendment no. 7 — Regulations, Her Majesty's Stationery Office, London, 1982.

4.32. BULL J.W. An analytical solution to the design of precast concrete pavements. *Int. J. Numer. Meth. Geomech.*, 1986, **10**, 115–123.

4.33. BULL J.W. and AL-KHALID H. An analytical solution to the design of footway paving flags. *Comput. Geotech.*, 1987, **4**, 85–96.

4.34. BULL J.W. The design of footway paving flags. *Highways*, 1988, April, 44–45.

4.35. BRITISH STANDARDS INSTITUTION. *Precast concrete paving flags.* BS 368: 1971. BSI, London.

4.36. BULL J.W. and AL-KHALID H. An analytical solution to the design of footway paving flags. *Comput. Geotech.*, 1987, **4**, 90–92.

4.37. BRITISH STANDARDS INSTITUTION. *Precast concrete kerb, channels, edgings and quadrants.* BS 340: 1979. BSI, London.

4.38. *The 'Beany Block' combined kerb and drainage system.* Marshalls Mono, Halifax, 1987.

4.39. RANKINE W.J.M. *A manual of civil engineering.* Griffin, London, 1880, 13th edn revised by W.J. Millar, 630.

4.40. DEPARTMENT OF TRANSPORT. *Specification for road and bridge work.* Her Majesty's Stationery Office, London, 1983.

4.41. TRANSPORT AND ROAD RESEARCH LABORATORY. *A guide to the structural design of pavements for new roads.* Road Note 29, Her Majesty's Stationery Office, London, 1970.

4.42. BRITISH STANDARDS INSTITUTION. *Specification for coated macadam for roads and other paved areas.* BS 4987: 1983. BSI, London.

4.43. BRITISH STANDARDS INSTITUTION. *Specification for rolled asphalt (hot process) for roads and other paved areas.* BS 594: 1973. BSI, London.

4.44. INSTITUTION OF HIGHWAYS AND TRANSPORTATION. *Providing for people with a mobility handicap.* IHT, London, 1986.

4.45. DEPARTMENT OF TRANSPORT. *Design considerations for pelican and zebra crossings.* TA 52/87. DTp, London, 1987.

5

Street lighting and illuminated traffic signs

The latest survey of street lights carried out by the Institution of Lighting Engineers in 1985 showed that there were some 4·8 million lights in England, Wales and Scotland. At current prices this represents an investment of some £1440 million. Highway and transportation statistics for 1986/87 showed an expenditure in excess of £160 million on lighting maintenance. In addition there are numerous illuminated traffic signs erected on our highways, which require electrical maintenance. These statistics give an indication of the scale of maintenance operations.

The past few years have shown a steady increase in the number of street lights and illuminated signs. More motorways and major traffic routes have been lit and with few exceptions lighting is being installed on new housing estates.

Against the background of increasing road traffic and a sharp increase in crime there is a growing public demand for more and improved lighting and a better standard of maintenance.

Recent government legislation calls for more competition in the public sector to reduce overall costs and provide better value for money.

All these developments have happened at a time when there has been a sharp decrease in public funds, which stopped or slowed down the work badly needed to arrest the decline in the standard of lighting and illuminated sign maintenance.

The mechanics of lighting maintenance are well known. However, there are often many economic, legal and political constraints that affect the way maintenance is approached and carried out. All these factors have an impact on the ultimate service that can be provided. In spite of all this there is still much scope for more efficiency and better utilization of the resources available.

5.1. Legal aspects

The Highway Act of 1980[5.1] updates previous legislation which empowers the Department of Transport and local highway authorities to provide and maintain lighting on highways for which they are responsible.

The Act does not require these authorities to install and maintain lighting, but Section 97 (i) gives them the power to do so. However, Highway Authorities may be sued for negligence resulting from failure to maintain the highway adequately and this includes street lighting.

The defence in accordance with Section 58 (i) is that they took reasonable care to ensure that the highway was not dangerous to traffic. This can be interpreted to mean that if street lighting is installed a reasonable level of inspection and maintenance is carried out.

Section 270 updates the differences set out in the Local Government Act 1966 Section 32[5.2] between 'footway' and 'road' lighting. The terminology in the Act is unfortunate as its primary purpose was to define the standard of the installation and did not attempt to interpret the lighting of footways or roads.

'Footway' lighting describes a system of lighting where no lamp is mounted more than 13 feet above ground or no lamp is more than 20 feet above ground and there is an interval of more than 50 yards between successive lamps in the system. 'Road' lighting is a system that does not meet any of the conditions described above. A 'system' means any three adjacent lamps.

The 1980 Act states that 'road' lighting is the responsibility of the Highway Authority. However, 'footway' lighting may be the responsibility of the Highway Authority, where lighting is regarded as a safety feature, or of a parish or district council, where lighting is provided for public security or amenity reasons. These councils are lighting authorities within their own rights.

A lighting authority may also install lighting on a public highway with the consent of the Highway Authority. It may provide a system of 'road' lighting, in which case the Highway Authority may take it over and maintain it thereafter. However, in such an event the Highway Authority does not become responsible for any costs or liabilities incurred in the installation.

Section 101 allows district councils to maintain street lighting, which is the responsibility of the Highway Authority on an agency basis.

Under Section 98 (i) a Highway Authority may delegate maintenance functions to lighting authorities. Section 98 (ii) defines this as an agency. This also empowers the Department of Transport to give lighting agencies for motorway and trunk roads to county councils.

By virtue of Section 43, Highway Authorities and district councils may bear any cost incurred by parish councils in maintaining public footpaths and bridleways. Consequently, they may pay for the maintenance of 'footway' lighting installed by parish councils.

The Local Government Act 1988[5.3] consolidates the Local Government Planning and Land Act 1980; Direct Labour Organisations,[5.4] together with subsequent Local Government Regulations, 1988.[5.5] This legislation requires local authorities to submit all general highways work, including maintenance exceeding £25 000, to competitive tender. The Regulations also decrease from 70% to 40% the maximum proportion of the aggregate of the previous year's amount of work valued below £25 000, which can be allocated to a direct labour organization without competition.

The 1988 Act clarifies the position of street lighting and amends Section 20 (i) of the 1980 Act (definition of maintenance work) by adding 20 (c) 'Maintenance of street lighting'.

The legal requirements for the illumination of traffic signs are set out in the Traffic Sign Regulations and General Directions 1981, Section 3.[5.6] The legal requirements for the illumination of speed limit signs are set out in the Traffic Sign (Speed Limit) Regulations and General Directions 1969.[5.7]

5.2. Responsibility for street lighting and illuminated sign maintenance

Street lighting and illuminated sign maintenance is the responsibility of Highway Authorities. They may carry out this work by

(a) direct labour (subject to current legislation)
(b) contract
(c) agency arrangements.

Within this framework responsibilities are divided between

(a) *Counties* — which may act as agents for the Department of Transport for the maintenance of motorways and trunk roads by using their own work force or contractors. As a Highway Authority they maintain lighting and illuminated signs direct or through agencies. The latter may incur agency fees on energy charges. In view of this there are proposals to bring the maintenance work back into the direct control of the counties. They may defray the cost of 'footway' lighting provided by parish councils.
(b) *London Boroughs and Metropolitan District Councils* — which act as agents for the Department of Transport for motorway and trunk road lighting and illuminated sign maintenance or exercise their own powers as highway authorities.
(c) *District Councils* — which may act as agents to the County Councils for lighting and illuminated sign maintenance and carry out the maintenance for 'footway' lighting for which they are directly responsible. They may be given lighting agency by the Department of Transport. Financially, they can contribute to the upkeep of 'footway' lighting installed by them or parish councils.

5.3. Maintenance functions

Maintenance functions include the following operations

(a) scouting of installations
(b) routine maintenance of lighting and illuminated signs, i.e. bulk changing of lamps and cleaning of lanterns
(c) non-routine maintenance of lighting and illuminated signs, i.e. inspection of lights reported faulty, replacing parts to bring lights back into operation and adjusting time control equipment
(d) inspection of electrical components in accordance with Institution of Electrical Engineers (IEE) Regulations
(e) structural inspection of columns
(f) painting of steel columns
(g) repairs following accident damage
(h) replacement of obsolete equipment

Table 5.1. All purpose roads — recommended values of luminance and uniformity ratios

Definition of road	Description of road	Traffic Volume		Average luminance cd/m²	Overall uniformity ratio	Longitudinal uniformity ratio
		Urban	Rural			
Primary roads	Trunk, some principal and 'A' routes. High volume of traffic roads between major conurbations. High speed roads. Dual carriageway roads	15 000	7000+	1·5	0·4	0·7
Main distributor roads	Important rural and urban traffic routes. Primary network of main roads in urban areas. Radial and district distributor roads. High volume of traffic but with close origins and destination	5 000	2 000	1·0	0·4	0·5
Secondary distributor roads	Basically 'B' roads and less important connecting roads in towns or between villages. Lower volume of traffic	1 000	500+	0·5	0·4	0·5
Local roads	Main estate roads and roads giving access to property	500	200	Not applicable	Not applicable	Not applicable

The maintenance of illuminated traffic signs, and in particular the lighting units, is normally carried out as part of the street lighting maintenance. Although the replacement of obsolete equipment is a maintenance function, a planned replacement programme may preferably be carried out independently from routine maintenance operations.

5.4. Management of street lighting maintenance

Most authorities responsible for street lighting maintenance have set up specialist units within their organization. Advances in lighting technology and expansion in the associated electrical works has led to the employment of electrical engineers and technicians to deal with the wide range of functions.

Few highway authorities have their own lighting departments. In most cases their specialists are attached either to the authorities' highways maintenance or traffic management section. The latter is normal practice where these specialist units deal with a wide range of functions including the maintenance of traffic signals (see also Chapter 6).

Whatever the approach it would seem good practice to distinguish between the 'client' and 'contractor' functions. This is advisable following recent changes in legislation affecting 'in-house' methods of maintenance. It would seem appropriate to treat direct labour organizations as separate contractual bodies, which need to be divorced from the client's organization. The arrangement would be in the interests of both parties.

5.5. Definition of street lighting

Lighting of roads is provided to meet the following needs

(*a*)   road safety — an aid to motorists and pedestrians
(*b*)   public safety — the prevention of crime and vandalism
(*c*)   amenity — lighting of public places, shopping centres and leisure areas.

To achieve a satisfactory standard of lighting the average luminance of the road surface should be sufficiently bright to reveal objects adequately at night. At the same time it is important to ensure good uniformity on every part of the road and avoid excessive patchiness. Disability and discomfort glare are to be avoided.

The required standard and level of lighting of various types of roads depends on the nature, importance and volume of traffic of the road to be lit.

The British Standard BS 5489: Part 2: Code of Practice for lighting of traffic routes provides a new concept of lighting design for all-purpose roads.[5.8] It recommends values of luminance and uniformity ratios for different types of roads.

The LAA Code of Good Practice[5.9] describes the road hierarchy used by highway authorities to assist in the determination of policies and priorities. These are categorized in order of importance and traffic volumes. Table 5.1 equates the recommended level of luminance and uniformity ratios with the hierarchy of roads defined in the LAA Code.

Table 5.2. Light sources for all purpose traffic routes

Lamp	Type	Wattage	Colour
Low pressure sodium	SOX-E	66, 91, 131	Monochromatic yellow
Low pressure sodium	SOX	90, 135, 180	Monochromatic yellow
High pressure sodium	SON	150, 250, 400	Golden white
High pressure mercury	MBFU	250, 400	White

Lighting is in general provided by lanterns mounted on 8–12 m columns. Lanterns are fitted with electric discharge light sources. The most common types of lamps used in order of their energy efficiency are shown in Table 5.2.

The efficacy of lamps is often described by the amount of luminous flux emitted per unit of energy consumed, i.e. lumens/watt. Low pressure sodium lamps provide the greatest output per unit of energy. The latest generation of SOX-E lamps (Fig. 5.1) are the most economical lamps available for street lighting purposes. Although of a slightly lower output compared with SOX lamps they should meet most of the requirements set out in the Code of Practice. High pressure sodium lamps (Fig. 5.2), although less efficient compared with the low pressure sodium lamps, have a longer life. Their better colour rendering properties make them more acceptable in public places such as town centres, conservation areas and places of leisure.

High pressure mercury lamps are still in general use for road lighting but are the least efficient and are being displaced by high pressure sodium lamps where white light requirements are called for.

A paper given at the Lightex '87 Conference, Blackpool, 'Lighting Criteria for Residential Roads and Areas'[5.10] examined the requirements for lighting of local roads and looked at the draft proposals for BS 5489:

Fig. 5.1. Range of SOX-E lamps

Fig. 5.2. Range of SON lamps

Table 5.3. Local roads — suggested lighting requirements

Definition of road	Description of road	Requirements for road, verge, footway or footpath	
		Average illuminance: lux	Minimum point illuminance: lux
Local road 1	Roads where public use at night is likely to be high or the crime risk is likely to be high or traffic usage is similar to a local distributor road	10·0	5·0
Local road 2	Roads where public use at night is likely to be moderate or crime risk is likely to be average to low or traffic is at the level of an access road	6·0	2·5
Local road 3	Roads, culs-de-sac, footpaths where public use at night is minimal and are for access purposes only or the crime risk is low or traffic usage is for access only	3·5	1·0

Part 3; Code of Practice for Lighting Subsidiary Roads and Associated Pedestrian Areas.

It would seem that, whereas in the past lighting on local roads was provided primarily to aid the motorist, in future the needs of the pedestrian are likely to be considered as paramount. There would also seem to be a need for the design to cater for illuminance to ensure that pedestrians are adequately revealed at night.

Table 5.3 shows the suggested criteria for the lighting of local roads according to the nature and needs of the areas to be lit. Lighting is in general achieved by mounting lanterns on 4–6 metre columns. Lanterns are fitted with electric discharge lamps. The more common types of lamps in order of energy efficiency are shown in Table 5.4.

More specialized lighting is dealt with in other parts of BS 5489; Parts 4–9 deal with special requirements such as the following

Table 5.4. Light sources for local roads

Lamp	Type	Wattage	Colour
Low pressure sodium	SOX-E	26, 36	Monochromatic yellow
Low pressure sodium	SOX	35, 55	Monochromatic yellow
High pressure sodium	SON	50, 170	Golden white
High pressure mercury	MBFU	50, 80, 125	White

(a) lighting of single level junctions and roundabouts
(b) lighting of grade separated junctions
(c) lighting of bridges and underpasses
(d) lighting near aerodromes, railways, docks, etc.
(e) lighting for town and city centres.

5.6. Inventory of street lighting and illuminated sign equipment

An up-to-date inventory is an essential ingredient of a good maintenance system. Many authorities are currently embarking on the setting up of a highway inventory, which amongst other things identifies the location of street lights and illuminated signs. Specialist assistance will be needed to record the technical data necessary to manage the lighting maintenance. This can be carried out either in-house or contracted out to specialist contractors. Additionally, computerized data capturing devices can be utilized for this task.

Data collected can be stored on record cards, which may be adequate for smaller authorities, or in a computerized format. Computerization is recommended for inventories containing in excess of 6000 lighting units.

The choice of the computer system depends on the quantity of information to be stored, and the monitoring and reporting facilities required. A microcomputer for the sole use of the smaller lighting department may be adequate. Larger departments may wish to make use of the authority's in-house minicomputer or mainframe computer.

An inventory of lighting equipment should preferably be developed on a database common to all departments of the authority. This will enable other information, e.g. accident data, to be related to street lighting.

All computerized highway inventory systems are based on unique identification of equipment in relation to the highway. This is achieved by recording a combination of road number, road section, metreage along the road and location in the cross-section. Measurements are made along centre lines of roads and footways. Street lights and illuminated signs are shown as point items together with the column or sign number displayed. Such systems can be digitized, enabling the production of record drawings based on Ordnance Survey plans.

The identification numbers on the columns or sign posts should be clearly visible both by day and night. They can be painted or, alternatively, plastic self-adhesive numbers on reflectorized backgrounds can be attached to the supports. Numbers 50 mm high are normally adequate. Number sequences should be kept to a minimum so that they can be read from slow moving vehicles during inspections.

In addition to the unique numbering of every street light and illuminated sign other relevant information and data will need to be recorded. This normally consists of such items as lamp type, wattage, lighting period, details of time control, lanterns and columns.

Such information is needed for maintenance and costing purposes. A brief description of the location of the equipment such as a house number or other geographical information can be useful to the maintenance personnel. Road names should also be recorded especially for minor roads

1. STREET LIGHTS

UNIT NO	DATE CONN	DRAWING NUMBER	LOCATION	T/C OWN	T/C CAB OWN	LANT DIST	LANT TYPE	MTNG HGHT	MTNG TYPE	LINK NODE	COST CODE	EEB NO	ITEM NO	WATTAGE	TYPE	TIME PRD
001	176	0000	A1 ROUNDABOUT TAKE OFF	1	H	COF	SE	12	ST	0	016	+	1156	180	SOX	X
002	176	0000	APPROACH TO R/A	1	H	COF	SE	12	ST	0	016	+	1156	180	SOX	X
003	000	0000	EASTBOUND TAKE OFF	1	H	COF	SE	12	ST	0	016	+	1156	180	SOX	X
004	176	0000	A1 APPROACH	1	H	COF	SE	12	ST	0	016	+	1156	180	SOX	X
005	000	0000	EASTBOUND TAKE OFF	1	H	COF	SE	12	ST	0	016	+	1156	180	SOX	X
006	176	0000	A1 APPROACH	1	H	COF	SE	12	ST	0	016	+	1156	180	SOX	X
007	176	0000	A111 APPROACH	1	H	COF	SE	12	ST	0	016	+	1156	180	SOX	X
008	176	0000	WESTBOUND TAKE OFF	1	H	COF	SE	12	ST	0	016	+	1156	180	SOX	X
009	176	0000	A111 APPROACH	1	H	COF	SE	12	ST	0	016	+	1156	180	SOX	X
010	176	0000	WEST BOUND TAKE OFF	1	H	COF	SE	12	ST	0	016	+	1156	180	SOX	X
011	176	0000	A111 APPROACH	1	H	COF	SE	12	ST	0	016	+	1156	180	SOX	X
012	176	0000	WESTBOUND TAKE OFF	1	H	COF	SE	12	ST	0	016	+	1156	180	SOX	X
013	176	0000	ROUNDABOUT WESTSIDE	1	H	COF	SE	12	ST	0	016	+	1156	180	SOX	X

2. SIGNS

UNIT NO	DATE CONN	DRAWING NUMBER	LOCATION	T/C OWN	T/C CAB OWN	LANT DIST	LANT TYPE	MTNG HGHT	MTNG TYPE	LINK NODE	COST CODE	EEB NO	ITEM NO	WATTAGE	TYPE	TIME PRD
001	177	0000	WEST CARRIGWAYBIGNALLSUK	1	H	ADS	FL	2	ST	0	016	+	2039	250	MBFU	X
002	177	0000	EAST CARRIGWAY	1	H	ADS	FL	2	ST	0	016	+	2039	250	MBFU	X

3. SUBWAYS

UNIT NO	DATE CONN	DRAWING NUMBER	LOCATION	T/C OWN	T/C CAB OWN	LANT DIST	LANT TYPE	MTNG HGHT	MTNG TYPE	LINK NODE	COST CODE	EEB NO	ITEM NO	WATTAGE	TYPE	TIME PRD
001	175	0000	WASH LANE SUBWAY	0	H	UUU	KE	3	RM	0	016	+	3206	2 * 20	FLUO	VIII
002	176	0000		0	H	UUU	KE	3	RM	0	016	+	3206	2 * 20	FLUO	VIII
003	176	0000		0	H	UUU	KE	3	RM	0	016	+	3206	2 * 20	FLUO	VIII
004	176	0000		0	H	UUU	KE	3	RM	0	016	+	3206	2 * 20	FLUO	VIII
005	176	0000		0	H	UUU	KE	3	RM	0	016	+	3206	2 * 20	FLUO	VIII

Fig. 5.3. Computerized street lighting inventory for the A1178

where road numbers are not normally displayed on site. Good information recorded initially can ultimately save much time and money. (Fig. 5.3 shows a typical inventory page.)

5.7. Energy costs

These can account for more than half of the lighting and illuminated sign maintenance budget. Costs vary according to the type of equipment installed and are a function of

(a) quantity of lamps installed
(b) types and wattage of lamps
(c) energy losses in discharge lamp control gear
(d) energy dissipated in time control equipment
(e) lighting period
(f) tariff offered by Electricity Boards.

Care should be taken when selecting equipment for street lighting and sign maintenance. Some parts when they fail can be replaced with more efficient equipment than that previously fitted. Small savings in energy consumption multiplied by large quantities of lighting units can show significant reductions in running costs.

Table 5.5. Schedule of discharge lamp loadings for street lighting energy charges

Lamp	Lamp type	Lamp watts	Circuit watts		
			Standard gear	Low loss gear	Optimum hybrid gear
Low pressure sodium	SOX	35	65	48	—
	SOX	55	84	67	—
	SOX	90	123	104	—
	SOX	135	175	159	—
	SOX	180	223	—	—
Low pressure sodium	SOX-E	26	59	41	33
	SOX-E	36	67	51	45
	SOX-E	66	104	83	81
	SOX-E	91	136	129	106
	SOX-E	131	178	—	151
High pressure sodium	SON	50	62	—	—
	SON	71	84	—	—
	SON	150	172	—	—
	SON	250	279	—	—
	SON	400	434	—	—
High pressure mercury	MBF	50	61	—	—
	MBF	80	94	—	—
	MBF	125	142	—	—
	MBF	250	275	—	—
	MBF	400	428	—	—

Lamps such as low pressure sodium SOX types can be replaced with lower energy consuming SOX-E types during bulk change operations at very little extra cost. Even when operated on existing standard or low loss control gear the savings can be considerable. The slightly lower light output of these lamps may well be acceptable when off-set against the reductions in energy costs.

When replacing obsolete lanterns, SOX-E lamps can be installed together with optimum hybrid control gear, which will practically halve the energy costs incurred with SOX lamps operating on standard gear.

Alternatively, less efficient high pressure mercury lamps can be replaced with high pressure sodium lamps of comparable light output. In most cases, if a planned conversion programme is carried out, capital costs can be recovered from energy savings in less than four years.

Table 5.5 gives details of the energy consumption of discharge lamp circuits currently agreed by Electricity Boards.

The use of part night lighting can make substantial contributions towards reductions in energy costs. However, savings can be off-set by the need for more sophisticated and often less reliable time control equipment, which can be affected by power cuts. There are strong arguments against part night lighting for reasons of crime prevention and public safety.

Most street lights and illuminated signs operate on unmetered supply. Electricity Boards throughout the country may use different methods for charging for the energy consumed. Costs are normally assessed on the quantity of lights installed, their total circuit watts, the time period they operate in and the unit cost of energy. The need for an up-to-date inventory is essential if these calculations are to be accurate. Experience has shown that where new surveys of lights are carried out for computerization purposes substantial errors are found — in many cases detrimental to the authorities concerned.

5.8. Performing lighting maintenance

Historically, street lighting maintenance was done either in-house by direct labour or by the local Electricity Board. The passing of the Local Government Planning and Land Act 1980 with subsequent amendments has changed this dramatically. It would seem that, in future, street lighting maintenance will be subject to competitive tendering procedures. This means that both direct labour organizations and Electricity Boards will need to take a much more commercial approach to be able to compete with the rapidly increasing number of private contractors.

Local Electricity Boards, by virtue of having to supply energy and provide and maintain electricity services to public lighting, were well placed to take on maintenance of the equipment. Local authorities were also empowered to enter into such maintenance agreements without competition. These arrangements invariably included the supply of all materials required to carry out the work. However, prices offered in those agreements often reflected the non-competitive nature of these arrangements, where Electricity Boards were required to compete for maintenance, contracts prices reduced substantially.

Maintenance carried out in-house by direct labour meant that the local authorities assumed direct responsibility for their actions. They had to provide their own depots, labour, plant and stores for materials, a very onerous task requiring much managerial resources and expertise. Direct control over operations, however, ensured a good standard of maintenance. Maintenance by private contractors, first introduced in the late 1960s, has since expanded with the result that there are now many competent contractors willing to compete for such work.

Whatever the arrangements it will be difficult to avoid involving the Electricity Boards as they are responsible for the service cable into the lighting unit. To overcome this situation many local authorities now provide their own street lighting cable network fed from the Electricity Board's network via feeder pillars.

Many lighting units are still fed through the fifth core in the Electricity Board's supply cables and are controlled from their sub-stations. As only their own personnel have access to these controls long delays can occur until switches are re-set following power cuts. Such systems should be replaced at the first opportunity so that local authorities can assume full control over the performance of their equipment.

Far-reaching changes can be expected in the near future. It is up to the local authorities to ensure that the new arrangements will provide the basis for a better street lighting service.

5.9. Preparation of maintenance contracts

The law now requires street lighting maintenance work to be offered for competitive tendering. DOE Circular 19/83[5.11] states that authorities should seek the best value for money for its ratepayers, through fair, unbiased competition between direct labour organizations and private contractors. Contracts should not contain irrelevant and extraneous requirements and conditions of contract that are anti-competitive in effect or intention. Contracts should be precise and clear in their requirements so that they can be easily interpreted by prospective competitors.

In common practice, tender documents should contain

(*a*) Instructions to Tenderers
(*b*) Form of Tender and Agreement
(*c*) Performance Bond (if required)
(*d*) Conditions of Contract
(*e*) Specification
(*f*) Bills of Quantities or Schedules of Rates
(*g*) Summary of Tender.

Most authorities have a standard format for the contractual arrangements as indicated in (*a*)–(*c*).

Conditions of Contract are usually derived from the Model Form MF1 General Conditions of Contract 1988.[5.12] These are amended as appropriate to suit the requirements of the work.

Specifications should be precise, setting out accurately the work to be performed and the frequencies at which the maintenance operations are to be carried out. British Standards and Codes of Practice should be quoted wherever appropriate.

Bills of Quantities or Schedules of Rates should describe and quantify the work to be performed to enable an accurate assessment of the cost to be made. Most lighting maintenance contracts have separate Bills of Quantities or Schedules of Rates for

- (a) routine cyclic maintenance, which includes bulk changing of lamps, cleaning of lanterns, and electrical and structural inspections of equipment
- (b) non-routine maintenance, which caters for repair of random faults found through scouting or other reports, and repair of vandal and accident damage.

Lighting maintenance contracts can be for labour and transport only, with materials supplied by the local authority, or be inclusive of all elements.

The County Surveyors Society in May 1985 issued model contract documents for the maintenance of street lighting and illuminated signs.[5.13] Report 3/1 and supplement 3/2 provide alternative labour and plant, or supply of materials inclusive arrangements, respectively.

It must be emphasized that the quantity of materials required to service adequately a maintenance operation is considerable and would require a substantial investment, with resulting increases in the cost of overheads. A private contractor who can diversify his operations would have greater purchasing power and utilization of materials.

Contracts should include guarantee periods for all equipment installed to be replaced at no cost to the local authority should it fail. Provision may also be made for a non-performance rebate clause to form part of the contract. This would make provision for predetermined sums of money to be deducted from contractors' accounts if lights remain out of commission longer than the stated prescribed period. This ensures that contractors complete repairs without delay.

In view of the large initial cost to contractors of setting up maintenance operations, the duration of contracts should be for the longest periods economically viable. Contracts should include break clauses or be of a set period with provision for extension should this be preferred. The Department of Transport recommends five-year contracts if this is possible.

Suitable price variation clauses need to be included in a contract in excess of one year to enable adjustment for inflation. These are usually based on indices compiled by the Department of the Environment.[5.14]

Payment for work carried out should be arranged on a monthly basis. This provides better cash flow essential for contractors and will help to monitor the client's expenditure.

Contracts should explain clearly methods of documentation required for certification of accounts. Works reports should itemize work done in accordance with the Bills of Quantities or Schedules of Rates and should quote unique identification of lighting units as contained in the inventory.

Where computerized maintenance programmes are used, direct data transfer between contractor and client can save much staff time and resources. Portable data capturing devices can be used for recording details of work carried out provided that non-scheduled repair items are kept to a minimum.

5.10. General maintenance

5.10.1. Scouting

Scouting accounts for a very small proportion of the overall cost of lighting maintenance. It plays a very important integral part, however, in the maintenance operations. The LAA Code of Good Practice[5.15] recommends fortnightly scouting in the winter and once every four weeks in the summer.

The Department of Transport code of practice for the maintenance of road lighting for trunk roads and trunk road motorways,[5.16] recommends fortnightly scouting for trunk roads and 28-day scouting for trunk road motorways throughout the year. This makes no allowance for the different burning hours during the summer and winter months.

The ILE Technical Report No. 14[5.17] examined the cost effectiveness of night time patrolling or scouting. It made a detailed study of the operation, frequencies and costs. The report investigated two methods of scouting in detail

(a) scout and report
(b) scout and at the same time carry out simple first line repairs

The report found little difference in the merits of the two methods but emphasized that the second method would only be suitable for certain situations such as residential roads in urban areas where traffic conditions allow this to be done in safety or on minor roads in rural areas. The report stressed that scouting at night is a constant danger to the operatives and every effort must be made to observe all health and safety requirements and equip the scouts appropriately to minimize the risks encountered.

Comment on the cost effectiveness of scouting reflected that it can only be judged effectively if it is recognized that there is a loss in cash terms to society when public lighting is inoperative. The benefits in lighting in the field of accident and crime prevention are well known.

The conclusion reached in the report was that if average conditions prevail the most cost effective scouting interval is 14 days in winter and that any saving achieved by extending this period is insignificant. There is also a limited financial justification for extending this interval to 21 days in the summer for urban side roads, if they can be economically separated from traffic routes. In most cases it will not be possible to justify an interval shorter than 28 days for scattered rural areas.

Records of scouting should be kept for a minimum of three years to ensure that details are available for insurance purposes and legal proceedings should they be called for.

Scouting may be carried out by the client or alternatively be included in the maintenance contract operations. Whichever method is used reports should be conveyed to the maintenance engineer for processing and authorization of work to be carried out. Some contracts specify that when scouting is carried out by the contractor only personnel not directly engaged on maintenance works should be employed.

Compliance with the Health and Safety at Work Act 1974 is obligatory. Methods of operations should be submitted to the local safety officers for comment. Vehicles used for scouting must be fitted with appropriate warning devices. For maximum cost effectiveness most scouting is carried out as a one-man operation. If this is the case then scouts should be provided with voice activated tape recorders for fault logging purposes.

In rural areas the use of prepaid postcards issued to selected members of the community could replace normal scouting operations. Because of the high cost of such cards the method is not recommended for use on a large scale.

5.10.2. Routine maintenance — lamp changing and lantern cleaning

Highway authorities determine lamp change policies and other street lighting maintenance levels, irrespective of whether the work is carried out in-house by direct labour or by contractors. There are two main policies for dealing with lamp replacements

(a) to burn the lamps to destruction and replace them as required
(b) planned cyclic replacement or bulk changing of lamps at predetermined burning hours, with premature failures replaced as necessary on a random basis.

There is much controversy concerning this subject and there are ardent supporters for both methods.

It must be stressed that discharge lamps used for street lighting have a long life. They may fade rather than fail. It may be more a question of the standard of service the authority wishes to achieve rather than the need for replacement.

A survey contained in the ILE Technical Report No. 17,[5.18] shows a wide variation among highway authorities. They range from random lamp replacement to cyclic planned replacement at 12 000 hours or a combination of both for different light sources.

Choosing the best policy may well turn out to be an economic minefield. The results depend on the method selected, the standard required and the cost of lamp replacement. Also, lantern cleaning carried out at the same time as the lamp change can affect the overall cost.

Random replacement of lamps can be twice as expensive as planned cyclic replacement. Although the burning period of the lamps is extended the labour and transport costs are increased due to the random nature of the operations.

A bulk change policy means that lamp replacements are planned, travel between lights is minimized and since random failures between bulk changes are fewer, a better level of service is achieved. There are variations on the theme of a planned replacement cycle.

(a) All lamps are replaced at the bulk change and any subsequent premature failures replaced with new lamps.

Table 5.6. Discharge lamp life

Lamp type	Total survivors: %				
	After 4000 burning hours	After 6000 burning hours	After 8000 burning hours	After 10000 burning hours	
Mercury	97	95	91	85	
Low pressure sodium	95	92	88	78	
High pressure sodium	97	95	92	90	

Table 5.7. Discharge lamp lumen maintenance

Lamp type	Maintenance: %				
	After 100 burning hours	After 4000 burning hours	After 6000 burning hours	After 8000 burning hours	After 10000 burning hours
Mercury (vanadate)	100	85	80	75	70
Low pressure sodium	100	97	92	85	75
High pressure sodium	100	94	92	90	88

(b) All lamps are replaced at the bulk change. Selected randomly replaced lamps, say during the last three months or approximately 1000 hours, are recovered and used for random replacements in the next cycle.

(c) Only lamps not previously replaced at random during a three-month period prior to the bulk change are changed in a planned cyclic fashion. Lamps have to be tagged or marked during the period leading up to the bulk change. Subsequently, new lamps are fitted for premature failures between the bulk changes.

In any case, planned bulk change lamp replacement specifications should cater for the free replacement of lamps failing in the initial period of the cycle. For discharge lamps a guarantee of 4000 hours is not uncommon for longer bulk change intervals. An initial failure of up to 6% of the total number of lamps installed can be expected during this period.

An alternative practice is to make all random lamp replacements an inclusive element of the planned lamp change cost. This is only practical for lamp change cycles up to 8000 hours. Such an arrangement makes the contractor entirely responsible for the performance of lamps and cuts administration costs.

The occurrence of lamp failures is not predictable although studies of lamp life may show a pattern. Even the orientation of lanterns in relation to prevailing winds may affect the lamp's performance, due to vibrations. Some lamps fail early in life under guarantee, some survive the average life and others may continue to operate with ever-decreasing performance.

In the end they all fail. Lamps cannot be used to the limit of their material duration as their life cycle is subject to operational conditions and the chemical activity within. Discharge lamps burnt to destruction can also damage the control gear.

Data shown in the ILE Technical Report No. 17,[5.19] based on information provided by the Lighting Industries Federation, may help in choosing from the options available and in formulating the policy to be adopted. Table 5.6 shows the number of surviving lamps that can be expected after selected burning hours. Table 5.7 shows the lamp lumen maintenance that can on average be expected under these conditions.

Manufacturer's data give figures for a representative quantity of lamps under optimum conditions. Results in the field may differ from these and lamps may show an accelerated failure rate. Batches of lamps supplied may vary considerably in spite of the quality control exercised in the factory.

Although lantern cleaning can produce a marked improvement in the performance of the installation, the reduction in light output due to the age of the lamps can only be remedied by their replacement. However, the two are inter-related and must be considered together when planning cyclic maintenance.

The effects of air pollution have decreased substantially since the Clean Air Act became law in 1956. Although the Marshall Report[5.20] and the LAA Code[5.21] recommend more frequent cleaning, it may now be considered appropriate to coincide this operation only with the bulk change of lamps. British Standard 5489: Part 2[5.22] provides maintenance factors for lanterns at various cleaning intervals.

Because of wide variations in conditions and circumstances governing the choice of bulk change frequencies, few recommendations have been made. The Department of Transport Departmental Standard TD 23/86[5.23] recommends the following bulk change cycle

(a)   low pressure sodium (SOX, SOX-E):   8000 hours, i.e. 24 months
(b)   high pressure mercury (MBFU):   8000 hours, i.e. 24 months
(c)   high pressure sodium (SON):   12 000 hours, i.e. 36 months.

For illuminated traffic signs fitted with high pressure mercury or fluorescent lamps, similar bulk change periods may be chosen.

In order to evaluate the average performance of street lighting it is possible to calculate the overall depreciation of light output from lanterns

Table 5.8. Average lantern lumen output at bulk lamp change periods

Lamp type	Wattage	Average lamp lumens: 2000 hours	Average output (DLOR) lumens:	Average lantern output in lumens bulk change at 8000 hours (SON 12 000 hours) lanterns IP54		
				Pollution category		
				High*	Medium†	Low‡
SOX	35	4 300	3 010	2 072	2 123	2 328
	55	7 150	5 005	3 445	3 531	3 871
	90	12 250	9 310	6 409	6 565	7 201
	135	21 200	16 112	11 093	11 367	12 462
	180	31 500	23 940	16 482	16 889	18 517
SOX-E	26	3 320	2 324	1 600	1 639	1 797
	36	5 410	3 787	2 607	2 671	2 929
	66	10 160	7 721	5 315	5 447	5 972
	91	16 620	12 631	8 696	8 911	9 770
	131	24 700	18 772	12 924	13 243	14 520
SON	50	3 100	2 170	1 457	1 512	1 660
	70	5 510	3 857	2 589	2 688	2 950
	100	9 500	6 300	4 230	4 391	4 819
	150	13 500	9 450	6 345	6 586	7 229
	250	24 000	16 800	11 281	11 709	12 852
	400	35 000	31 500	21 152	21 955	24 097
HPM	80	3 550	2 485	1 710	1 753	1 922
	125	5 800	4 060	2 795	2 864	3 140
	250	12 000	8 400	5 783	5 926	6 497
	400	20 400	14 280	6 361	10 074	11 045

* In centre of large towns and heavy industrial areas.
† In semi-urban, residential and light industrial areas.
‡ In rural areas.

for different bulk change periods. This calculation is a function of the average lamp lumens (2000 hours), the downward light output ratio of lanterns (DLOR) provided by manufacturers, the pollution factor, and lamp light output depreciation based, e.g. on the bulk change period recommended by the Department of Transport for trunk roads and motorways. Table 5.8 shows the average lumen output at bulk change periods.

As lighting hours vary considerably during the summer and winter months it is important to choose maintenance cycles that are aggregates of complete years. This means that lamps are always changed at approximately the same time and burning hours. This also ensures an even pattern of expenditure over the bulk change cycle. Any deviation from this, although not impossible, would need careful monitoring and planning. It could not be recommended without computer facilities.

The ILE Technical Report No. 17[5.24] concludes that a lumen output of between 65% and 75% of the initial lantern (DLOR) value can be recommended as the figure for lamp replacements, but as complaints from the public regarding low light output are rarely received, the cost of the overall lamp replacement policy is the prime factor to be considered when deciding on a planned cyclic replacement policy. This means that the main issue that will determine the length of time lamps remain in service can be summed up as

(a)   acceptable safe limits of level of light
(b)   the overall cost of the lamp replacement policy.

Based on the information available it is possible to obtain the average cost of planned cyclic maintenance. A simple way of demonstrating the cost effectiveness is to calculate the annual cost of the operation by the following formula

$$AC = (BC + RR + LC)/T$$

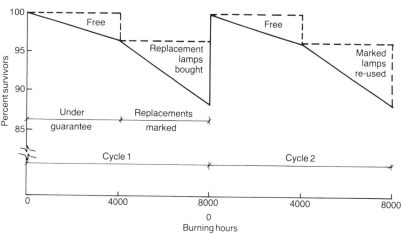

Fig. 5.4. Lamp bulk change cycle

where AC is the annual cost of the planned maintenance operation; BC is the cost of bulk change over the frequency chosen inclusive of labour, transport and materials; RR is the cost of random replacements of lamps during the bulk change cycle inclusive of labour, transport and materials; LC is the cost of cleaning of lanterns over the chosen bulk change cycle; and T is the time period chosen for bulk change cycle in years.

Figure 5.4 shows a typical 8000 hour bulk change cycle, using marked lamps for random replacements for random failures, after the first year.

In conclusion the indications are that planned cyclic maintenance provides more value for money and a better service to the public. The choice of level of service may well be governed by technical, financial and political factors. In the end it will be the task of the authority concerned to decide on the policy to be adopted, based on information provided by the lighting engineer.

5.10.3. Non-routine maintenance — repair of failures

Street lights and illuminated signs are made up of numerous components. Every item is subject to deterioration in service and subsequent failure. The life expectancy of these components is very unpredictable and many of them will fail in a random fashion.

Statistics show that at the recommended scouting frequencies approximately 2% to 3% of lights have failed for one reason or another. Expressed in other terms it has been established that over 50% of the total lighting installation is likely to develop a fault during any one year. The older the equipment the greater is the occurrence of a fault. Failures can be divided into electricity supply or component faults. Other failures result from accident and vandal damage or just deterioration due to the age of the equipment.

Repairs are initiated from reports following scouting, routine inspections, reports or complaints from members of the public, councillors, police or other sources.

The standard of maintenance depends entirely on the scouting frequency and repair cycle adopted by the authority concerned. Maintenance operations should be arranged so that every light found out of commission during the scout is repaired before the next scout, if this is practicable. There are sometimes reasons why this is not possible due to the involvement of other parties concerned with the installation. Other remedial works to equipment, not affecting its operation, can receive a lower priority, unless action is required for safety reasons.

The Department of Transport Departmental Standard TD 23/86[5.25] sets out the maintenance requirements. It must be stressed that these requirements apply to motorways and trunk roads with all their inherent maintenance problems. The standard classifies defects into two categories

    (a) *Category I*: defects that require prompt attention because they result in unacceptable quality or insufficient lighting, or when structural or electrical hazards are present

    (b) *Category II*: defects which are less serious and can be left until the next routine or repair visit.

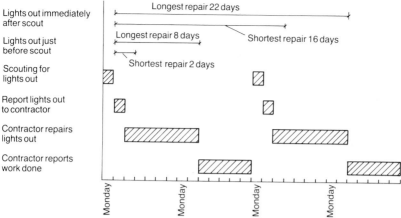

Fig. 5.5. Typical 14-day scouting and repair cycle

It is recommended that certain Category I defects which constitute a structural or electrical hazard are dealt with as soon as possible, but in any case within 24 hours. All other faults shall receive permanent repairs within a maximum period of 14 days of them being reported.

Category II defects may be left for up to 6 months, unless it is reasonably possible for them to be attended to with the Category I defects in the vicinity.

These arrangements fit in very well with scouting frequencies recommended in the ILE Technical Report No. 14,[5.26] which is normally adopted by local authorities for their own roads. Experience has shown that when using a contractual approach to lighting maintenance, a 14-day repair cycle is the shortest time that can reasonably be achieved. In practice the maintenance operation is subject to the scouting cycle and how soon after a visit the defects can be repaired. Fig. 5.5 shows a typical repair cycle.

Assuming that, on average, the same number of lights fail every day, then, from Fig. 5.5, the average repair time based on a fortnightly scout is 12 days. The best time that can be achieved is two days and at the worst it may take 22 days to bring a light back into operation. Any improvement on such repair times may well escalate costs. Computerization can help to speed up these procedures.

Non-routine maintenance costs represent the largest slice of the maintenance budget. It is therefore in this area that the biggest savings can be achieved by good management.

Random repairs of defects require a vast stock of materials to achieve the objectives set out. Consequently, it is essential to standardize replacement items as much as possible. Too much emphasis is given to the replacement of components, especially columns and lanterns to match existing fittings. With the rapid progress in the design and manufacture of columns and lanterns, the latest type on the market is invariably more efficient and cheaper than the superseded types, which may still be available but at a greater cost.

Columns and lanterns can be specified by their shape, size and performance, providing a standardized base for competition among manufacturers. Other components that are not visible are interchangeable provided that they meet specifications and fit the equipment.

It is fairly common to experience longer delays in repairs when remedial works fall outside the direct control of the highway authority, as for instance, when faults develop in the electricity supply cables owned by the Electricity Board. It is important to establish good contacts with personnel responsible for these cable repairs and to set up a system of exchange of information so that progress can be monitored.

In the event of accident damage occurring, emergency measures need to be taken in many cases to make the installation safe initially and to effect speedy repairs. Again, good liaison with the Electricity Board is required when electricity supply cables are involved.

5.10.4. Maintenance of high mast lighting

High mast lights are considered to be structures. This means that they require periodic structural inspection. Most of them are fitted with winches capable of lifting maintenance personnel to the top of the masts in purpose made cradles. Such winches and wire ropes have to be tested and will need certification. The Department of Transport in Departmental Standard BD 22/84[5.27] sets out requirements for the structural inspection of high mast lights on the Department's roads.

It is normal practice to carry out maintenance in two-yearly cycles as follows.

First, part maintenance involves

(a) the general inspection and lubrication of all winch components and pulleys

(b) full operation of the power drive mechanism and inspection for wear of wire ropes

(c) the inspection of the lantern carriage, electricity supply, cable anchorages, lanterns and electrical components.

Full maintenance is the same as part maintenance and in addition involves

(a) test loading of wire ropes with a maintenance cradle before it is used to carry personnel

(b) inspection of mast surfaces for paint deterioration

(c) inspection of head pulleys and fixings

(d) testing of lightning earthing installation at the base as recommended in the British Standard Code of Practice BS 6651[5.28] and CP 1013.[5.29]

It is advisable for specialist high mast manufacturers to be commissioned to carry out these inspections. When high mast maintenance is included in maintenance contracts these requirements should be specified. The ILE Technical Report No. 7[5.30] gives detailed specifications for the design, manufacture, installation and maintenance of masts.

5.10.5. Maintenance of street lighting columns — painting

Whether dealing with existing steel lighting columns or new replacement columns, both will need protective paint treatment during their life. All steel lighting columns currently manufactured leave the factory with some protective coatings such as galvanized or metal sprayed finishes. A sealant undercoat is also available for metal sprayed finishes.

Galvanized steel lighting columns are normally erected without further treatment. However, it is recommended that protective paint is applied after a period of between seven and ten years.

If metal sprayed finishes are chosen, then the time span before the first maintenance is required depends on the standard of the initial paint application.

New galvanized or zinc sprayed finishes will require the application of an etch or calcium plumbate primer to achieve proper adherence of subsequent coats of paint.

Existing steel lighting columns will need some treatment before they can be repainted. The most common treatment is to chip or scrape off loose paint and wire brush, followed by degreasing the surface with white spirit and spot priming.

For both old or new steel lighting columns the initial preparation is followed by the application of successive coats of paint. The ILE Technical Report No. 9[5.31] gives a detailed description of the treatment and requirements for paint finishes.

For durability the application of a combination of phosphate primer and micaceous phosphate primer with a finish coat of micaceous oxide paint is recommended. For aesthetic reasons the top coat can be replaced with a good quality undercoat and gloss paint finish. With existing steel lighting columns some of the applications can be omitted depending on the state of the existing paint finishes. For selection of paint colours, BS 4800[5.32] should be referred to.

Work should be carried out only in dry weather conditions. Painting during the winter months is not recommended. Special care should be taken to ensure that remedial treatment for existing columns is carried out before there is much evidence of corrosion.

5.11. Materials

5.11.1. Lighting columns

There are three basic types of lighting columns in general use. These are made of steel, concrete or aluminium. In addition, cast iron replica period columns and high masts are manufactured and marketed for special applications.

Columns are made to conform to BS 5649: Parts 1–9.[5.33] In this new standard many changes have been made with the aim of improving the quality of lighting columns in use today and ensuring that various manufacturers produce goods to the same specification.

Columns used on trunk roads and motorways have to meet additional requirements specified by the Department of Transport in their Technical Memorandum BD 26/86.[5.34]

A Lighting Column Quality Assurance Scheme has been set up and will be jointly administered by the British Standards Institution and Lloyds Register Ltd. Columns manufactured under this scheme will incur a small extra cost, but will save the cost of independent inspection.

Lighting columns are made to meet certain conditions and geometry of the highway. Because of the camber of the road, columns need to be set back a minimum of 0·5 metre from the kerb on urban roads and 1·0 metre on roads with high speed traffic. To support lanterns, normally positioned over the road channel, columns have to be fitted with bracket arms. The bracket projection is defined as the horizontal distance from the column centre line to the point of entry in the lantern. The nominal height of columns is the vertical distance from ground level to the point of entry of the bracket arm into the lantern. To avoid the optical illusion of lanterns drooping when they are fitted at right angles to the columns, bracket arms are manufactured with a minimum up-lift of 5° above the horizontal.

Steel lighting columns. Steel lighting columns are made from either circular hollow sections or tapered octagonal or multi-sided steel folded sections. They are generally referred to as tubular or folded steel columns. Tubular columns can be made from parallel sided steel tubes or tapered by extrusion from steel tubes. Parallel sided tubular columns consist of a larger diameter base compartment with a smaller diameter shaft forming the upper section. Columns can be supplied either with roots or with flange places for fixing to prepared bases. Cranked roots are also available. Bracket arms are attached with stainless steel socket screws and should be located by means of a positive anti-rotation device.

Steel columns are manufactured in 4–5 metre nominal heights, and are treated in the factory by hot dip galvanizing or by shot blasting and metal sprayed zinc or aluminium finishes, with an acrylic sealant as an optional extra. Column interiors and roots are treated with black bituminous paint.

Base compartments are fitted with non-hygroscopic hardwood back-boards for the mounting of electrical components and brass earth studs.

Concrete lighting columns. Concrete lighting columns are made from reinforced spun concrete or prestressed concrete, and such columns should carry the British Standard Institution Kite Mark. Columns are made in various shapes and sections, finished in natural texture or smooth ground surface and will require no further treatment or maintenance.

Base compartments are generally fitted with cast aluminium doors and hardwood back-boards.

Bracket arms can be supplied in reinforced concrete finish or made from galvanized steel tube, and should be located by means of an anti-rotation device. Concrete columns are manufactured in 5–12 metre nominal heights.

Aluminium lighting columns. Aluminium lighting columns are made from either tubular aluminium sections with cast aluminium bases or folded aluminium sheets. They are made in 5 and 6 metre nominal heights, and are available for post top mounting or with a choice of bracket arms. Aluminium columns do not require painting or maintenance, and can be supplied with roots or with flange base plates. Base compartments are fitted with hardwood back-boards and earthing points.

Cast iron columns. Replica period cast iron columns are now available for specialist schemes in connection with restoration of historic streets and areas. They normally consist of cast iron base compartments with the shafts being constructed of normal steel tube embellished with cast iron ornaments and ladder bars. They can be supplied with roots or bolt-on bases.

High masts. High masts are made from tubular or folded sheet steel and are available in heights of 20–50 metres. They are supplied complete with flanged base, head frame, winch apparatus and all wire ropes and electrical cables. Electric winch power tools and maintenance cradles are available as an optional extra.

5.11.2. Posts for illuminated traffic signs

Posts should be made from tubular sections complying with BS 6323[5.35] or be of rolled steel joist types complying with BS 4.[5.36]

All posts and bracket arms should be shot-blasted, rust-proofed and finished in traffic sign grey by means of one of the following

- (*a*)   a self coloured coating of stoved epoxy
- (*b*)   a fluidized bed or extruded PVC finish
- (*c*)   a chlorinated rubber finish
- (*d*)   painted standard traffic sign grey colour 693 to BS 381C[5.37] with appropriate undercoats.

Posts should contain a base compartment for electrical components or be capable of being fitted with separate boxes to be strapped to the post section. Structural design should take into account the load on sign plates due to wind pressure. Signs in general are dealt with in Chapter 7.

5.11.3. Street lighting lanterns

Lanterns should comply with the latest edition of BS 4533.[5.38]

The choice of lanterns will depend on where they will be used. It is important to avoid disability glare. An object that is just visible in the absence of glare will tend to merge into the background with the increase of disability glare. The percentage by which the background luminance must be increased, to make an object visible again, is referred to as the threshold increment (TI). Control of TI will ensure that discomfort glare is kept to a minimum. For high speed roads a TI of not more than 15% is recommended. This is important in rural areas where there is a lack of reflecting background, which tends to increase the glare experienced. In other locations a TI of not more than 30% should be aimed for. With this higher limit of TI, longer spacing of lanterns is possible. Lanterns are divided into two categories. Those with

- (*a*)   a moderate threshold increment (MTI) which will meet the maximum TI requirement of 15%
- (*b*)   a low threshold increment (LTI) which will meet the maximum TI requirement of 30%.

The protection of the lamp housing against ingress of dirt or water should be to IP 54 minimum as recommended in BS 5490[5.39] and BS 5489.[5.40]

The selection of lanterns depends on the design criteria for road lighting installations set out in BS 5489, Appendix A and B.[5.41] Data required for design calculations are provided by the lantern manufacturers. Some manufacturers provide isoluminance templates with their lantern data. Computer programs for lighting design are also available.

Modern technology has made it possible to design lanterns and optics that minimize the losses. A downward light output ratio (DLOR) of 0·7 is now generally accepted as normal when specifying lanterns. However, a DLOR in excess of 0·8 can now be achieved.

Lanterns are supplied with integral control gear or separate gear for fitting into the columns. Although integral lanterns have been chosen by the Department of Transport for their road network and in particular for motorways, the additional weight of the control gear leads to increases in the structural strength of the lighting column with consequential extra cost. Base compartments in lighting columns can in most cases adequately accommodate control gear, making the use of integral lanterns superfluous.

Lanterns should be designed to give easy access to lamps and associated electrical terminations. Sockets for photoelectric cells can be specified to be fitted during assembly.

Special attention should be paid to the external finishes of lanterns. Very bright and reflecting materials can be quite unacceptable for aesthetic reasons in sensitive areas. Also, sunlight reflecting from lanterns in daytime can cause discomfort to the road user.

5.11.4. Sign lighting units

These units should meet the requirements set out in the Traffic Sign Manual. Exterior type lighting units should be constructed to be attached to traffic signs by means of bracket arms or free standing for use with large advance direction signs. Control gear should be integral with lanterns whenever possible. Lighting units should be supplied with factory fitted photoelectric cells. The protection of the housing against ingress of dirt and water should be to IP 54 specification. Lanterns should be fitted with twin fluorescent lamps or with twin high pressure mercury lamps as required to avoid complete failure of illumination.

With internally illuminated signs the lighting equipment forms an integral part of the sign. They are normally supplied by specialist sign manufacturers. Parts are not generally interchangeable and in the event of damage can take a long time to obtain.

5.11.5. Lamps

Lamps should meet requirements set out in the British Standards where applicable. British Standard 3767[5.42] deals with low pressure sodium vapour lamps and BS 3677[5.43] with high pressure mercury vapour lamps. Fluorescent tubes are covered in BS 1853.[5.44]

Lamps used should be of a type and wattage generally made by more than one manufacturer and should be interchangeable with the control gear. Special lamps produced by only one manufacturer should be avoided in view of the lack of competition in future. Some manufacturers may offer large discounts for initial installation of such specialist types of lamps to ensure the need to buy replacements from them in the future, invariably at a premium.

Manufacturers offer guarantees for the lamps which they supply. Some will offer replacements for short life lamps on a pro rata basis depending on the number of hours in operation. Others will give a blanket guarantee up to a given number of burning hours. As it is difficult to keep track of the burning hours of lamps and also prove it, the latter arrangement is preferable. As batches of lamps vary considerably in life and performance, some form of guarantee is essential.

Special care must be taken in the storage of new lamps and the disposal of used ones because of the fire risk from lamps containing sodium and the toxic properties of other lamp ingredients. For disposal of large quantities of lamps the local authority concerned with the disposal of toxic or dangerous waste should be consulted.

5.11.6. Discharge lamp control gear

Control gear should meet requirements set out in the British Standards where applicable. British Standard 4782[5.45] deals with ballasts for low pressure sodium, high pressure sodium and high pressure mercury lamps, and BS 4017[5.46] with capacitors for use with tubular fluorescent, low pressure sodium and high pressure sodium discharge lamp circuits.

Where possible, ballasts should display the British Standard Kite Mark. All control gear should have all live parts adequately protected and should be fitted with earth terminals. Capacitors must provide a power factor correction of not less than 0·85 lagging. All gear should be fully compatible with standard lamps supplied by manufacturers.

Pre-wired gear trays are available for traffic sign lanterns and are now also being marketed for other discharge lamp circuits. They can be fitted with quick release plug and socket terminals for removal during maintenance operations. By using interchangeable gear trays, faulty equipment can be tested and repaired in the workshop for future re-use. Pre-wired gear trays are recommended for new work. This will ensure that circuits are correctly wired at all times whichever contractor carries out the installation works. Circuit watts ratings of control gear are shown in Table 5.5.

5.11.7. Photoelectric controls or time switches

Photoelectric controls have become the most widely used form of switching street lighting and illuminated signs. They are supplied either as one part units which mate into sockets fitted to street lighting or traffic sign lanterns or as two part units with the photo-cell part fitted into the lanterns and the switch accommodated in the base compartments of columns or posts.

Photoelectric controls should meet requirements set out in BS 5972.[5.47] Switching levels are pre-set in the factory depending on criteria required by the user. Most Electricity Boards have tariffs for certain ranges of switching levels. There can be substantial differences between these ranges in energy costs. Consequently, care should be taken when determining this policy.

Photoelectric controls fitted with thermal switches or electronic solid state devices are available. The latter devices are more accurate but are likely to be more expensive. Unless there are differences in the tariffs quoted by the Electricity Board, little is gained by opting for the more expensive units.

Most photoelectric controls are designed to fail in the 'on' positions. This ensures that lights will not fail when the photoelectric device becomes defective. Although this will provide a better level of service to the public, the disadvantage is that defects will need to be located during daytime inspections.

There are currently two types of photoelectric controls on the market for

(*a*)   dusk-to-dawn operation
(*b*)   part night operation.

The latter is of the electronic type fitted with a microprocessor, which will determine intermediate switch 'off' and 'on' times between the normal dusk-to-dawn operation. The advantage of these devices is that in the event of power failures the part night timing cycle will reset after one night during which it will operate on a dusk-to-dawn cycle.

If time switches are used it is recommended that they are of the synchronous motor type fitted with solar dials with two 'on' and 'off' switching provisions. Switches should be fitted with a spring reserve or emergency battery to operate the timing mechanism during power failures. When purchasing time switches it is necessary to specify the geographical latitude of the location where they will be used.

5.11.8. Cable terminations in columns and fuses

Cut-outs for cable terminations in street lighting columns and posts should be made from substantial moulded plastic. They should incorporate drip proof enclosures with sealing chambers and separate terminals for live and neutral conductors. A fuse carrier suitable for cartridge fuses or a miniature circuit breaker should be accommodated. Cut-outs should be suitable for taking service cables in straight terminations or looped services. Clamping devices for earth continuity between service cables and electrical equipment in lighting columns and illuminated signs should be provided.

Fuses should be of a high rupturing capacity type to BS 1361[5.48] or BS 88[5.49] specifications.

5.11.9. Underground cables and joints

Local authorities have a choice when designing electrical networks. In urban areas where power cables are available as part of the Electricity

Board supply network, it is likely to be cheaper to request for an un-metered supply to lamp columns or illuminated signs from the public supply cables. In other locations and especially when lighting is provided as part of major road systems, private cable networks may be considered more economical and a better proposition for future maintenance activities. In such cases the Electricity Board supply is terminated in feeder pillars owned by local authorities from which the private cables are radiated.

Underground cables are normally supplied with copper or aluminium conductors. British Standard 6346[5.50] deals with aluminium conductors, PVC insulated and aluminium strip armoured, and PVC sheathed 600–1000 volt grade cables. British Standard 6364 also caters for copper conductors, PVC insulated and steel wire armoured, and PVC sheathed cables. Concentric cables can also be used for street lighting services.

Joints are available in kit form and can be supplied either with mechanical conductor joining clamps or crimping devices. These should be complete with earth/armouring continuity straps and clamps. Cold pouring sealing compounds consisting of a combination of resin and hardener are generally used and are introduced into the joint casings. Shrink-on sleeves are also available for water-proofing joints. Jointing kits should be tested to the Electricity Council Engineering Recommendation C64,[5.51] and compounds should meet the requirements of ERRC/M687.[5.52]

5.12. Plant

Street lighting maintenance operations require the use of specialist plant. For low level work on lighting columns below 6 metres nominal

Fig. 5.6. Hydraulic platform   *Fig. 5.7. HIAB lifting appliance*

height, fixed lightweight platforms attached to the van chassis of the 'transit' type are often used. These units provide limited flexibility, but are relatively cheap to purchase and very economical to operate. However, due to current policies of erecting lighting columns at the back of footways and the increasing inaccessibility of installations as a result of car parking problems, small hydraulic platform vehicles may be considered more practicable.

For maintenance at levels in excess of 6 metres nominal height, various forms of hydraulic lift platforms (Fig. 5.6) mounted on chassis fitted with workshop and storage lockers are now generally used. Many of these are fitted with interlock systems to prevent the boom being extended over an adjacent carriageway below 5·5 metres.

Column erection is carried out by means of HIAB (Fig. 5.7) or ATLAS type lifting appliances attached to lorry chassis. These have adequate lifting capacity for erecting new columns, but may be restricted for removal of columns. Over-load warning systems are not obligatory as with cranes, and care will have to be exercised by the operator when undertaking the removal of old lighting columns, in particular concrete columns.

Special cranes are needed for the erection of high masts on prepared foundations. Plant operators should be consulted before embarking on such operations.

Trenching machines are now generally used for the laying of underground cables. These machines are basically wheeled or tracked vehicles incorporating bucket or toothed chain loops. Special trenching machines are also available for excavating cable trenches along embankments. Mole ploughs can be employed as an alternative method of cable laying. Cables are fed into grooves cut by plough blades attached to the rear of tractors. There is no need for back-filling as the ground will return to its natural position after a few days.

Cable trailers are found to be more efficient for laying of long sections of power cables. However, cables should be pulled into position on cable rollers to avoid damage to sheathing caused by dragging over rough ground.

Unless plant can be adequately utilized it is unlikely to be more economical to hire from reputable plant hire firms.

5.13. Traffic safety and control

It is the contractor's responsibility to provide, erect and maintain such temporary traffic signs necessary to comply with recommendations contained in Chapter 8 of the Traffic Sign Manual.[5.53]

However, street lighting maintenance works, due to their short duration, are exempted from the more stringent requirements set out for longer roadworks. For maintenance not exceeding 15 minutes, reduced signing may be permitted with the agreement of the authority concerned. A useful Code of Practice has been prepared by Staffordshire County Council,[5.54] which sets out recommendations for short duration stops.

It is very important to stress the need for good traffic management when carrying out street lighting maintenance works. Apart from the danger to road users from obstruction caused by lift vehicles, the risk to the operators must be emphasized. All vehicles are required to be fitted with flashing warning lights and clear danger markings at the rear. Many lift vehicles are now fitted with impact absorbing devices.

5.14. Electrical safety in public lighting operations

Electricity can be dangerous and fatal. The Health and Safety at Work Act 1964[5.55] places responsibility on all persons engaged in work to ensure the safety and welfare of themselves and others. When dealing with electrical installations it is important to emphasize the safety aspects required. There are many data sheets, technical reports, codes of practice, advice notes, guidance notes, manuals and other publications available dealing with this subject.

The ILE Code of Practice for Electrical Safety in Public Lighting Operations[5.56] provides comprehensive guidance and recommendations to personnel engaged in working with electrical installations.

The Engineering Recommendation G 39[5.57] gives guidance to local authority's and contractor's personnel and authorization procedures to enable such persons to isolate equipment connected to the Electricity Board's unmetered supply.

Personnel issued with permits must be competent and must have received a recognized course of training in electrical engineering. An authorizing engineer should be appointed in every authority to deal with the authorization procedures and the issue of permits to competent persons. Permits should be for a maximum period of three years after which they should require renewal. Persons infringing any of the safety regulations should forfeit permits.

Personnel engaged on electrical installations are required to comply with IEE Wiring Regulations,[5.58] and many Electricity Boards also have published guidance notes.[5.59]

Special care must be taken by personnel dealing with emergencies affecting lighting columns following motor accidents. If there is evidence of damage to Electricity Board cables, the Board's emergency services must be notified without delay. When private cable networks are affected, the main supply must be isolated before any remedial measures are taken.

5.15. Planned replacement of lighting equipment

As mentioned previously the most economical way to carry out replacement of obsolete equipment is by a planned cyclic replacement programme. This will ensure that the lowest quantity discount prices can be obtained from manufacturers and installation contractors. Good forward planning will also enable the Electricity Board to programme the disconnection and reconnection of lighting columns at the lowest possible cost.

When carrying out the replacement of equipment that has reached the end of its life the opportunity should be taken to install the replacement equipment to a standard that will meet the latest recommendations contained in BS 5489: Parts 2–9. This will ensure that the lighting installation is renewed and at the same time improved to the correct standard.

In the trade, the life of a lighting column is considered to be in the region of 25 years. In practice columns properly installed and treated well will last 40 years or more. Lanterns and other electrical components may need replacing at least once during such a time span. Such replacements can also be carried out in a planned fashion once the correct replacement cycle can be established.

Planned cyclic replacements will need substantial financial provision. By including such expenditures in the authority's service plan adequate funds can be assured, making it possible to plan such operations on a long-term basis. The benefit obtained by a planned replacement programme will ultimately result in a reduction in maintenance costs.

Failure to provide a planned replacement programme will ultimately increase maintenance costs when dangerous equipment has to be replaced randomly. In the end, large sums of money will have to be found when lighting equipment has deteriorated to the point where it has to be changed anyway.

Acknowledgements

Photographs of maintenance vehicles are by courtesy of D. Webster Ltd and photographs of lamps are by courtesy of Philips Lighting Ltd.

References

5.1. *Highway Act 1980.* Her Majesty's Stationery Office, London, Sections 43, 58(i), 97(i), 98(i), 98(ii), 101.

5.2 *Local Government Act 1966.* Her Majesty's Stationery Office, London, Section 32.

5.3. *Local Government Act 1988.* Her Majesty's Stationery Office, London.

5.4. DIRECT LABOUR ORGANISATION. *Local Government Planning and Land Act 1980.* Her Majesty's Stationery Office, London.

5.5. *Local Government (Direct Labour Organisation) (Competition) (Amendment) Regulations 1988 (SI 1988 No. 160).* Her Majesty's Stationery Office, London.

5.6. *Statutory Instruments 1981 No. 859 Road Traffic, The Traffic Signs Regulations and General Directions 1981.* Her Majesty's Stationery Office, London, Section III, ch. 15.

5.7. *Statutory Instruments 1969 No. 487, The Traffic Signs (Speed Limit) Regulation and General Directions 1969.* Her Majesty's Stationery Office, London.

5.8. BRITISH STANDARDS INSTITUTION *Code of practice for the lighting of traffic routes.* BS 5489: Part 2: 1987 Road Lighting. BSI, London.

5.9. LOCAL AUTHORITY ASSOCIATION. *Highway maintenance. A code of good practice.* Appendix 2, Local Authority Association, London, 1983.

5.10. SIMONS R.S. *et al.* Lighting criteria for residential roads and areas. *Lightex '87 Conference 1987,* Blackpool. Institution of Lighting Engineers.

5.11. DEPARTMENT OF THE ENVIRONMENT. *Local Government Planning and Land Act 1980 — Direct Labour Organisation Year 3.* Her Majesty's Stationery Office, London, 1983, Circular 19/83.

5.12. INSTITUTION OF MECHANICAL AND ELECTRICAL ENGINEERS and ASSOCIATION OF CONSULTING ENGINEERS. *Model Form MFI General Conditions of Contract 1988.*

5.13. COUNTY SURVEYORS SOCIETY. *Model document for the maintenance of public lighting and signs.* Report No. 3/1 and 3/2, 1985.

5.14. DEPARTMENT OF THE ENVIRONMENT. *Monthly Bulletin,* Construction Indices. Specialist Engineer Installations. Index No. 1. Cost of Labour for Electrical Installations. Index No. 2. Cost of Materials for Electrical Installations and Monthly Bulletin Construction Indices. Civil Engineer Index No. 2. Cost of Plant and Equipment. Index No. 8. Cost of Derv Fuel. DoE, London.

5.15. LOCAL AUTHORITY ASSOCIATION. *Highway maintenance. A code of good practice,* London, p. 20.

5.16. DEPARTMENT OF TRANSPORT. Highways and Traffic Departmental Standard TD 23/86 *Trunk road and trunk road motorways. Maintenance of road lighting.* Table 1: *Inspection requirements.*

5.17. INSTITUTION OF LIGHTING ENGINEERS. *The cost effectiveness of night-time patrolling.* Technical Report No. 14, 1984.

5.18. INSTITUTION OF LIGHTING ENGINEERS. *A study of lamp replacements for discharge sources 1982.* Technical Report No. 17, pp. 9–10.

5.19. INSTITUTION OF LIGHTING ENGINEERS. *A study of lamp replacements for discharge sources 1987.* Technical Report No. 17, Tables 1 and 2.

5.20. *Report of the Committee on Highway Maintenance 1970.* Her Majesty's Stationery Office, London, 125, 126.

5.21. LOCAL AUTHORITY ASSOCIATION. *Highways maintenance — a code of good practice,* London, p. 20.

5.22. BRITISH STANDARDS INSTITUTION. *Code of practice for lighting of traffic routes.* BS 5489: Part 2: 1987. BSI, London, p. 28, Table 4.

5.23. DEPARTMENT OF TRANSPORT. Highways and Traffic Departmental Standard TD 23/86 *Trunk road and trunk road motorways. Maintenance of road lighting.* p. 7, Table 3.

5.24. INSTITUTION OF LIGHTING ENGINEERS. *A study of lamp replacements for discharge sources 1987.* Technical Report No. 17, p. 7, para. 8.

5.25. DEPARTMENT OF TRANSPORT. Highway and Traffic Departmental Standard TD 23/86 *Trunk roads and trunk road motorways. Maintenance of road lighting.* p. 3, ch. 4.2.

5.26. INSTITUTION OF LIGHTING ENGINEERS. *The cost effectiveness of night-time patrolling 1984.* Technical Report No. 14.

5.27. DEPARTMENT OF TRANSPORT. Departmental Standard BD 22/84, *Inspection of structures.*

5.28. BRITISH STANDARDS INSTITUTION. *Code of practice for protection of structures against lightning.* BS 6651: 1985. BSI, London.

5.29. BRITISH STANDARDS INSTITUTION. *Earthing.* CP 1013: 1965. BSI, London.

5.30. INSTITUTION OF LIGHTING ENGINEERS. *High mast lighting 1976.* Technical Report No. 7.

5.31. INSTITUTION OF LIGHTING ENGINEERS. *Protective coatings for steel street lighting columns 1980.* Technical Report No. 9.

5.32. BRITISH STANDARDS INSTITUTION. *Specification for paint colours for building purposes.* BS 4800: 1981. BSI, London.

5.33. BRITISH STANDARDS INSTITUTION. *Lighting columns.* BS 5649: Parts 1–9. BSI, London.

5.34. DEPARTMENT OF TRANSPORT. *Steel Lighting Column Design 1988.* Technical Memorandum BD 26/86.

5.35. BRITISH STANDARDS INSTITUTION. *Specification for seamless and welded steel tubes for automobile, mechanical and general engineering purposes.* BS 6323: Parts 1–8: 1982. BSI, London.

5.36. BRITISH STANDARDS INSTITUTION. *Specification for hot-rolled sections.* BS 4: Part 1: 1980.

5.37. BRITISH STANDARDS INSTITUTION. *Specification for colour for identification coding and special purposes.* BS 381C: 1980. BSI, London.

5.38. BRITISH STANDARDS INSTITUTION. *Specification for light distribution from road lighting lanterns.* BS 4533: Part 103: 1981. BSI, London.

5.39. BRITISH STANDARDS INSTITUTION. *Specification for classification of degree of protection provided by enclosures.* BS 5490: 1985. BSI, London.

5.40. BRITISH STANDARDS INSTITUTION. *Code of Practice for Lighting of Traffic Routes.* BS 5489: Part 2: 1987. BSI, London, p. 28, Table 4.

5.41. BRITISH STANDARDS INSTITUTION. *Code of Practice for Road Lighting for Traffic Routes.* BS 5489: Part 2: 1987, Appendix A and B. BSI, London.

5.42. BRITISH STANDARDS INSTITUTION. *Specification for low pressure sodium vapour lamps.* BS 3767: 1982. BSI, London.

5.43. BRITISH STANDARDS INSTITUTION. *Specification for high pressure mercury vapour lamps.* BS 3677: 1982. BSI, London.

5.44. BRITISH STANDARDS INSTITUTION. *Specification for tubular fluorescent lamps for general lighting service.* BS 1853. BSI, London.

5.45. BRITISH STANDARDS INSTITUTION. *Specification for ballasts for discharge lamps.* BS 4782: 1971. BSI, London.

5.46. BRITISH STANDARDS INSTITUTION. *Specification for capacitors for discharge lamps.* BS 4017: 1979. BSI, London.

5.47. BRITISH STANDARDS INSTITUTION. *Specification for photo-electric control units for road lighting.* BS 5972: 1980. BSI, London.

5.48. BRITISH STANDARDS INSTITUTION. *Specification for cartridge fuses for AC circuits.* BS 1361: 1986. BSI, London.

5.49. BRITISH STANDARDS INSTITUTION. *Specification for cartridge fuses for voltages up to and including 1000 volts AC and 1500 volts DC.* BS 88. BSI, London.

5.50. BRITISH STANDARDS INSTITUTION. *Specification for PVC insulated cables for electricity supply.* BS 6346: 1987. BSI, London.

5.51. ELECTRICITY COUNCIL. *Testing procedure for approval of joints for cables.* Electricity Council, London, 1969, Engineering Recommendation C64.

5.52. ELECTRICITY COUNCIL. *Derivation and use of specification for cold pour compounds.* Electricity Research Centre, 1974. Report ERRC/M687.

5.53. DEPARTMENT OF TRANSPORT. *Traffic Sign Manual.* Her Majesty's Stationery Office, London, ch. 8.

5.54. STAFFORDSHIRE COUNTY COUNCIL. Code of Practice for Signing in Conjunction with Intermittent Minor Street Works. *Staffordshire Green Book.* Staffordshire County Council, 1980.

5.55. *Health and Safety at Work Act 1974.* Her Majesty's Stationery Office, London.

5.56. INSTITUTION OF LIGHTING ENGINEERS. *Code of Practice for Electrical Safety in Public Lighting Operations 1981.* ILE, London, 1981.

5.57. ELECTRICITY COUNCIL. *Model code of practice covering electrical safety in the planning, installation, commissioning and maintenance of public lighting and other street furniture.* Engineering Recommendation G39, 1979.

5.58. INSTITUTION OF ELECTRICAL ENGINEERS. Regulations for electrical installation. *I.E.E. Wiring Regulations.* 1981, 15th edn.

5.59. INSTITUTION OF ELECTRICAL ENGINEERS. Notes on guidance on characteristics of supply. *I.E.E. Wiring Regulations and Installations to be Connected to Protective Multiple Earthed Systems 1986.* Eastern Electricity Board, 1986, 15th edn.

6

Traffic signal maintenance

6.1. Special maintenance requirements of traffic signals

6.1.1. The nature of a traffic signal system

Modern traffic control systems are an example of electronic intelligence being distributed around the highway network. Some of this includes communication to central offices, usually with computers (see, e.g., Fig. 6.1). While there is a general specification in BS 505[6.1] much more detail is provided in numerous Department of Transport specifications.[6.2]

The essential feature of control is a traffic signal controller that contains at least one microprocessor and switches the traffic signals on and off at calculated intervals. The simplest possible arrangement, therefore, comprises an electricity supply, the signal controller in its cabinet, the traffic signals to be switched and interconnecting cables. Such a system would be able to switch the signals purely on a predetermined basis, using an internal clock. This is known as fixed time signalling.

For nearly 50 years it has been normal UK practice for traffic signals to respond to individual vehicles. For this purpose vehicle detectors are placed in (induction loop detectors) or near (microwave and ultrasonic detectors) the road, and connected to the signal controller. This is known as vehicle actuated signalling.

Additionally, there can be advantages in interconnecting signal controllers so that traffic can progress unhindered between junctions at a predetermined speed. This may be through interconnecting cables directly between the controllers or through a regional or central computer. The latter arrangement is known as Urban Traffic Control (UTC). In some UTC systems, the detector information is used by the central computers rather than by the signal controllers. Interconnection between controllers and the control centre may use dedicated circuits or circuits rented from a telephone company; data transmission systems are usually used.

Supplementary equipment, particularly for UTC and motorway control systems, can include roadside telephones and closed-circuit television. Two-way communication is needed and in the case of television the high grade picture circuits may use fibre optics.

6.1.2. Maintaining the integrity of the system

Control systems differ from passive elements, like roads, in that all the separate components must function correctly for the system as a whole to be seen to be operational. Malfunctioning of components of the system occurs on a random basis and is not the result of gradual degradation, so cannot be reliably countered by generous design. A single malfunction can seriously degrade the overall performance or even render the signals inoperative. Clearly, the control logic is designed to contain the consequences of single faults of vulnerable items such as signal lamps, vehicle detectors and interconnections. However, the degree of degradation experienced is serious enough for there to be a need to find such faults and respond to them promptly. The concept of periodic inspection to

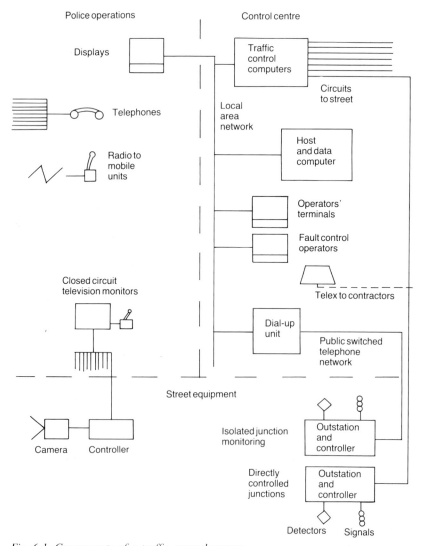

Fig. 6.1. Components of a traffic control system

remedy wear and tear or to anticipate life expiry is relatively less important; indeed, in some cases, disturbance of the equipment for inspection may increase the risk of faults.

6.1.3. Economics of better maintenance

Some studies have identified the proportion of signal faults and their consequences in terms of traffic delay. Using normal assessment techniques, these studies indicate that the capital costs of quite complex automatic fault reporting systems can be recouped (in terms of reduced delays) in a few months.

6.1.4. Special situations

Traffic signal systems on motorways have many different features. Most of them are owned by the Department of Transport, which has very tight control over specification. Many of the components, such as signal assemblies in central reservations, present access problems. Special mention is made of them later.

Signals at roadworks are relatively inexpensive and yet have to contend with severe operational circumstances. The environment is particularly harsh on temporary work, involving lack of proper protection from weather and physical buffeting, either on site or when being transported to site. In these adverse circumstances, interconnections have to be made and are not as well protected as in permanent installations. Finally, the people installing the signals are unlikely to have proper training or the ability to understand quite simple signal setting procedures. Not surprisingly, the settings of most road works signals are not optimal and create visible unnecessary delays, which encourage drivers to ignore the signals.

6.2. Organization of signal maintenance

6.2.1. Supplier maintenance

Until 1970, UK traffic signals were maintained by the supplier who undertook, under a maintenance contract, to make periodic inspections and respond when called out. Usually, the whole installation at a junction (or even within a whole highway authority) was supplied by one company. This loose contractual arrangement, and the destructive effect of heavier traffic on vulnerable rubber pad vehicle detectors, meant that the majority of junctions suffered from faults at any one time. Some changes had to be made.

6.2.2. Performance contracts

The first change, already in operation overseas and introduced successfully by the Greater London Council in 1972,[6.3] involved performance standards and financial controls. This has been developed to the stage of a Department of Transport Standard[6.4] and draft contract,[6.5] which are used on the Department's own roads and are recommended to other highway authorities. The contract requires a range of regular inspections or actions (such as lamp changing) at regular intervals.

*Table 6.1. Maintenance classifications**

Maintenance class	Class L	Class M	Class N
Contract hours	8.00 a.m.–5.00 p.m. Mondays–Fridays (excluding bank holidays)	7.00 a.m.–7.00 p.m. Mondays–Saturdays (including bank holidays)	6.00 a.m.–8.00 p.m. Mondays–Saturdays (including bank holidays)
Attendance on site for urgent faults	Within 8 contract hours	Within 8 contract hours	Within 4 elapsed hours
Attendance on site for non-urgent faults	Within 40 contract hours	Within 24 contract hours	By 8.00 p.m. next contract day

* Attendence for urgent faults out of hours and out of hours on Sundays should also be stipulated by the authority.

The second change was necessary when equipment at a junction could come from several different suppliers. This arose firstly with the data transmission for UTC systems and later when alternative suppliers bid successfully for signal controllers at junctions where traffic signal aspects were not to be changed. Hence, one organization must be able to maintain equipment supplied by another. In the end, the maintenance contractor can be a specialist and not a supplier at all; the emergence of such firms around 1980 significantly improved the competitiveness of maintenance.

Random faults are covered by the periodic maintenance contract payment. The contractor is encouraged to reduce the number of such call outs and hence improve his profit by ensuring that repairs are efficiently executed. Faults due to damage are the responsibility of the control system owner rather than the maintenance contractor. The contract provides for repair orders (usually to a price schedule rather than by individual estimating) to be issued and work implemented immediately.

6.2.3. Draft form of contract

The contract requires call out within a specified time, depending on the nature and location of the fault. 'Urgent' faults are defined as

(a) all signals unlit
(b) signals failing to change
(c) excessive traffic queues or abnormal conditions
(d) signals damaged and in a dangerous condition.

An on-call emergency service to rectify items failing due to fair wear and tear is recommended from 8.00 a.m. to 6.00 p.m. Mondays to Saturdays excluding bank holidays (known as 'contract hours'). This should include attendance within 8 contract hours (or 8 hours for urgent faults arising out of the contract hours) for urgent faults, and within 24 contract hours for non-urgent faults.

Non-performance rebates are also recommended for failure to attend within the specified periods. This should be at the rate of 2·5% in respect of the first excess period and 10% in respect of each subsequent excess period in response to a fault report; the excess period is defined as 8 contract hours for urgent faults and 24 contract hours for non-urgent faults. A further non-performance rebate is payable if there are more than eight faults per year to the signal controller itself; the contractor can protect himself from this rebate, if he believes a controller is unmaintainable, by having it removed from the contract.

Different contracts can apply in different circumstances, e.g. extensive urban areas need, and can afford, faster response than signals remote from a depot in a rural area. While individual authorities stipulate their own standards, the draft form of contract recommends (for repair of equipment not covered above) the contract hours stated in Table 6.1.

6.2.4. Fault reporting centres

The need to control response times (by levying financial rebates) on performance contracts meant that the call out orders had to be formally given. Ideally, this is through a dedicated fault control centre having records of equipment performance at each site. Since time is of the essence either telephone calls must be rigorously timed and their contents formalized or, better, the orders must be placed electronically, e.g. by telex or fax. Out of normal operating hours, initial call outs can be applied through commercial telephone answering services. Previous arrangements whereby police and other agencies notified faults directly to contractors had already proved to be ineffective (messages were imprecise, late and inaccurate) and out of keeping with contractual control.

The fault reporting centre can then analyse performance of contractors and equipment.[6.6] It has, for example, been found sensitive enough to identify abnormal lamp failure rates attributable to an incompetent operative or change in manufacture. It is also necessary to monitor whether the faults in a particular piece of equipment have become so numerous as to indicate that the life of the equipment has expired or that maintenance has been incompetent.

A technical inspectorate is necessary. In response to information from the fault control centre, the inspectorate should visit a sample of sites. On a random basis this should verify that response and repair times have been as stated, that simple repairs are not being declared as more complex (with longer permitted repair times) and that the equipment is being left in good working order. On a sample basis, some repairs may require destructive inspection, e.g. to check that loop cable joints have no air voids. On a more structured basis, particular classes of equipment or fault should be more thoroughly inspected. This was, for example, the basis for the creation of a new induction loop detector specification[6.7] when site visits revealed that the majority of faults were not attributable to loop cables being cut, as had previously been thought. One of the requirements was to provide better protection of the circuits as they passed under the kerb, as indicated in Fig. 6.2.

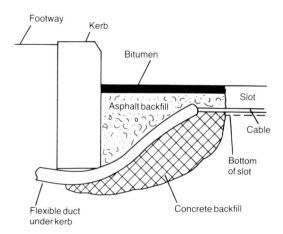

Fig. 6.2. Detector cable and passage under kerb

6.2.5. Automatic fault reporting

The weakness in the system described above is the time taken for any report of a fault to be received. Some authorities have routine functional inspections at intervals as short as six weeks. In the UK, such arrangements have seldom lived up to their claims, and faults have had to wait for police or members of the public to notice them, for faulty lamps to be removed in the lamp change cycle, or for the annual periodic inspection.

To produce immediate fault reports, remote monitoring arrangements have been introduced in the UK.[6.8] An additional microcomputer in the controller measures vehicle detector inputs, UTC input signals and lamp currents, and deduces whether the junction equipment is operating correctly. If not, using a normal telephone line (known as PSTN — Public Switched Telephone Network), it dials the central office equipment and reports the fault. Ultimately, the central office equipment is a computer, which then initiates and records the whole sequence of repair events, including actually placing an order on the contractor. Central computer control can achieve dramatic reductions in the proportion of equipment faulty at any one time, e.g. from 50% to 5% for certain timing faults and for detectors.[6.8]

6.2.6. In-house maintenance

Some authorities use their own staff for some or all of the maintenance. Introduction of such a system may be more economic than using contracts. Provided the organization is efficient and management demands high standards this can be effective. However, staff numbers in public authorities are often subject to overall and perhaps arbitrary restriction, and the conditions of employment do not permit adequate sanctions to ensure high performance; in maintenance activities any slippage from the highest standards quickly leads to seriously unsatisfactory performance.

For in-house maintenance it is therefore strongly recommended that the full organization required for contractual maintenance should be set up, including formally specified attendance times, electronic fault reporting and call-out arrangements and formal requirements to attend out-of-hours. Monitoring of attendance performance and the technical performance of the equipment in the field should be monitored by an independent team.

6.3. Traffic signal controllers

6.3.1. The core of the system

A modern traffic signal controller is a microcomputer having different modes of operation, enabling it to provide fixed time control, vehicle actuation and urban traffic control (via a data transmission unit), and including automatic management aids such as an accurate clock for time-of-day switching or coordination with other controllers, a memory of different settings, special logic and facilities for monitoring its own performance and that of the lamps and detectors connected to it. The safety of the motorist is protected primarily by a duplicated system of guarding against unwanted simultaneous green signal displays, but also by using some time setting thresholds that cannot be violated. Proper maintenance of the traffic signal controller forms the core of the signal maintenance contract.

In essence there are few degradable components in the signal controller, e.g. lamp switching relays have now been replaced by electronic switches. Periodic (annual) inspection is therefore aimed at functional checking, and only occasionally need anything be adjusted or replaced, e.g. batteries every five years. Faults, however, do occur much more frequently than the once in two years specified in MCE 0141.[6.9] The faults can be difficult to diagnose, even though the microcomputer keeps elaborate fault logs, which can be accessed by plugging in a handset or portable diagnostic computer. Skilled maintenance staff are essential and may be less readily available (particularly in remote areas or overseas) than the less skilled staff needed for faults such as lamp replacement. To overcome this, some overseas equipment provides more modular fault diagnosis, with lamps on the modules not requiring computer interrogation in the first instance; there is, however, some loss of flexibility.

6.3.2. Routine maintenance

A few routine tasks are still necessary, including lubrication of door locks, replacing of seals and painting of sheet steel cases (not to mention removal of unwanted advertisements). Note that outside the UK, special heat-reflecting paint may be necessary.

6.4. Signal aspects

6.4.1. Different types

Signal aspects fulfil different functions. Normal traffic lights provide red, green or amber aspects to control vehicular and pedestrian movements. Standard ones are 200 mm in diameter; those with stencils which block some of the light, such as for pedestrians or arrows for turning movements, are 300 mm in diameter. A signal head may contain from one (a single filter arrow) to seven aspects facing in one direction, and other clusters facing different directions. The total number of aspects at a junction varies, is typically 30, and tends to rise progressively as more sophisticated control is introduced.

The signal head may also contain box signals to advise of regulatory restrictions, such as banned turning movements. These signs use those normally prescribed for them in the Traffic Signs Regulations.[6.10]

On motorways, signals are dot-matrix panels. Earlier ones had a lamp at each matrix point, giving rise to a substantial maintenance commitment. Currently, fibre optics are used so that each different legend can be powered by a single standard tungsten halogen lamp. Additionally, there are flashing amber and perhaps red lamps. The period of operation of these lamps is, or should be, limited to obtain long effective lamp life.

6.4.2. Routine maintenance needs

Most UK signal aspects are now made of polycarbonate, which does not need painting. Some special components such as variable message signs, either on motorways or the boxes on signal heads, may require such painting. If painting is required it is vital to avoid painting the seals, which then become brittle and leak.

The aspects do still accumulate dust so must be opened for the reflectors and lenses to be cleaned, taking great care not to scratch them.

6.4.3. Lamp supports — access

On the street, signal heads are supported on posts set in concrete. Access is obtained from a suitable ladder. Since lamp changing is normally carried out live, there should be someone else present to rescue the operative in the event of electric shock. In practice it is assumed that members of the public fulfil this role.

Some signal aspects are less accessible, say on a 6 m high mast arm over the road. An elbow or other special vehicle is needed to obtain access. This can be expensive and time-consuming, and access may be limited to times of light traffic.

On motorways and similar special-purpose roads, access to gantry signals is obtained via walkways on the gantries. There may be special precautions to prevent tools and equipment being dropped on passing traffic. Signals on central reservations pose greater problems, in principle requiring lane closure for any attention to them.

6.4.4. Lamp supports — maintenance

Modern (since 1970) UK traffic signal posts are plastic sheathed steel and require no regular attention. Mast arms and gantry structures of various types require maintenance appropriate to their construction material. In view of the difficulty of access they are commonly made of maintenance-free materials.

6.5. Signal lamps

6.5.1. Life variation

Lamps have a limited life. Incandescent lamps in the UK are normally 50 W low voltage tungsten halogen lamps having a nominal life of 3000 hours. Allowing for the periodic operation of traffic signals on streets, this represents six months. Note that amber lamps burn for less time, but do not reach the temperatures required for the halogen cycle to operate reliably, so have a similarly useful life. In some applications some lamps are on for significantly more than half the time and have a lower life. Thus, the 'red man' and green traffic aspect at pelican crossings are on most of the time and burn out prematurely, so a more frequent replacement cycle is necessary.

6.5.2. Lamp changing

In the UK, periodic bulk lamp changing is normal. Alternatively, with a very fast response maintenance organization, replacement can be limited to occasions of call out. This is not suitable in the UK, firstly because the fault may be present for a long time before being reported (prior to the advent of remote monitoring) and secondly because of the high cost of having to attend to deal with a single lamp. An alternative compromise is to change all lamps at a function when, and not before, one is reported as having failed. This may be economic in urban areas (where minimum routes between junctions are not relevant), using remote monitoring.

Some lamps have longer lives, particularly the fluorescent lamps of box signs. They should be dealt with separately or on a proportion of lamp-changing visits. Overseas traffic signal lamps have lives of 5000 or 8000 hours. This is at the expense of considerable loss of luminous efficacy. Such long-life lamps could be useful at sites with difficult access, such as mast arms over the road. Although no British specification exists, there is a case for providing such installations with higher power (150 W) long-life lamps.

Lamp-changing cycles and faults should be closely monitored. In a bulk changing system the random faults should not exceed 1·5% of all lamps per year. Deviations from this indicate sub-standard lamps, poor operatives (tungsten halogen lamps fail prematurely if wrongly handled) or failure to change lamps at the correct times. This figure applied to 30 lamps per junction amounts to a call out every two years, and this is the commonest single fault category requiring a call out.

6.6. Vehicle detectors

6.6.1. Different types

Early detectors of the pneumatic type are now not usually used. Heavy traffic and powerful brakes reduced their lives to two years or less. When they were abandoned their metal frames were difficult to remove and were often left in place until removed during carriageway maintenance. Temporary pneumatic detectors were commonly pinned to the surface for traffic counting. They needed weekly inspection to ensure that the pins and clips were secure. The clips, or the whole tube, were replaced if necessary. After a short time they deformed a flexible road surface.

Tribo-electric detectors are used in a few specialist cases; they are similar to pneumatic detectors, comprising a line across the road, but the sensitive element is more securely protected in a slot.

The commonest detectors are and will continue to be induction loop detectors (Fig. 6.3), laid in slots cut 100 mm (less in concrete) into the surface. They may appear as 2 m rectangles, diamonds 2 m across or chevrons 1 m wide, covering as much of a traffic lane or approach as is necessary. Commonly, three detectors per lane occur in the last 40 m of each approach and may be serviced via feeder cables laid in one or more carriageway slots leading to the traffic signal controller in which the electronic equipment is housed. Occasionally the distance from the controller or the number of detectors is too great and a supplementary pillar is provided on the footway for the electronics. One detector type, not used in the UK, has the electronics permanently buried in the carriageway.

Microwave (doppler radar operation) vehicle detectors may be provided at pelican crossings and are standard for road works signals. They point in the direction of the oncoming traffic and must be accurately aligned to detect vehicles at the correct distance (0–40 m). They are cheaper than

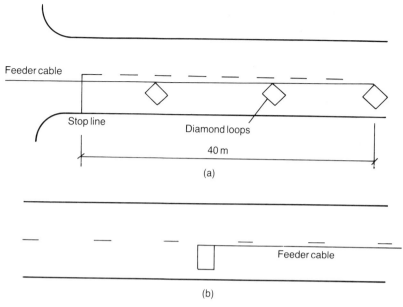

Fig. 6.3. Loop detector patterns for standard British traffic control systems: (a) 'System D' loops at junction; (b) loop for SCOOT control system

induction loops because of the absence of a connecting cable, and they are not exposed to any carriageway movement or damage, but their traffic detection performance is imprecise.

Ultrasonic detectors are common in Japan and find specialist application elsewhere. They are mounted overhead, thus requiring a special pole that may be unsightly. Although immune to carriageway problems, they have difficulties of their own. The detection zone is deflected by wind acting both on the support and on the sound waves, and they suffer interference from traffic noise.

Infra-red detectors are now being developed in the UK. They can be mounted to face along or across the road and detect vehicles occupying a defined zone of road as seen from their position. It is too early to give any idea of their maintenance requirements.

Detectors do not always occur close to junctions. They may be provided up to 200 m away to classify traffic speeds on the approach. They may occur throughout a street network to measure traffic flows or detect queues for a UTC system. They may occur on streets or motorways for regular traffic surveying purposes; in this case they may be controlled from a free-standing battery-powered traffic counter, or the counter may have data transmission to a central point.

6.6.2. Maintenance requirements

Detector faults are responsible for much system underperformance. They are usually under-reported, misunderstood and poorly repaired. The

Greater London Council pioneered improvements in specification, installation and maintenance techniques of induction loop detectors following the discovery that half its junctions had detector faults.[6.7] Although it was commonly thought that these faults were attributable to carriageway movement and failure (often due to statutory undertakers' activities), study showed that the then approved detector design was inherently unable to cope with normal climatic variation.

Apart from the introduction of self-tuning electronics, the specification insists on the use of robust cable, full depth properly cleaned slots, careful back-filling of the slots and a proprietary impregnated heat-shrunk joint with the feeder cable. Special treatment was specified when crossing beneath kerbs. A proportion of joints is excavated as quality control of installation.

Since similar care is required for replacements during maintenance, there should be a special section of the maintenance contract directed to a specialist detector team, if necessary provided by a specialist contractor. Detector fault rectification should still be subject to contractual performance controls, although clearly longer, say a week, must be allowed for detector loop replacement.

A vital requirement is to monitor detector operation, since poor performance caused by detector faults is not readily understood by motorists and the police. Modern signal controllers contain detector fault monitoring logic; in essence, if the detector is not operated in a given period the fault flag is set and the fault lamp lit on the controller case. The detectors are designed to fail when they are in the 'on' condition, and this is also monitored. Remote monitoring systems have the advantage that this information is immediately used to instigate further investigation and rectification.

6.6.3. Pedestrian push-buttons

Pedestrian push-buttons suffer many of the same problems as detectors. Although failure to operate is apparent to pedestrians, they do not understand the significance of the 'Wait' light and may think that some other feature of the traffic signal control has been set to their detriment. More usually, the button fails permanently 'on', thereby causing traffic delays in response to non-existent pedestrians.

The key solution is again monitoring, by the signal controller or by remote monitoring system. Earlier UTC systems can be set to monitor pedestrian push-buttons by noting the occasions when particular signal phases appear and relating this to time of day (there should not be too many pedestrians present in the middle of the night).

6.7. Interconnections

6.7.1. Electricity supply

In the UK the electricity supply is the area Electricity Board's responsibility. Service is satisfactory, apart from some delays in provision. The supply may include provision of an earth connection, the integrity of which is vital. Power supply failure is unusual.

6.7.2. Local cabling

All junctions require cabling between the signal controller and the signal heads. In the UK these cables are 'daisy-chained' from pole to pole, and one route to each aspect is adequate. There may also be signal cables from detectors, push-buttons and links to other controllers. These should ideally be in separate cables from those carrying mains voltage to the signal aspects, but may be in the same ducts.

Standard armoured multi-core signal cable is used for all purposes, laid direct in the ground under footways and in ducts under carriageways.

The life of the cable network may exceed that of other junction equipment. Recabling is expensive and undertaken reluctantly. However, deterioration of insulation can seriously affect the green–green conflict monitoring circuitry in the signal controller and must be rectified. Similarly, deterioration of earth connections has this effect and can cause signal aspects to light feebly or when they should not. The earth connection is carried round the junction on the cable network, since ground resistance is too unpredictable to earth reliably the signal poles. It is usual to specify spare cable cores, which can be used to accommodate future expansion or to replace a faulty core without having to recable. Otherwise fault repair times can be extended.

6.7.3. Data communication

The UTC systems require longer distance communication. In a few systems dedicated cables are used, but more usually circuits are rented on the British Telecom or other telephone network. These are interfaced by in-station and out-station data transmission units. Access by telephone engineers has to be allowed, and the controller design has to be approved, particularly in respect of protection of live parts.

Circuit faults should in no circumstances exceed one day's loss per year. Even this can be serious in circumstances where several junctions depend on one circuit to the central computer. In spite of agreements for priority service it is frequently difficult to achieve prompt fault rectification. An UTC organization should charge a competent manager with the task of liaising with the telephone company. Such liaison involves identifying knowledgeable contacts in all relevant parts of the telephone network.

Some UTC systems and most remote monitoring systems use the PSTN. An advantage is greater reliability since only the circuit from the traffic signal controller to the nearest exchange is dedicated to this use. Other circuits in the network are shared with other users so that there is adequate service even when faulty circuits are taken out of use.

6.8. Computer maintenance

6.8.1. Configuration precautions

This section is of course applicable only to UTC and remote monitoring systems with central computers. For many years doubts over computer reliability led to provision of duplicate computers. This had additional advantages of allowing software development and of running off-line signal optimization or administrative programs on the spare computer.

Great care is necessary in such systems to ensure that the back-up computer is provided with up-to-date data at the moment of takeover — in many systems this was not the case and the standby computer had to restart the system with consequent short-term dislocation of signal timings. With the increase in computer reliability the standby requirement became less necessary. With the decrease of computer cost, there is now less need to share computers between users. It is therefore becoming less common for new systems to have specific standby computers.

Standby is nowadays available in the signal controllers themselves, since they have a substantial library of plans to provide reasonably efficient standby control.

It is also becoming more common to have a central office with several interconnected computers assigned to different tasks. While this does not provide a standby arrangement there is more likely to be a suitable spare computer available in the event of long-term failure. In any case, since relatively standard computers are now used, a replacement may be obtainable and spare parts should be more readily available.

It is important that failures should be safe. Since data transmission failure must always be guarded against by the local signal controllers, computer switch off is readily handled. More difficult faults are those related to data corruption. In these cases the computer may send erroneous instructions to the local signal controller. Although blatantly unsafe conditions (such as conflicting green displays) are avoided by the local controller, some highly undesirable conditions can arise; these may include the signals being 'stuck' and not changing. To guard against these eventualities the computer program contains overlapping 'watchdog' checks. It is also desirable to provide an obvious switch so that police or security staff can, as a last resort, switch off.

6.8.2. Computer advantages

Computers can materially assist traffic signal maintenance. The recording and automatic reaction to signal faults has already been mentioned. An interconnected computer system can readily contain a traffic signal database covering both permanent and on-line information. It is therefore possible, with or without operator intervention, for the computer to instigate regular checks of numerous aspects of controller and system performance. When a fault has been detected, remedial action can be put in hand, both by initiating call out and by selecting fall-back control settings.

Good data capture can be built into such a system and this further enhances the computer's ability to analyse fault performance statistically and therefore identify significant trends.

6.9. Physical damage

6.9.1. Roadworks

Roadworks have long been accused of damaging vehicle detectors and other equipment. The effects are real even if they have at times been exaggerated.

Excavations damage cables. Loop detectors are particularly vulnerable. They cannot be replaced at exactly the same site when there is a risk of serious carriageway instability. It is usually adequate, and acceptable in traffic control terms, for the loop to be moved or reshaped to avoid the excavation. Such a move does require liaison with the traffic engineer who will have a better understanding of traffic control implications and may wish to alter some control settings. Some traffic authorities mark the corners of induction loops to discourage statutory undertakers from damaging them.

Excavations can also damage cables to signal poles, linking cables between junctions, and circuits (particularly dedicated ones) to UTC centres. Good organization is necessary to ensure that repairs are made promptly; these problems have crippled some systems for years.

Burning-off and resurfacing may damage induction loops. They should be fully tested after such an operation and if necessary recut.

6.9.2. Traffic accidents

Signal poles are frequently hit in traffic accidents. Prompt attendance may be necessary to protect live cables. Once this is done, and provided sufficient poles remain to provide safe control the signals may be switched on again. If the pole is merely leaning, a suitable contractor may jack it vertical; cable insulation should be checked, and any other appropriate examination made.

Signal controllers in the UK are mounted in surprisingly vulnerable positions on footway edges. This is intended to avoid conflict with building owners, to minimize circuit lengths and to allow a signal maintenance engineer to see the signal aspects and traffic movements when diagnosing faults or altering settings. Loss of a signal controller is usually serious. A complex controller may be difficult to replace quickly. It is therefore good practice to keep spare controllers of each type in use for this purpose. Ideally, these should be of the largest version used, and configuration information should be kept available to minimize the time to replace.

6.9.3. Liability

If the culprit damaging signal control equipment can be identified, reimbursement can be claimed. For traffic accidents this is successful in only a minority of cases. For excavation damage it is seldom attempted, although useful on occasion as a salutary reminder to contractors and statutory authorities.

6.10. Legal issues

It is common for parties to an accident at traffic signals to claim that the signals contributed to the accident. Usually the claim is that simultaneous greens were displayed. This is highly unlikely considering the duplicated conflict monitoring in the signal controller — in the UK, conflict monitoring circuitry is itself checked at frequent intervals. An honest engineer may, however, admit that he cannot be absolutely certain that such a condition had not occurred.

Unfortunately, witnesses may state that they saw conflicting green displays. Such a statement may well carry more weight with a court than properly assessed risks of a well-designed system. Such witnesses are often badly situated to make such statements anyway. Often they were not in a position to see both the claimed conflicting aspects (a point to pick up in cross-examination), and had judged vehicle movements instead. It is of course quite likely that vehicles could pass a signal at amber or even red and therefore mislead the witness.

In such circumstances, the Department of Transport's standards and approval procedures can be called in aid. These have been designed explicitly to ensure that signal equipment is safe, and have been backed by actual tests and experience. For this approach to succeed it is essential that all the normal standards have been followed.

6.11. Closed-circuit television
6.11.1. Installation

Many UTC systems and the control of motorways, bridges and tunnels are frequently assisted with closed-circuit television (CCTV). This comprises cameras located at good viewpoints on buildings or on special masts 6–11 m high. Many of these cameras are mounted to provide rotation in two dimensions (pan and tilt) and have zoom lenses. They have various other controls for their electronics and for wiping the cover glass. They are connected via high-grade circuits (often fibre optic) to the control centre. Some circuit capacity is used in the reverse direction for control purposes.

Sometimes each camera is connected to a single monitor in the control room. More usually circuits are switched, either remotely to economize on circuit capacity, or within the control room(s) so that the pictures can appear to and be controlled by the desired operators.

6.11.2. Maintenance

Considerable routine and call-out maintenance is required. It is generally difficult to keep the camera tubes in good condition (they are adversely affected by street and vehicle lights) and various other detailed adjustments have to be made. Although most of the camera electronics are detached and located in convenient positions, access to the cameras themselves is a problem.

The normal maintenance arrangement is again contractual, using the supplier's specialists. Often the terms offered by the supplier are inadequate and expensive, so that compromise is involved. Fortunately, in only a few installations such as tidal flow systems is the CCTV essential for normal operations; hence the lower level of reliability can be tolerated.

6.12. Motorway control systems
6.12.1. Provision

The systems for motorway control are similar to those for tunnels and bridges. In all cases there is controlled ownership of the road. The Department of Transport owns and has designed much of the UK motorway control equipment in some detail. Some 2000 specifications are listed in Ref. 6.2.

The equipment comprises

(a)   matrix signals mounted on gantries (urban) or in the central reservation (rural); the pattern of legends on adjacent signals is automatically controlled by one of the central control computers in response to the operator keying in his requirements for one signal; correct signal operation is regularly monitored by the computers

(b)   motorist aid telephones on the hard shoulder, giving automatic connection to the police control centre

(c)   detector stations for recording traffic patterns and, more recently, detecting congestion to warn the police to set the signals

(d)   CCTV monitoring of the more critical junctions or sections of road

(e)   weather stations to detect the presence of fog or ice

(f)   a multi-circuit communication system (more recently fibre optic) laid along all motorways to interconnect the above equipment and the control computers

(g)   control centres for each police force and section of motorway

(h)   five pairs of networked computers strategically located on the communications network to be able to service the above equipment, even when some of them are faulty

6.12.2. Maintenance

Some of the specifications[6.2] deal with provisions specifically for maintenance. The actual maintenance is usually by contract direct to the Department of Transport. Maintenance and reliability figures have not generally been published.

6.13. Traffic signals at roadworks

6.13.1. Equipment

Similar equipment is provided to control shuttle working of general traffic at temporary roadworks, and to control the conflict between general traffic and construction plant at road construction sites. The main difference is the signal poles, which are on tripods for the former and sunk in the ground for the latter.

Roadworks traffic signals suffer some of the harshest environmental conditions for traffic signal equipment. The equipment usually comprises two to four sets of signal aspects. Each signal pole has a microwave vehicle detector so as to give and retain right of way (within pre-set periods) for any moving traffic (a nudge circuit periodically provides right of way in case an approaching vehicle has gone undetected). The controller is a small box or may be within one of the signal aspects, and the whole is connected together with as many 100 m multicore cables as necessary. Power at industrial voltage (centre-point earthed at 110 V for safety) is provided by an internal combustion engine generator or transformed from the mains. A notice board advises drivers where to stop and should be located as close as traffic conditions permit to the signals so that the detectors function properly.

6.13.2. Maintenance

The generator requires periodic lubrication. All the equipment requires cleaning. Otherwise, maintenance is largely by repair of obvious faults. The major difficulty is in having the timings correctly set, often by staff unfamiliar with the niceties of traffic control. As the length of the protected area varies, the settings should be changed to suit, but frequently are not. Some counties run special inspection teams to attempt to raise the standard of roadworks signalling. Some of the suppliers cooperate with these schemes.

References

6.1. BRITISH STANDARDS INSTITUTION. *Specification for road traffic signals.* BS 505: 1971. BSI, London.

6.2. DEPARTMENT OF TRANSPORT. Movement control circular. *MCS Circular 206/207.* Traffic Control Division, Bristol, 1986 (and later).

6.3. HUDDART K.W. Experience in new arrangements for traffic signal maintenance. *PTRC Summer Annual Meeting.* University of Sussex, 1972.

6.4. DEPARTMENT OF TRANSPORT. All-purpose trunk roads maintenance of traffic signals. *Departmental standard TD 24/86.* London, 1986.

6.5. DEPARTMENT OF TRANSPORT. *Draft model invitation to tender for authorities inviting tenders for the maintenance of traffic signal installations.* Letter of 27 November, London, 1981.

6.6. BLASE J.H. Computer aids to large-scale traffic signal maintenance. *Traff. Engng Control*, 1979, **40**, No. 7, July, 341–347.

6.7. HEAD J.R.H. A new specification for inductive loop detectors *Traff. Engng Control*, 1982, **23**, No. 4, April, 186–189, 199.

6.8. OASTLER K.H.S. Maintenance of traffic signals in London. *Traff. Engng Control*, 1985, **26**, No. 3, March, 104–108.

6.9. DEPARTMENT OF TRANSPORT. *Microprocessor based traffic signal controller for isolated linked and urban traffic control installations.* MCE 0141, Traffic Control Division, Bristol, 1984.

6.10. *The Traffic Signs Regulations and General Directions.* Her Majesty's Stationery Office, London, 1981.

7

Aids to movement

7.1. General considerations

The annual carnage on Britain's roads is second only to heart disease in the number of lives lost and cannot be regarded with equanimity by any civilized society. Taking account of the age groups involved, it is indeed surprising that a public outcry is not more in evidence. As discussed in Chapter 9, accident statistics are likely to grossly underestimate the number of conflicts and, therefore, the overall costs of vehicular accidents to the community.

The aims of a highway transport system are for

(a) a safe highway environment
(b) a reasonable level of comfort
(c) optimum speed consistent with (a) and (b) and in relation to legal and community restraints
(d) minimum outlay on energy, the costs of wear and tear on machinery, and the highway and its furniture.

Some of the variables affecting the achievement of the above aims include

(a) the driver's skill and condition
(b) vehicle capability and condition
(c) the quality of the highway as designed and its maintenance
(d) traffic types and density
(e) prevailing weather conditions
(f) transmission and reception of necessary information.

The contributions that can be made by maintenance organizations are now considered.

Driver skills are checked at the initial test in terms of the ability to control the vehicle safely and show knowledge of the highway code. Great dependence is placed on the subsequent acquisition of practical experience in order to deal adequately with the demanding needs of urban or motorway traffic situations. Eyesight and concentration are also vital factors in the ability of drivers to recognize and respond to information from other vehicles and highway systems. Impairment of these faculties, whether for health reasons or from the all too frequent abuse of stimulants, becomes a police matter after an accident but, because many drivers are in fact unaware or unwilling to acknowledge the erosion of their skill, highway systems must be arranged to minimize the consequences. It is established that driver skill is a significant contributory factor in the majority of accidents, but the means of improving such skill at an acceptable cost has so far eluded the authorities. Positive results are being achieved however from the study of accident data collected by the police and applied by highway engineers to identify causes and if possible to devise methods of improving sites showing a recognizable problem. Techniques and equipment used in these studies are illustrated in Chapter 8.

Advances in vehicle design and tyre technology have produced transport with much improved performance, and research into the mechanics of collision has led to the use of seat belts and the provisions of crushable zones in the modern car, giving some protection to occupants. The disparity in size and weight of commercial vehicles and cars nevertheless results in major damage in accident events, especially on high speed roads and in inclement weather. The maintenance of information systems is of critical importance in reducing the risk of late decisions by drivers.

The condition of the vehicle, although subject to regular checks, is known to suffer from damage caused by lack of carriageway repair. Such 'hidden costs' are at present not taken into account in the justification of general maintenance budgets, but are none the less real costs to the community. A proportion of accidents are caused by mechanical failure in the vehicle, and where this results in damage to highway property, there is again an influence on the maintenance engineers workload.

Highway design clearly affects capacity, and the ease with which traffic negotiates the system. Awareness of evolving problems, either in materials or the recognition of accident 'black spots' should be cultivated by the maintenance engineer, who often has the job of carrying out minor modifications. Valuable progress can be made by ensuring that this sort of information is recorded and fed back to design staff. Improvements (e.g. to skid resistance to eliminate an accident black spot) must be recorded permanently in a database that is available to engineers planning future resurfacing work, so that an appraisal of the effectiveness of such measures can be made.

Traffic types and density have a significant effect on the longevity of a highway, and therefore on the frequency of maintenance necessary. Few long journeys can now be undertaken without encountering the delays caused by maintenance works, and this can be regarded as an unavoidable feature of life in the future. In the context of the massive flow of traffic, most people can understand the nature of the problem, whilst not necessarily sympathizing with some of the methods and timescales. Among engineers, there is rising concern about the damage being done to the less comprehensively designed roads, which all too often are being subjected to the passage of commercial vehicles far larger and heavier than envisaged when such roads were built. The longitudinal cracking and edge damage are clear to all, but what may be less evident is that critical amounts of damage can occur after only a few passes of the larger vehicles. In severe cases, full and costly reconstruction of the carriageway becomes necessary. In some areas, this problem is so acute that the suggestion was made that some roads be removed from public liability. Knowledge of the load spectrum commonly using the road network, including the level of use by abnormal indivisible loads, referred to in Chapter 11, is clearly of interest to the maintenance engineer, and a useful development is the portable weighing equipment with computerized recording facilities, on which research has been done by the Transport and Road Research Laboratory (TRRL).[7.1.]

Weather conditions can have a marked effect on traffic flow, due in part to the effects on visibility, and also on the important aspects of vehicle control such as steering and braking. Problems are most severe in the winter months, as dealt with in Chapter 10, but, at all times, the highway authority has a duty to ensure safety. Not least among the available safeguards is the system of temporary and permanent signs detailed in the Traffic Signs Manual,[7.2] which gives guidance on the type, style and positioning of signs to suit most circumstances. It should be noted that many of the signs and markings require covering Traffic Orders, and that the accuracy of placing, in accordance with such orders, is in some cases critical.

From these general considerations, it is clear that the safety and enjoyment of driving is related to the quality of engineering, and the attention given to maintenance of the many facets that make up the highway environment. Road signs, placed to warn drivers of approaching potential hazards, indicate regulatory control, or supply local amenity information, form a valuable aid to travel, but care must be exercised to avoid a confusing multiplicity of signing.

In the maintenance context, repair of signs becomes necessary due to

(a) accident damage
(b) vandalism
(c) changes resulting from new works
(d) deterioration due to age or weathering.

Activities will be considered under the headings road markings, signs mounted on posts and structures, and temporary signs.

7.2. Road markings

Transport and Road Research Laboratory studies[7.3] indicate that 'the contribution to safety, and to improved traffic flow, made by white lines, markings, and reflective studs, makes them now an indispensible feature of modern roads', a conclusion which is echoed by the Organisation for Economic Cooperation and Development (OECD). The effectiveness of all lining depends on cleanliness, achieved by regular street cleansing, and the action of rainfall and vehicular movement. This is essential to maintain the reflective properties of the solid glass beads (SGB, until recently called ballotini) which can be incorporated in, and applied on to surface markings. SGBs improve night time visibility by picking up and reflecting vehicle headlights, in much the same way as the lenses in reflective road studs perform. Solid glass beads should only be used with white road markings, since there is no necessity to see yellow 'no parking' markings quickly at night. However, there is an exception, this being the yellow transverse bar markings used at high speed approaches to roundabouts, in which SGBs and also calcined bauxite, to improve skidding resistance, are incorporated. A specification for solid glass beads is included in BS 6088.[7.4]

A summary of the desirable qualities for road markings would include

(*a*) high visibility at all times
(*b*) durability compatible with cost
(*c*) acceptable antiskid properties
(*d*) ease of application
(*e*) rapid drying
(*f*) acceptable shelf life for storage
(*g*) application methods that ensure the safety of operatives.

7.3. Materials for lining and road markings

7.3.1. Road paint

Road paint is usually a petroleum based pigmented liquid, applied in a wet film thickness of some 400 microns (0·4 mm) and offering quick drying characteristics of between 5 and 15 minutes, depending on weather conditions and formulation. Application is normally by machine mounted spray equipment, either by an air spray fitted with masking discs, or by an airless spray, in which the pressurized liquid and special nozzles give a clean edged result without masking discs.

Both types can be pedestrian controlled or truck mounted, and can be fitted with reflective bead dispensers. Specifications and tests for road paint are given in BS 6044.[7.5] The use of brushes or aerosol dispensers is also practicable for limited areas of paint. Paint is cheaper than thermoplastic markings, and is particularly suited to sites where a build up of thickness is to be avoided, e.g. where water would be trapped, or for reasons of economy, such as at roadworks, or for seasonal parking restrictions where a long life is not required. A summary of specifications for road marking materials is given in Table 7.1.

7.3.2. Thermoplastic markings

Thermoplastic markings are composed of a mixture of aggregates, pigment, SGBs, and a plasticized resin, which binds the components and acts as an adhesive to the surface. Delivered in block or powder form, the material is heated to a temperature between 150°C and 180°C in a boiler, and is usually applied to the surface, using hand-held screed boxes (Fig. 7.1), to a thickness in the range 1·5 to 5 mm. Once applied, the material solidifies within 60 seconds, allowing almost immediate trafficking. Special shapes (e.g. cycle lane logos) are formed with the aid of pre-cut stencils. Most line marking is applied by lorry mounted spray machines (Fig. 7.2), working with the material at a temperature of about 200°C, and to a minimum specified thickness of 1·5 mm. The lorry travels at a speed of 8–10 km/h, and since the line cools and sets rapidly, minimum traffic disruption is caused. Control of thickness and definition is difficult with this type of equipment, and an alternative is the pumped extruded line machine. Although slower, typically at 4 km/h, this machine applies a line some 3 mm thick with good definition of the edges, but due to the greater thickness of material, cooling is slower and a water spray is needed to reduce the risk of 'pick up' by following vehicles. These machines are increasing in popularity, and are likely to displace the more common spray marking types. British Standard 3262 (Parts 1–3)[7.6] covers the specification, site assessment, and routine applications of hot applied thermoplastic road markings.

7.3.3. Pre-formed pliable plastic markings

Pre-formed pliable plastic markings are also available, some being self adhesive, and these types have the advantage of ease of application, requiring no specialized equipment or skilled labour. These markings are,

Fig. 7.1 (left). Hand operated thermoplastic application machine

Fig. 7.2 (below). Major sprayplastic machine

Table 7.1. Summary of specification for road marking materials*

THERMOPLASTIC

Test	Standard	Specification	Reason
Laboratory			
Binder content	18–22%	BS 3262[7.6]	Adhesion, durability
Luminance	70 white, 50 yellow		Daytime visibility
Heat stability	65 white, 45 yellow		Stability of colour after heating
			Safety
Skid resistance	45 minimum		Reflective ability/ night-time visibility
Glass bead content	20%		
Road trials:	Class A 24 months	BS 3262[7.6]	Durability
certification	Class B 12 months	BS 3262[7.6]	Durability
Application			
(a) Resin based products	BS3262[7.6]	Durability	
Spray 1·5 mm thick (white)			
Spray 0·8 mm thick (yellow)			
Screed 2·5 mm thick (white)			
(b) Rosin based products			Durability
Spray 2·0 mm thick			
Screed 3·5 mm thick			Durability
(c) All products		DTp Specification for Highway Works[†]	Durability
2–5 mm thick (except yellow)			

PAINT

Laboratory Bead retention	> 90%	BS 6044[7.5]	Night-time retroreflectivity
Luminance	83 white, 58 yellow		Daytime visibility
Hiding power	> 90% white, > 80% yellow		Covering quality of paint
No pick-up	< 15 min at 350 μm		Maximum drying time
Skid resistance	45 minimum		Safety
Road trials: certification	Class A 12 months	BS 6044	Durability
	Class B 6 months	BS 6044	Durability
Application	315–400 μm thick	DTp Specification for Highway Works†	Durability

* Summary only of the main standards and specifications. Only white products are tested in the road trials. BS 381C defines permitted colours, in particular for yellow. No standards exist for pre-formed materials. A British Standard guideline is under consideration for removable tapes (not to be confused with cheaper, non-reinforced temporary tapes). Removable tapes are specified for use at roadworks. Their use on DTp roads has to be approved by the Department after road trials.

† DTp Specification for Highway Works requires that only Class A materials be used.

however, relatively expensive, and tend to be reserved for situations where their particular advantages outweigh the extra cost, an example being at motorway contraflow sites, where high reflectance and quick removal are valuable properties. Many pedestrian crossings have been installed using this type of material, and good service life has been achieved, provided that detachments were seen and attended to promptly; in general, though, this material forms a small element of the road marking market.

7.3.4. Life of road markings

Studies by the TRRL, on materials used on a heavily trafficked, straight running road, indicate the following life expectancies

(a) inset thermoplastic (mastic): about five years
(b) superimposed plastic strip: about eight to ten years
(c) superimposed thermoplastic: one to two years
(d) sprayed thermoplastic: one to two years
(e) paint: less than one year, probably three to six months, according to the density of traffic.

Fig. 7.3. Marking removal — hot air lance

7.4. Removal of road markings

During periods of roadworks, temporary traffic diversions, or because existing markings have become worn or redundant, road markings may need to be removed or obscured, either temporarily or permanently. This can be achieved by

(a) burning off with a hot air lance (not to be recommended where the public are close to the works, as the fumes are toxic) (Fig. 7.3)

(b) scabbling with mechanical flails or multi-head scabbling machine. This can remove most of the existing line, even when a build up of material occurs due to successive lining operations, but is not able to completely remove all marking material from the interstices of the surfacing. The resulting surface after treatment forms a good key for new markings, and the method can also be used to clean existing markings obscured by oil and rubber deposits

(c) obliteration of existing markings using black paint or thermoplastic. This is a cheap and quick method, but has the disadvantage of a relatively short life, and if not regularly inspected could lead to

Table 7.2. Inspection of road markings and studs

Type of carriageway*	Inspection intervals (markings)		
	Paint	Thermoplastic	
		Spray applied	Screed applied
Single carriageway roads			
7·3 m up to 10 000 vpd†	1 year	2 years	2 years
7·3 m over 10 000 vpd	6 months	1 year	1 year
10·0 m up to 15 000 vpd	1 year	2 years	2 years
10·0 m over 15 000 vpd	6 months	1 year	1 year
Dual carriageway roads			
Two lanes up to 20 000 vpd	1 year	2 years	2 years
Two lanes over 20 000 vpd	6 months	1 year	1 year
Three lanes up to 30 000 vpd	1 year	2 years	2 years
Three lanes over 30 000 vpd	6 months	1 year	1 year
Road studs			
Fixture	During lane closures for other purposes unless faults occur in significant groupings, in which case specific closures for inspection of studs is necessary		
Reflective conspicuity	To be checked annually during the hours of darkness (usually with markings and signs).		

* Traffic flows given represent the annual average daily (24 hours) flow in both directions.
† Vehicles per day.

the original line or sign reappearing. The finished result looks untidy

(d) obliteration of the original marking, temporarily or permanently, using black preformed tapes

(e) other methods, which include the use of shot or grit blasting, and controlled high pressure water equipment.

The above methods of removal will all be visible to some extent, unless the marking is being overlayed by new material. Skill is needed to try and simulate the texture of the adjacent road surface when removing markings, otherwise the smoothness will be misleading to motorists in wet or sunny conditions and under artificial lighting, and such surfaces can be hazardous to two-wheeled vehicles in the wet.

7.5. Inspection of markings

Maintenance routines must include regular inspections of all road markings, minimum recommended frequencies being shown in Table 7.2 for Department of Transport roads. For motorways and trunk roads, two categories of action are defined by the Department of Transport[7.7]

(a) urgent — requiring action within 28 days, e.g. defective, 'Stop' or 'Give Way' signs, or double continuous white lines

(b) less urgent — not requiring action for at least six months, and to be collected for inclusion in a programme of planned routine maintenance.

The LAA Code of Good Practice[7.8] does not stipulate categories of defect and timescales for repair, but clearly indicates that important markings and signs are to be replaced as soon as possible within the prevailing budgetary constraints.

7.6. Skid resistance of markings

All materials used in the carriageway wearing course need adequate skid resistance properties, especially where substantial areas are involved. Two-wheeled vehicles are particularly at risk from abrupt changes in surface characteristics. Inevitably, with the currently available materials, the high speed skid resistance of road markings must be a compromise, because to be clearly visible, the marking must be relatively smooth, and therefore a texture depth comparable with that normally required for, say, hot rolled asphalt, cannot be achieved.

Department of Transport Standard TD 26/86[7.9] covers the maintenance of road markings on trunk roads and motorways. The approach taken is to measure the skid resistance of only those markings that could be associated with above average accident rates. The small areas involved in road markings means that the only practical method of obtaining comparative values is by using the TRRL Pendulum Tester. According to perceived risk, the value required for longitudinal lines is greater than 45, that for large areas of letters, numerals or arrows is greater than 55, and that for transverse yellow bar markings at high speed approaches to roundabouts is greater than 65.

The specification for Highway Works[7.10] specifies a skid resistance value for road markings of not less than 45, except in certain locations, where the designer may select a value of not less than 55. It is assumed that all these values refer to measurements taken in the laboratory on materials proposed for use, rather than in situ field measurements of the material in service. Details of the method of carrying out the test are given in BS 3262 (Appendix G)[7.6] and the use of the portable skid resistance tester is described in Research Note 27.[7.11]

7.7. Reflecting road studs

Road studs are used individually, or in combination with line markings, as a means of demarcation, as for instance on the approach side of pedestrian crossings, and in the case of reflectorized studs to increase the visibility of marking to motorists after dark. The use of studs shall be in accordance with General Direction 31 of the Traffic Signs Regulations and General Directions 1981 (Statutory Instrument 1981, No. 859) and the guidance given in the Traffic Signs Manual, Chapter 5. All studs for use in this country shall be subject to Department of Transport approval for both design and method of fixing, and must satisfy the requirements laid down in BS 873 (Part 4),[7.12] together with road trials of 12 months for permanent studs and three months for temporary studs. A list of the types of stud which are currently acceptable is given in the appendix to Circular Roads 7/84,[7.13] and is shown in Table 7.3.

Attention is drawn to the care needed in choosing an appropriate type, bearing in mind possible difficulties due to the use of snow ploughs in some areas, the regularity of use by cyclists, and the overall expected traffic flow on the road. Particular emphasis is placed on the method of fixing, which must be in accordance with the manufacturer's agreed instructions, in order to avoid the risk of loosened studs becoming a traffic hazard for which the maintaining authority could be liable.

7.8. Road signs

Road signs form a large and valuable part of highway 'aids to movement', and may be grouped under the headings

(a) regulatory signs — either mandatory or prohibitive
(b) warning signs
(c) informatory signs.

The Traffic Signs Manual[7.2] gives details of the requirements for design, positioning and illumination of the above signs, together with instructions concerning any necessary approvals for type and size. The highway authority has a duty to provide necessary signs.

Sign maintenance comprises:

(a) periodic cleansing
(b) repair of accident damage
(c) replacement of lighting components
(d) cyclic painting of frames and supporting structures.

Table 7.3. List of approved road studs incorporating reflectors

Type*	Supplied by	Approved for use on	Specified in manufacturer's drawing no.	Approved fixing instructions
Catseyes	Reflecting Roadstuds Ltd. Boothtown, Halifax, West Yorkshire: tel. Halifax (0422) 60208	All markings on all roads except for the right hand edge carriageway markings where amber studs are required	† RRL 190 (standard or short type) † RRL 191 (long type) † RRL 192 (square type) RRL 265 (angle type) RRL 266 (short type) RRL 267 (long type) RRL 272 (flush kerb type)	Paving Instructions 1984 edition (red)
Stimsonite 88	Amerace Ltd. Brook House, Northbrook Street, Newbury, Berks RG13 1AH: tel. Newbury (0635) 4919	All roads, but see paragraph 5 of Circular‡	SK 919 Issue C	IPM July 1984 (supersedes February 1975)
Catastud	Berger Traffic Markings Ltd. Fossway, Midsomer Norton, Bath BA3 4AY: tel. Midsomer Norton (0761) 414824	All roads, but see paragraph 5 of Circular‡	MK 1/CS/001	Berger Document No. 17484
Catastud Deep Fix Epoxy	Berger Traffic Markings Ltd. Fossway, Midsomer Norton, Bath BA3 4AY: tel. Midsomer Norton (0761) 414824	All roads, but see paragraph 5 of Circular‡	30947A — body 30947B — receptor 30947C — screw	Berger Document No. 17484A
Prismo II	Prismo Universal Ltd. Rowfant, Crawley, West Sussex RH1D 4NF: tel. Copthorne (0342) 714949	All markings on all roads, but see paragraph 5 of this Circular‡	M 2448/1 Issue E	Prismo Document No. PR II 1001
CTM — hot melt adhesive type	Berger Traffic Markings Ltd. Fossway, Midsomer Norton, Bath BA3 4AY: tel. Midsomer Norton (0761) 414824	All roads as temporary reflecting studs, but see paragraph 5 of this Circular‡	19484	Berger Document No. 9484
CTM — self adhesive type	Berger Traffic Markings Ltd. Fossway, Midsomer Norton, Bath BA3 4AY: tel. Midsomer Norton (0761) 41824	All roads as temporary reflecting studs, but see paragraph 5 of this Circular‡	19484A	Berger Document No. 9484A

*CTM: Contramark Temporary Marker.   †No longer in production.   ‡Department of Transport Circular Roads.

The object should be to keep all traffic signs legible and visible as far as possible at all times in relation to the road use and traffic speeds. Standards recommended in the LAA Code of Good Practice[7.8] are given in Table 7.4.

For trunk roads and motorways, advice on sign maintenance is given in the Department of Transport Departmental Standard TD/85.[7.14] Normally, much of the sign maintenance and inspection routine will be integrated with the programme of street lighting maintenance, described in detail in Chapter 5.

7.8.1. Access to signs

For all but the large gantry signs, described in Chapter 11, access will be by ladder or lorry-mounted platforms. In some cases lane closures will be needed, with the consequent temporary signing specified in Chapter 8 of the Traffic Signs Manual.

7.8.2. Visibility of signs

In addition to the cleaning of signs, highway authorities, in order to avoid possible claims following accidents and to enhance safety, must ensure that signs provided are clearly visible to highway users. Among steps to be taken are the removal of any obstructing foliage and the control of parking which may affect sight lines.

Table 7.4. Standards for sign maintenance as recommended in the LAA Code of Good Practice[7.8]

Illuminated signs and bollards	
Scouting for illumination	Winter every two weeks; summer every four weeks
Lamp changing	Burn to destruction
Internal inspection and cleansing	Annually, including supports
External cleaning	As required, but at least annually
Replacement and repair of damaged signs and bollards	To be made safe within 24 hours. Important warnings and regulatory signs to be permanently repaired as soon as possible
Painting of supports and frames	When required
Electrical tests	Not exceeding five yearly
Non-illuminated signs and bollards	
General condition	Inspection once per year after cleaning and after dark
Cleaning	As required, but at least annually
Replacement and repair of damaged signs	To be made safe within 24 hours, permanent repairs to be according to the degree of danger. Important warning and regulatory signs should be replaced as soon as possible
Painting of signs and supports	As required

7.8.3. Gantry signs

Gantry signs of the motorway type, spanning several lanes, require periodic structural examination, and should be included with other structures in the programme of registration and inspection, as described in Chapter 11. Such signs are likely to involve advance planning of maintenance and full lane closures. On high speed roads, illuminated early warning signs built into the system for such occasions, facilitates this work.

7.8.4. Temporary signs

Roadworks can increase the risk of accidents if not properly signed. The standards adopted should be in accordance with the Traffic Signs Manual, Chapter 8, and various subsequent amendments, but in all too many instances falls short. In the road environment, road cones can soon become dirty, and energy failures in battery powered lamps can rapidly reduce the effectiveness of warning systems, particularly in cold weather. Movement by passing vehicles, vandalism and theft are also a problem affecting temporary installations. Regular inspection, fuel and battery replacement, and lens cleaning, are, therefore, fundamental requirements when dealing with temporary works, together with the washing of advance warning cones and signs and the alignment of fenders and barriers.

7.9. Road cones and lamps

7.9.1. Road cones

Road cones, fitted with reflective sleeves, have become standard equipment for highway works, and offer a highly flexible means of directing traffic and delineating roadworks of all kinds. Deposited and collected from slow moving lorries, long lengths of coning can quickly be established. Detailed specifications are given in BS 873 (Part 8).[7.15]

7.9.2. Road lamps

Two main types of road lamp have been developed: oil lamps and battery powered lamps. Specifications for both types are given in BS 3143.[7.16] Of prime importance is that the power output from lamps is adequate and meets the required intensity and performance standards for the duration of the periods between inspections. In winter conditions, some battery lamps will have difficulty in reaching and maintaining these standards throughout a complete weekend for instance, and equipment trials should be conducted before relying on supplier's claims. Choice of lamps tends to be conditioned by the relatively high cost of replacement, since most lamps suffer from theft, damage from vehicles and vandalism, and hence have an operational life of as little as two to three weeks. Some protection is afforded if lamps can be adapted to be fixed to other items of plant, such as skips or timber baulks, to discourage casual removal.

7.10. Sign amendment

Ensuring that the information conveyed by signs is accurate may seem to be a statement of the obvious, but regular damage to bridges occurs where sub-standard headroom clearance is incorrectly shown on the approach signs, often where road resurfacing works have changed the carriageway levels. Such signs must be adjusted within a tolerance of 75 mm of the actual clearance available, allowance being made for the effects of lorry wheelbase and any sag in the profile of the road. Where bridges are subject to weight restriction or are undergoing repairs necessitating traffic control, advance signing over a wide area may be needed to reduce traffic disruption, and in some cases the assistance of the publicity media gives valuable advance warning and eases traffic difficulties.

7.11. Minor works signing

Minor roadworks, and typically the many trench operations of the Public Utility Companies, can create potential hazards for the road user if not properly signed. The speed of traffic and the type of road will govern the size of sign required, and the type needed is covered in the Traffic Signs Manual, Chapter 8, and later amendments. The duration of obstructions should be minimized, and this can sometimes be helped by the use of steel plates or temporary bridging devices, which can if necessary be fixed to the road surface. It is worth emphasizing that highway authorities should have a system of records for road opening applications, and efforts should be made to co-ordinate any series of operations in the same area to minimize the period of traffic disruption, and also the scale of damage to the road structure. In this respect, research is in hand in some areas to develop computer-aided record systems. The present liabilities for dealing with temporary and permanent reinstatement of Public Utility Authority trenches is likely to change if the recommendations of the Horne Report[7.17] are implemented.

7.12. Pedestrians and other groups

Included in 'aids to movement' are the needs of pedestrians and groups such as the disabled, cyclists and the special consideration to be given to facilitating the flow of public transport. Maintenance organizations will often be involved in the implementation of minor improvement schemes, and should also be given the opportunity to comment on the implications of schemes prepared by others, which affect the highway.

Examples of schemes which need comment from maintenance organizations, and which have effects on the future activities and costs of maintenance are as follows.

7.12.1. Bus lanes

Marked by a continuous white line, and signed to operate at prescribed times, these facilities are now a common feature of urban life. In London, many have been accentuated by the use of a surface dressing comprised of 10 mm red stone chippings applied on a resin binder (Fig. 7.4). Contra-flow lanes have also been constructed, with kerbs separating the opposing traffic streams. Due to the limited movement available to buses in these lanes, some problems were experienced with pushing of the asphalt surfacing. Among the remedies tried were the use of stiffer mixes, and also a special cement grouted macadam (see Chapter 3, Part II).

Fig. 7.4. Installation of 'red bus' lane using red chippings

7.12.2. Facilities for the disabled

Warranted attention has been drawn in recent years to the needs of the disabled, both in access and safety terms. Among the many needs, the following improvements have relevance to highways

- (*a*) dropped kerbs at crossing points
- (*b*) the provision, where possible, of ramped approaches to footbridges and subways
- (*c*) contoured paving at pedestrian crossings (see also Chapter 4)
- (*d*) improved control of pavement parking
- (*e*) improvement in the general standard of maintenance, particularly footway surfaces. This is important for all highway users, but can be of particular importance to the disabled.

7.12.3. Segregation

Accidents can sometimes be prevented or reduced by the introduction of segregated facilities for different classes of traffic, and this can also show advantages in the resulting flow. An example of this approach is the prohibition of pedestrians, cyclists and learner drivers from motorways. Similarly, paths restricted to use by cyclists offer some relief from the dangers inherent in main road travel, albeit with regular and critical areas of conflict at junctions. Guidance and control of pedestrians, particularly in busy urban shopping centres is often achieved using guardrailings, with the aim of directing pedestrians to the con-

trolled crossing points, subways or footbridges. The provision and maintenance of suitable signing, and a high standard of maintenance of
these facilities encourages their use, and removes any excuse for taking
risks unnecessarily.

7.12.4. Critical junctions and locations

Traffic congestion at key sites, such as bridges, tunnels and major junctions, soon leads to widespread and costly repercussions elsewhere
in the road system. At such sites, the provision and maintenance of
control and information equipment, as described in Chapter 6, can be of
considerable help in identifying problems, and allowing relieving action
to be taken. Other factors, which can reduce the impact and time taken
to deal with accidents, include for instance, effective fire fighting equipment and communication systems in tunnels, and contingency planning
to deal with accidents on elevated roads agreed between the highway
authority, police, and the emergency services. In many situations, the
availability of trained staff and resources, such as exist in maintenance
organizations, is a vital element in reducing both the effects of accidents
on traffic, and damage to property on or adjacent to the highway.

7.12.5. Anti-skid measures

In Chapters 8 and 9, the nature and consequence of highway anti-
skid measures are discussed, together with methods used to identify
and test prevailing conditions. In addition to providing a reduction in

Fig. 7.5. Application of calcined
bauxite anti-skid surfacing

Fig. 7.6. Application of slurry surface
dressing

the number of wet road skidding accidents, the application of improved road surfaces at junctions, crossings and sharp bends can be regarded as an aid to movement generally, and in both respects can be shown to be cost effective. At present, only the accident saving element is directly taken into account in scheme justifications. At the upper end of the scale among anti-skid treatments is calcined bauxite in an epoxy resin binder (Fig. 7.5) used as a surface dressing. The material gives long-term sideways force coefficients of 0·75, probably the highest value for natural materials, and offers a long service life of about ten years. Other treatments at lower initial cost include

(a) surface dressing by conventional methods, or slurry seals (Fig. 7.6); this is mainly limited to less heavily trafficked roads, although trials of more recent materials have taken place for trunk road and some main road use in London

(b) resurfacing with replacement wearing course, paying attention to chipping rate and quality

(c) retexturing by means of flails, grit or hot air blasting, according to the existing surfacing material; this treatment, however, may not restore a high skid resistance for a sustained period if aggregate polishing is the underlying problem.

7.13. Other highway measures

A number of other measures falling within the 'aids of movement' category and requiring maintenance are

(a) road humps and the associated signs
(b) width restrictions and the associated signs
(c) height restrictions and the associated signs.

The design of such features and subsequent maintenance needs to ensure adequate drainage and be of such construction that vehicles are not tempted to ignore their presence, causing mutual damage. Regular inspection, and inclusion of all such items in the highway inventory are helpful in ensuring public safety and attention to necessary repairs.

Acknowledgements

The author wishes to thank members of the County Surveyors Society and the County Engineer of Devon for assistance in the preparation of this chapter, and also Messrs. Prismo Universal for the loan of slides used in Figs 7.1–7.6.

References

7.1.   PRIEST R.A.F. and MOORE R.C. *Equipment and techniques for commercial vehicle axle load surveys in the United Kingdom.* Transport and Road Research Laboratory, Crowthorne, 1981.

7.2.   *The traffic signs manual.* Her Majesty's Stationery Office, London, 1983.

7.3.   JAMES J.G. and REID J.A. *Notes on the costs, lives, and effectiveness of various road markings.* LR 285, Transport and Road Research Laboratory, Crowthorne, 1969.

7.4. BRITISH STANDARDS INSTITUTION. *Specification for solid glass beads for use with road marking compounds and for other industrial uses.* BS 6088. BSI, London, 1981.

7.5. BRITISH STANDARDS INSTITUTION. *Specification for pavement marking paints.* BS 6044. BSI, London, 1987.

7.6. BRITISH STANDARDS INSTITUTION. *Hot applied thermoplastic road marking materials.* BS 3262 (Parts 1–3). BSI, London, 1989.

7.7. DEPARTMENT OF TRANSPORT. *Code of practice for routine maintenance.* Publications Sales Unit.

7.8. *LAA Code of Good Practice.* Association of County Councils, London.

7.9. DEPARTMENT OF TRANSPORT. TD 26/86.

7.10. DEPARTMENT OF TRANSPORT. *Specification for Highway Works.* Her Majesty's Stationery Office, London, 1986.

7.11. *Research Note 27.* Transport and Road Research Laboratory, Crowthorne.

7.12. BRITISH STANDARDS INSTITUTION. BS 873 (Part 4). BSI, London.

7.13. DEPARTMENT OF TRANSPORT. *Circular Roads 7/84.*

7.14. DEPARTMENT OF TRANSPORT. *Departmental Standard TD/85.*

7.15. BRITISH STANDARDS INSTITUTION. BS 873 (Part 8). BSI, London.

7.16. BRITISH STANDARDS INSTITUTION. *Road danger lamps.* BS 2143 (Parts 1–4). BSI, London.

7.17. HORNE M.R. *Roads and the utilities.* Report, Department of Transport, Her Majesty's Stationery Office, London, 1985.

8

Road assessment and management systems

This chapter gives a brief introduction to a series of concepts and techniques that can be studied under the generic title of Maintenance Management Systems (MMS). Figure 8.1 indicates that MMS comprise a variety of sub-systems that in some way collect and manipulate data relating to the highway.

These sub-sets are by no means exhaustive, but it will be recognized that some elements relate to physical entities, some to concepts and some to decision-making processes. Two fundamental types of data relating to these elements may also be identified — that which relates to physical entities, e.g. a lighting column and that which relates to some measurement relevant to serviceability, e.g. the degree of corrosion occurring within the said lighting column. Surveys relating to such elements are usually identified as 'Inventory' in the former case and 'Condition' in the latter.

In the following pages, emphasis is given to the managerial concepts, strategies and overview knowledge required when considering MMS. Detailed descriptions and methods of operation of various items of equipment have been avoided as far as possible since in the vast majority of cases the published literature is already extensive.

8.1. Budget considerations

Budgeting for planned maintenance forms the most essential part of any highway management system and it is vital to realize that the cost of the system is itself an integral part of any budget plan. This cost is represented by the initial cost of establishing the system, and by the costs which then follow as an inevitable consequence of servicing and managing the system.

It is probably fair to say that, in general, managements within the UK highway industry have been slow to realize the full potential of such systems, have failed to give sufficient consideration to the longer term budgetary implications and have not recognized the fundamental 'lever arm' principle which is at work prior to system selection — i.e. the cost of the decision-making process in selection of an appropriate system(s) is minute when compared with the magnitude of costs arising from decisions made using the chosen system. It is most important therefore that managements should plan to set aside sufficient resources at the conception stage for them to investigate thoroughly a range of alternative strategies, evaluate appropriate systems, prepare short, medium and long term budgetary plans and exercise utmost skill and professional judgement before embarking upon a project that has financial implications well into the next century. These implications are discussed in more detail later, but are crucial to the success or subsequent failure of any logically designed management system, and their importance cannot be overemphasized.

Many decisions must be made on relatively sparse information, the consequences of which are often far reaching, and may not become obvious until very much later. Accordingly, the budgeting process should be divided into a series of planned phases, starting with system conception, and proceeding in logical steps to a fully implemented and maintained system. This will form the primary driving force of the management decision-making process within the organization responsible for maintaining a highway network.

At the conception stage much thought should be given to the way in which future budgets will be prepared, and some estimation has to be made as to the significance of possible legislative developments, changes in funding methods, and the longer term resource requirements. It is obvious that these considerations give rise to difficult questions, which are essentially long term, whereas in the UK in particular, the political

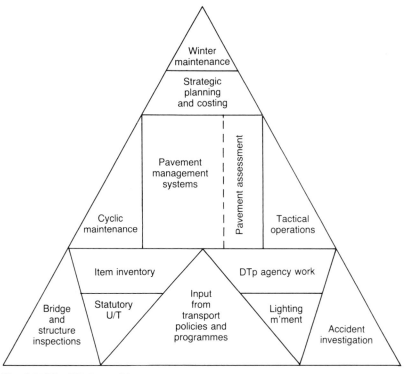

Fig. 8.1. The 'Highway Maintenance Management Systems' jig-saw

process, and hence financing, is short term. This conflict is inevitable, given that much effort has been expended in evolving road design processes to yield a 'life' of the order of 10, 20 or 40 years (depending on traffic), and any maintenance management system must be applied consistently over a number of 'lives' if it is to prove its cost effectiveness. Politicians, however, continue to view the civil engineering requirements inherent in road maintenance as part of the economic regulator and, as this conflict is unlikely to disappear, it is a challenge that managers must face.

Traditionally, budgets have tended to be formulated on an annual basis. Such a process is unlikely to aid the development of a sensible management system, a fact which was well recognized in the case of civil engineering by Banwell[8.1] and in the case of maintenance by Marshall.[8.2] Nevertheless, it is only recently that there has been any serious attempt to introduce rolling programmes founded on the 'moving cursor' principle, wherein over- or under-expenditure in any given year does not have traumatic consequences for the continuing and consistent application of a programme. Unfortunately, the fact that a system based on this precept has been introduced is no guarantee for its continuation, as legislators are frequently prone to change the rules concerning public expenditure.

At the system conception stage consideration should be given to which of these two procedures (or their generic variants) are likely to form the basis of budgeting over the initial few years. This may have important consequences in respect of system selection and capacity.

In an annual system, negotiations take place each year with the funding authority; traditionally, such procedures often revolve around the amount spent in the previous year (or on similar activities when there is no direct comparison) and are prone to political manipulation. In such cases, sudden increases can be just as disruptive as sudden decreases. This type of budgetary control is best suited to an ad hoc approach often known as 'crises management' wherein funds are allocated in response to visually imminent destruction of the asset. Such visual indicators, although persuasive to the media and hence public opinion, are not much use for planned maintenance management systems.

In so far as there is any value in this type of budgeting it can yield a one-off or infrequent subvention of funds, which can be used by management to undertake a sample survey of the highway network designed to indicate the magnitude of the maintenance task. By its very nature, however, it is prone to the errors of any sampling system and it cannot indicate trends — the most vital part of any cost-effective decision making process.

A sensible approach to the problem of setting an appropriate budget for the establishment and operation of a management system may be to view the cost as akin to an insurance premium. This could take the form of a high initial cost to buy 'the cover', viz. the establishment cost followed by a reduction in premium as a result of a no claims bonus, i.e. the avoidance of over-expensive repairs by the adoption of planned replacements where they are inherently preventative. In this way it is reasonable to argue the case for a fixed percentage of the current capital value of the asset to be allocated anually in order to provide a fund base. As the stock (the amount of highway) increases/decreases the budget will be subject to automatic reassessment. It should be noted that the term 'amount' of highway was used rather than length because the nature of the highway (complexity, traffic loading, design parameters, climatic exposure, etc.) all have an important bearing on the calculation of the 'risk'.

If this procedure is adopted, together with the concept of a rolling programme, it is possible to design an appropriate management system, which can be introduced progressively, can be designed to yield trend data and can be applied in a hierarchical manner commencing with those highways, premature deterioration of which is likely to cause the public the greatest monetary loss and inconvenience.

A very thorough analysis of the methods used in the UK to set the budget for the structural maintenance of motorways and all-purpose trunk roads has been described by Gaffney.[8.3] This work describes the procedures in use or proposed for the period 1986–89 and yet it is interesting to note that in 1988 changes were already being made to the time scales for relevant surveys, alterations and possible improvements made to the priority accorded to surface characteristics and part way through the year, the reintroduction of a moratorium on expenditure.

The trunk road and motorway network, while carrying a substantial proportion of the traffic, particularly heavy goods vehicles, forms a relatively small part of the total highway network, e.g. the English motorway network comprising 1% of the stock but carrying 27% of road freight. Nevertheless the bulk of the traffic is carried on roads maintained by highway authorities other than the Department of Transport. Most journeys start and finish on non-trunk roads despite the fact that many vehicles involved are at the limit of UK loading restrictions. Increasingly onerous financial restrictions on the freedom of such authorities has had a severe effect on the operation of maintenance programmes for their highways. This fact, although slow to become visually obvious to the travelling public, has been confirmed by the National Road Maintenance Condition Survey.

In preparing budgetary proposals, therefore, it is apparent that for the foreseeable future, consideration must be given to the likely disparity between central government funding and that which is, in theory at least, under local control. As stated earlier, in order to implement a maintenance management system, a reasonable term security of funding is essential. It is interesting to note that notwithstanding central government's difficulties it has been fairly successful in enabling its agent authorities to embark on the first stages of a maintenance management system by the adoption of the Code of Practice for Routine Maintenance.[8.4] It remains to be seen whether this security of funding is carried through into successive budgets, since to be effective it must continue for some decades.

At local level, similar decisions must be taken and long-term commitments envisaged if the full advantages are to be gained from a management system. It is suggested that at least 2·5–3·5% of the maintenance budget be reserved for this continuing and long-term operation. That leaves open the question of the appropriate additional subvention required as 'start-up' costs. Assuming the start-up is spread over a three-year period something in the order of 5–10% per annum needs to be reserved. The proportion will be dependent primarily on the system capacity and complexity.

As an aid to the decision making process a series of questions is posed at the end of this overview section. It is considered that by answering these questions, managers will be enabled to envisage a maintenance management system strategy suitable in terms of magnitude, capacity for development and credibility appropriate to their needs. By costing the various elements, the budgetary requirements will become apparent.

When a management system is in operation the objective data obtained need to become by far the most important element in establishing the budget for the actual maintenance. It is as well to appreciate at the outset that such a procedure is likely to give rise to conflicts of interest.

If a comprehensive maintenance management system is established as a result of decisions taken at system conception stage, then consideration must be given to the mechanism that is to be adopted for the production of future budgets. It is these subsequent budgets that will control the resources necessary to implement the planned maintenance programmes derived from the results of the various condition surveys. Since budgets are usually prepared on an annual basis the first major problem to be encountered is a conflict between the timing of data collection plus evaluation, and the deadline for estimate submission. For various technical reasons, as explained later, the data collection season in the UK is confined primarily to the period April–September for much of the important structural and surface characteristic surveys. Estimate submissions for budget preparations are usually required within this period (in the Department of Transport's case close to the half-way stage). Such administrative mismatches mean that data are neither as comprehensive, up-to-date nor as valid as they could be, and that the resulting budget is weakened.

Before completing consideration of the budgetary process, there is one other fundamental problem that management must resolve. This problem is in the nature of a dilemma between system credibility and flexibility. A numerate system, which is accurate in terms of data collection and in evaluation is rational, can maintain credibility only if it is applied rigorously. Unfortunately, such logical application may mean the diversion of funds to projects that are quite contrary to public perception and aspirations. As an example, consider the case where the evaluation may indicate that the most cost-effective use of certain funds is to carry out preventive maintenance on a particular part of the highway and accept that another part is going to fail completely. To the public this latter situation may also be obvious because of the visual condition and they will not condone the use of scarce funds for what appears to be unnecessary works elsewhere. There exists therefore a powerful temptation to exercise some 'judgement' or to 'take note of political realities', understandably so if there is a danger that funds voted for implementing the management system could be withdrawn. Yet every time such 'judgement' is exercised a little more inaccuracy creeps into the system and a little more credibility is lost. Hence, although it is virtually impossible to prevent some weakening of the system, management must be quite ruthless in keeping control.

Often the budgetary process requires that a convincing case is presented to non-technical persons responsible for deciding on the level of funding. In order to secure sufficient and continuing support for resources to maintain the system during the crucial early years of implementation, so that its inherent value may be recognized, some early successes are vital. The situation is not dissimilar to that in football management — demonstrate superiority or perish! Budgets must be prepared by management with the utmost care and precision, with adequate regard for what is truly within the capacity of the organization to attain and, having thus decided, they must present unyielding resistance to any attempt to pare down the proposal to meet some ill-conceived arbitrary limit.

Such a procedure wastes meagre resources because if the scheme has been properly prepared and budgeted, less than the designed scheme will, by definition, produce non-viable data. This is worse than no data, since being misleading, it undermines the credibility of the system. Far better to spend what resources exist on a little more durable blacktop.

8.2. Funding

Although careful analysis of requirements and a planned forward strategy for implementation of the system sets the size of the budget, it does not of itself provide the funds. Traditionally, such funds have been obtained from central or local government either separately or in combination. In the UK in recent years, however, local expenditure has been particularly constrained with the result that highway authorities have been forced to proceed with the introduction of comprehensive management systems at a much slower pace than is desirable if, within a reasonable time scale, real cost-effective benefits are to be obtained. The problem is particularly acute in the case of the initial expenditure necessary to install and manage the early life of the system. There exists a classical 'Catch 22' situation in that the initially poor return on the investment often precludes the investment itself.

In order to mitigate this problem a number of local highway authorities in the UK combined with the Department of Transport to provide joint funding for a study into a comprehensive Pavement Management System (PMS). The results of this preliminary study were published in late 1988.[8.5]

By acting in concert the parties to the study gained the advantage of speed and security of funding, enabling a more thorough-going analysis to be accomplished than that which any individual member could undertake. The project has now reached the stage when the parties must decide whether to proceed to implementation or not. If a sufficient number of authorities do decide to proceed it is quite probable that the UK will soon acquire the means to implement a PMS that will be as good as or better than any of the embryonic systems available in Europe or the USA.[8.6]

In the USA, developments associated with pavement evaluation are being funded through the Strategic Highway Research Program (SHRP). It is possible that, in the future, UK administrations may well give consideration to a form of funding similar to that adopted for the SHRP in allowing a virtually direct transfer of revenue raised from motor transport to be used for financing road improvements/maintenance and their associated management systems. Some of these suggestions are already being voiced,[8.7] but in the meantime it is expected that UK companies and universities will benefit from research contracts placed by the SHRP as a result of the Department of Trade and Industry (DTI) initiatives. The results of the DTI mission to the USA are published in reference 8.8.

Other possible sources of funding to provide the essential pump priming necessary to initiate MMS in the UK may come through World Bank contracts, research fellowships and private initiative. Experience to date suggests that there will have to be a substantial degree of co-operation and a combination of funding during the vital development phase of MMS expected in the late 1980s. To a large extent much of the essential research, particularly in pavement evaluation, necessary for input to a PMS has been undertaken in the last decade or so, but the crucial development phase has, as yet, not been funded adequately. This is a continuing challenge to managements.

In the immediate future it is likely that UK local authority spending will be subject to a radical revision of current rules brought about by the introduction of the community charge in place of rates, and the failure of existing legislation to achieve sensible objectives. These changes envisage a return, in part, to a system almost of loan sanction as operated in the 1950s and 1960s. This would have the effect of allowing the development of MMS funded within a more consistent and sensible application of financial control. On the one hand if the capital element is allowed to be funded by loans and recycled receipts from the sale of assets, while on the other hand revenue expenditure (i.e. running costs) once freed from central control can be budgeted for within the community charge, then it is possible to foresee more secure funding. The precise details of the proposed changes have to await parliamentary approval but meanwhile the Treasury White Paper Cmnd 441 and the Department of the Environment's Consultation Paper: Capital Expenditure and Finance, should be scrutinized so as to aid the decision making process in respect of funding PMS and MMS.

8.3. Standards

Effective maintenance requires that appropriate standards are specified and an objective means of monitoring performance in relation to those standards are instituted. Surprisingly little work had been done in respect of initiating such standards for UK roads prior to the work of the Marshall Committee in the late 1960s, whereas the major railway networks of the late 19th and early 20th century had developed quite sophisticated and successful systems designed to ensure consistent standards. This dilatory approach in respect of highways probably arose from the parochial way responsibilities were delegated, coupled with operations which lacked the prestige of new work.

Even today it is interesting to note that in the developing countries it is only very recently, in response to pressure from, and the lead given by, the World Bank that attempts have been made to set standards.[8.9] Elsewhere in the developed world attempts to introduce comprehensive standards are continuing in Japan, Poland, Denmark, France, USA, South Africa, New Zealand, Australia and many more. In the UK the post-Marshall period witnessed a sustained attempt by central and local government to establish sensible guidelines. As maintenance engineers grappled with the various problems, a divergence of emphasis between rural and urban situations became apparent, culminating in the establishment of two distinct systems of assessment reflecting differing priorities/standards and environments. These two systems — CHART (Computerized Highway Assessment of Ratings and Treatments) and MARCH (Maintenance Assessment Ratings and Costing of Highways) — became the dominant methods in the late 1970s and early 1980s. At this stage the differences in assessment methods are inconsequential and it is necessary only to note the effect within a feedback loop of the relative importance attached to the standards for particular types of deterioration.

The setting of appropriate standards has proved to be a difficult objective because it is inherently related to the continuation of a given level of funding. The original suggested 'standards' proposed by Marshall et al.[8.2] were overtaken very quickly by the effects of events elsewhere in the world, culminating in severe reductions in expenditure levels. These standards were found to be incapable of achievement within the constraints subsequently imposed, but it is important to note that the committee never proposed that their suggestions should be given the status of absolute standards — indeed they proposed 'suggested' target values and 'initial standards' for certain parameters. Unfortunately, there were a number of attempts through the courts to change the status of 'suggestions' to 'recommendations' and hence to enforceable standards. Blakey[8.10] has argued the case for standards to be objective and national as a means of promoting the case for adequate funding whereas others have made a case for standards to be evolved which reflect the likely level of funding available and have some degree of flexibility in implementation. In an attempt to come to terms with this problem the Local Authorities Code of Good Practice,[8.11] the Department of Transport's Code of Practice for Routine Maintenance and Departmental Standards (e.g. HD15/87),[8.12,8.13] together with papers by Garrett[8.14] and Cottell[8.15] on whole life costing, have introduced the concept of investigatory, warning and intervention levels.

The debate will no doubt continue between the protagonists for absolute standards (i.e. standards uninfluenced by location, funding provision, etc.) and those satisfied with comparative standards (i.e. is it better/worse, or the same as before?). Comparison with absolute standards does not preclude the latter questions. In the case of absolute standards, however, it must be borne in mind that these standards are to a large extent influenced by perception and aspirations of the travelling public, e.g. what level of bumpiness (roughness) is acceptable and what level of visibility restrictions is tolerable. When these arguments involve accident potential more 'heat' is generated than 'light' since there is bound to be an emotional reaction so that the setting of standards becomes a matter of controversy.

By far the best attempt to set some acceptable standards for the majority of roads is that given in the revised LAA Code of Good Practice due to be published in 1990. Whereas the earlier work[8.11] was somewhat constrained in terms of existing methods of assessment, the revised version should prove to have benefited from the continuing work of the County Surveyors' Society, the Maintenance Special Activity Group and the Pavement Assessment by Special Vehicles SAG (MSAG and PASV SAG).

Whatever and however standards are set, it is vital that they enjoy the confidence of the end users as being applicable, enforceable and within practical/financial realization. These requirements are more likely to be attained if the system is prepared in accordance with the principles of Quality Assurance (QA) since this is primarily a management procedure. Firstly, QA schemes require documented standards against which performance can be measured and hence ensure fitness for purpose, i.e. applicability. Secondly, such schemes must have a means of dealing with non-compliance, i.e. enforceability, and thirdly, each scheme is tailored to meet the requirements of the participants in that, the checking systems are designed to ensure that, what it is agreed shall be done, is being done, i.e. practical and giving confidence.

In QA terminology non-compliance results in managerial action to correct — in maintenance terms this postulates the need for some means of regular assessment coupled with a planned response — in other words, a means of appraisal.

8.4. Appraisal

Appraisal can be defined as estimating the value of an asset. In the context of highway maintenance the value of the asset is a monetary equivalent of all that which comprises the highways and its intrinsic value to the community. This will include, *inter alia*: the value of the land; the energy and construction cost relevant to all the highway fabric, viz. foundations, drainage, pavement materials, etc.; the environmental benefit to the community arising from its presence not only as represented by travel–time costs but also as a linear conduit for all the life-enhancing services provided by statutory and other undertakers; and, in rural areas, as a habitat for flora and fauna. Surprisingly, some of these factors tend not to be recognized as part of the asset until they cease to function. All are important nevertheless, needing to be preserved and renewed as necessary. In order to achieve this desirable state of affairs it seems sensible to arrange for any appraisal to be both systematic and rational. The main advantage of using systematic assessment methods is the ease with which comparative values can be obtained. If the methods were purely subjective and haphazard in application it would be virtually impossible to ensure that, between competing demands, resources were allocated on an equitable basis or that the most important obligation of endeavouring to preserve the value of the asset was being fulfilled.

To be of use, however, a rational system is required, i.e. one which requires the determination of meaningful parameters. There is not much point in systematically obtaining the 'wrong' information. The primary objective is to ensure that the methods used result in cost-effective remedial measures being applied in an order of priority that makes sense. This priority order may not be the same as that perceived desirable by those not involved in the decision-making process. As explained previously this can give rise to conflict which has to be accepted as an unfortunate side effect. Having considered the essential factors associated with budgets, funding, standards and the rationale for an appraisal system, thought can now be given to available systems and techniques. If the foregoing is being used as a guide to the creation of a MMS, before proceeding further the reader should have answered, or attempted to answer, each of the ten fundamental questions listed in Table 8.1.

8.5. Pavement assessment — an overview

An essential part of any MMS is some form of pavement assessment (PA), which can be founded on visual or mechanistic measurements. In the former there is bound to be a subjective element, while in the latter case objectivity is paramount. There is no reason, however, why both measurement systems cannot be employed in a logical fashion, and indeed by careful tailoring of the systems some of the difficulties inherent in too rigid an application of objective data can be avoided.

Since PA is a technology that is developing rapidly it is also inevitable that there will be some overlap between the systems, particularly when a technique is discovered to be extremely useful in aiding interpretation within the 'other' system (e.g. knowledge of cracking), and its extent and distribution are not only vital ingredients of a visual assessment method, as in CHART, but are also essential inputs to the interpretation of deflection information. It should be borne in mind therefore, when reading the rest of this section, that the split between visual and mechanistic is not absolute but merely a convenient way of grouping various techniques.

While it is possible to envisage MMS which discounts PA data and is based primarily on historical cost data, such a system is at a disadvantage in reacting to demographic and other changes, e.g. a rise in water table, cf. the London basin. A system that carefully monitors the performance of the pavement over a period of time, detects trends and has a built-in response mechanism is more logical and is advocated. By an analysis of the answers to the ten fundamental questions listed in Table 8.1 it is possible to develop an appropriate strategy for the creation of the PA system.

It is best to start by considering the size of the network to be monitored and the resources (staff, finance, bought-in assistance) available. Where the network is relatively small, e.g. some tens of kilometres confined to an area of fairly consistent geology, topography, climate and traffic, it is doubtful whether anything other than a carefully applied visual system is justified. Nevertheless, this approach can cause difficulties if, in order to acquire funds, some breach of an objectively measured intervention level has to be demonstrated.

At the other extreme a large network covering an extensive area will involve, almost inevitably, changes in geology, traffic, etc. At this level of complexity, the personal and subjective knowledge of pavement condition is likely to be shared amongst a number of individuals rather than the one or two typical of limited areas. Quantifying this subjective information becomes increasingly difficult, hence greater reliance must be placed on

Table 8.1. Ten fundamental questions for Maintenance Management Systems

1.	What is the size of the network that must be maintained? (It is advisable, in order to cope with multi-lane, multi-level highways, etc. to define this in terms of lane kilometres rather than length.)
2.	Is all this network to be subject to rigorous analysis within the MMS? If not what proportion? If a proportion, is this fixed or will it grow with time other than for demographic reasons? (Demographic change is inevitable, but is relatively slow whereas a decision to increase the network being monitored by incorporating a class of highway hitherto outside the system can have quite devastating implications, e.g. capacity for data collection, storage, retrieval and phasing decisions to meet budget considerations.)
3.	Is there a fundamental, secure, unambiguous location referencing system in operation? Is it robust and does it cope with all highway configurations and all speeds of data collection? (This is the key question in bringing diverse data into one integrated system, which, with a database approach, enables unstructured questions to be posed, alternative strategies investigated, and a multiplicity of choices reduced to a relatively few costed options on which decisions can be made with confidence.)
4.	Is the computer system necessary to handle the requirements for MMS in place, fully tested, supported by adequate numbers and quality of staff? Are the source data secure, protected against mismanagement and mischievous intent (hackers)? (Once a MMS is in place an exceptionally large proportion of management's decision making process is dependent on the viability of the computing system — within a few years of commencement manual back-up systems are virtually unworkable and probably no longer supported. At this stage the management are most vulnerable to the effects of computer systems failure.)
5.	Having considered the answers to the foregoing will the computer system be based on mainframe, mini- or micro-computers or a mixture thereof?
6.	Will all the decision-making processes be confined to one location or is the management structure diversified and in different physical locations? Are there various levels of staff with both input and output requirements of the system? Where are they located — are they connected by local or wide area computer networks?
7.	What type of data (e.g. numeric, alpha-numeric, descriptive, graphic and visual picture) is envisaged as being available on the system? Will this relate to inventory or condition or both?

rational and objective measurements. Once the leap between subjective and objective systems is made another dimension then becomes apparent. Objective mechanistic systems lend themselves to relatively high speed data collection and hence large quantities of data. Although a case can be argued for the pruning of this mass of data by careful statistically controlled sampling, in practice the process is fraught with difficulty. Consequently, in addition to the network being large, the density of data available per kilometre is also likely to be very much larger. Computer handling and storage capabilities then become a critical element in system design.

(The answers to questions 5–7 inclusive, to a large extent will define the computing system requirements and hence its limitations. It is vital to bear in mind the ultimate requirements and objectives of the system at the earliest stages since there is little point in deciding to initiate a system that may require a complete rewrite of software, or major changes to hardware and communications links in order to support graphic displays subsequently found necessary to enable the full benefits of the system to be obtained.)

8. How often will data be upgraded? Will the previous data be readily available in order to indicate trends?

9. Is there a hierarchical system of data importance in operation?

10. Does the system have a procedure for coping with changes to the geometry and extent of the highway network before, during and after the changes?

(The answers to these questions will define the usefulness of the system. Since a highway network is dynamic some data are out of date soon after collection while other data are probably viable for some time. Data relative to an inventory of items may well fall into the latter category while condition information relates to the former. As an example, data relating to surface characteristics are relevant to the network at the time the survey was undertaken and must always be 'tied' to both the geometry and the surfacing material. It may be necessary, for legal reasons, to store the network relating to this data for some considerable time. In the UK the shortest period is likely to be six years to account for the Statute of Limitation, together with one year extra to account for change-over dates and other logistical problems. The 'life' of the surfacing probably represents the other extreme. Inventory data relating to numbers of things or their physical presence on a particular highway may be sufficient for planning cyclic maintenance schedule routes, etc. even if it is partly out of date. New road locations must be able to be identified by the system, preferably from design stage forward, so that vital geotechnical data are built in to the fundamental understanding of the pavement behaviour. Similarly, traffic is likely to be present on the road often long before an official change is made to the road number or the route that it supersedes. The system must cope with this problem otherwise data relevant to an 'old' road may be allocated to the 'new' or vice versa.)

These implications have obviously been considered by the authors of the joint Department of Transport/LAA study into PMS.[8.5]

It is suggested that there will be a fundamental procedure involving a three-pass process irrespective of differences in implementation.

Pass 1   Coarse condition survey leading to determination of overall network condition, of trends, of total budget requirements and of priorities for further investigation.

Pass 2   A detailed condition survey to determine priorities for detailed design of major roads.

Pass 3   Detailed design and costing for all roads.

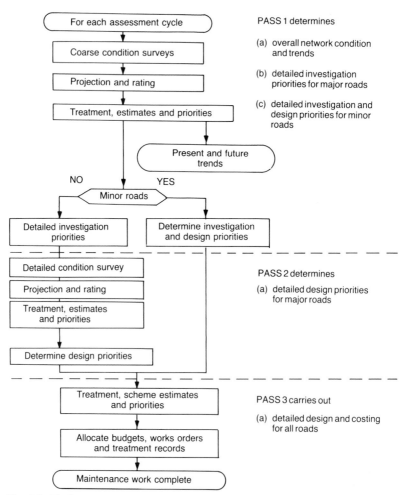

Fig. 8.2. Highway Maintenance Management Systems — pavement management. Overall structure of PMS Pass 1: determine network trends and detailed investigation priorities

It will be observed that the proposals envisage that minor roads are not subjected to the full rigours of a detailed condition survey. Such surveys generate a large amount of data and by dispensing with this pass the requirements for data storage are reduced substantially.

This study[8.5] is the result of substantial investigation and research; it is recommended for further reading.

The flow diagram shown in Fig. 8.2 is an overview of the structure of the proposed PMS, while Fig. 8.3 indicates how network trends and detailed investigation priorities are intended to be determined. Although the study proposes the use of many available techniques and shows how appropriate systems could be integrated into a comprehensive management system for the pavements it must be remembered that as yet these are proposals. Attention has been drawn previously to the fact that imple-

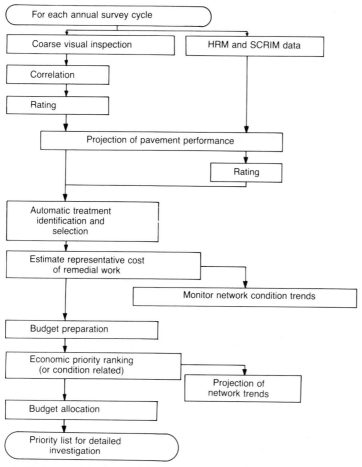

Fig. 8.3. Highway Maintenance Management Systems — PMS network trends

mentation of even these modest proposals will need continued co-operative funding.

8.6. Visual inspection techniques

In spite of advances in electronics and the ready accessibility of powerful computers, the human senses remain the most adaptable unit of mobile combined hardware and software available for use in inspection procedures. Their very sophistication, however, gives rise to difficulties since the in-built feedback systems are so highly tuned that subjective evaluations become commonplace without the initiator being aware of the fact. Hence inspection systems that rely on visual methods have often been designed to suppress these influences and 'program' the inspector to act as an automaton. The reason for this becomes obvious as soon as the reports produced are being used, not in a comparative sense based on one person's perceptions, but in conjunction with similar reports from a multiplicity of sources.

The first substantive attempts at codifying visual inspection data were made during the early 1970s as a support operation to the work of the Marshall Committee. The Transport and Road Research Laboratory (TRRL) published a Technical Note (TN708) in June 1972 entitled 'Methods of Assessing Structural Maintenance Needs for Highways' and methods of assessment discussed therein became the foundations for the CHART system. Since that time there have been numerous references in the technical literature describing methods of operation, shortcomings and improvements to the system, together with various enhancements to the associated computer programs. It is considered that those listed in the bibliography will be found useful guides to the operation of the process. In general terms CHART indicates the length of the highway to be considered for treatment and the relative priority that should be accorded to it.

At various times attempts have been made to incorporate data other than those acquired from visual surveys, e.g. from deflection or surface characteristics. Such attempts have not been particularly successful although the later versions of the processing suite do provide for some processed data to be included. The main problem with all compilations of data is the lack of a simple, accurate and robust location referencing system that is universal in application, enabling data from diverse sources to be merged.

Until the abolition of the Metropolitan County Authorities, considerable development work continued with the other major visual assessment system, viz. MARCH. This system tended to be favoured by maintenance authorities as being more suitable for evaluation in urban areas and possessed an undoubted advantage in respect of costing. Inevitably the abolition caused the destruction of knowledge teams, dissipation of expertise and delayed development. In the long run, however, some benefit may be obtained from the opportunity thus presented to combine the best features of MARCH with CHART. These developemnts are in progress and no doubt will be included in improved assessment systems.

Initially, CHART and similar surveys were carried out with nothing more sophisticated than a notebook, pen and linen tape. It soon became obvious that the process was slow and laborious, hence attempts were made to increase speed by using pre-printed stationery both in the field and office in order to simplify data collection/entry. A procedure using staff trained to recognize specific defects and enter their findings in a standard format required subsequent vetting and coding prior to computer punching: it became known as the *transfer* method. It was still tedious, had some possible disadvantages in respect of transcription errors, but required less expert staff. The alternative, of course, was to allow the coding sheets to be completed directly by the inspector. The disadvantages of this *direct* method included the additional expertise required and the slowness of the actual data collection (although the total process may be faster). Slowness in data collection, however, increases the danger to both operators and public since the period of occupation on a live carriageway is increased. It has long been recognized that any data collection system that impedes traffic flow is itself a continuing source of danger.

At this stage of development improved portable electronic devices for data collection, distance measurement and visual recording began to appear on the market with increasing frequency. The future for visual inspection systems is likely to be influenced more by these developments than any others.

Initially data collection speed was improved by the use of portable electronic 'memory' devices of which 'Data Ports' and 'Husky Hunters' are typical and still in regular use.

Although some local authorities (e.g. Surrey and Bristol) had carried out feasibility studies of condition monitoring using 16 mm cine film the costs were prohibitively expensive, negating much of the early developments. By the early to mid 1980s developments in video recording had so improved that those authorities such as the GLC, Surrey, Kent and Berkshire, who were undertaking extensive inventory, structural and surface characteristic surveys, began to make increasing use of the technique.

Many of the early recordings, using reasonably good quality domestic equipment, were found to be perfectly adequate for the purpose of aiding the editing of SCRIM (Sideways-Force Coefficient Routine Investigation Machine) surveys. Engineers using the tapes soon discovered that a very large amount of useful inventory data, plus some condition data, could be collected at the same time for a fraction of the cost of walking surveys. The ability to move and survey at normal traffic speed means that a large part of the danger element both to survey teams and to the travelling public is obviated. Experiments made by the author to prove high speed location referencing quickly demonstrated that useful data could be acquired at speeds up to 70 mph.

By using high quality equipment however, accuracy and decoding is significantly enhanced. A number of commercial organizations and various authorities currently use or provide video surveying services. One of the most advanced uses of this technique by Berkshire County Council

*Fig. 8.4 (above).
Berkshire County Council
— Inventory Survey
Vehicle*

*Fig. 8.5 (right). Berkshire
Inventory Survey Vehicle
(interior showing bar code
work station)*

is aimed at the collection of inventory data and has been described by Budden.[8.16] A specially adapted micro-bus vehicle (Figs 8.4 and 8.5) is equipped with high quality video recording gear, magnetometer location referencing and near-side/off-side observation work stations. Operators at these work stations can observe various inventory items and by means of a bar-code keyboard rapidly match the observed item with the complementary image on the work table. A stroke of a light-pen encoder fixes the item into the record accurately aligned to the highway network. Simultaneous video recording, front or rear view, provides a comprehensive record of the majority of highway features.

While these most advanced features, together with additional anticipated developments as associated with video recording, offer the engineer a very powerful tool they do not eliminate the need for certain physical/visual inspections. No device has yet been marketed that can look down a manhole or gulley pot while travelling at normal traffic speed.

8.7. Objective systems

The visual and subjective systems discussed previously can be used quite successfully to aid an assessment about the need for certain items of maintenance to be undertaken. Nevertheless, owing to the fact that they are essentially reactive to a deterioration in condition their use as a predictive tool is severely limited.

Wherever a pavement assessment system forms part of a comprehensive MMS, the ability to predict future budgetary demands becomes one of the most powerful assets for managing as opposed to reacting. It has long been argued that major economic benefit is gained by choosing the correct

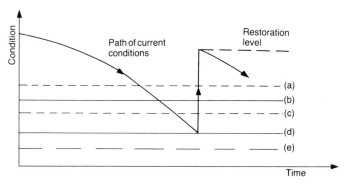

Fig. 8.6. Highway condition levels: (a) warning level — the level at which the road is approaching a critical condition; (b) optimum intervention level — the level at which the proposed treatment will minimize the total costs, i.e. the cost/benefit of maintenance action is most advantageous; (c) public acceptability level — the level below which the public do not expect standards to fall; (d) actual intervention level — the level at which the proposed treatment is carried out, this being dependent on the finance available; (e) legal acceptability level — the level below which the road condition should not fall based on legal requirements such as the Highways Act

time in the life of any pavement to apply remedial measures. Child[8.17] has demonstrated that the well-known deterioration path diagram can be redrawn to indicate various 'levels' of condition, which can be considered by management as crucial decision-making moments. This diagram is reproduced in Fig. 8.6.

Millard and Lister[8.18] suggested criteria for pavement maintenance designed to preserve the value of the asset. Much of the research carried out at the TRRL in the post-war period has been orientated towards developing apparatus to enable objective measurements to be made of the amount (and more latterly the rate) of deterioration.

Having developed such apparatus the exciting prospect of being able to predict what will happen to a pavement becomes a possibility. Research in recent years has been giving ever more attention to this attainment of the maintenance engineer's 'holy grail'. It is doubtful whether anyone involved would underestimate the difficulties, but within the last decade considerable progress has been made into turning these desires into everyday practical reality. In order to achieve this objective three fundamental types of apparatus are required

(a) a structural evaluation device
(b) a means of measuring surface characteristics
(c) a rapid means of making an overall assessment so that resources for (a) and (b) can be employed in the most cost-effective manner.

In addition to these primary devices a surprisingly large amount of ancillary apparatus and supporting data has been found to be necessary in order to make full use of the inherent, but sometimes latent, capabilities of the evaluation systems. These requirements include measurements of traffic, axle loading and distribution, measurements of thickness, strain, voids and density, and details of accident distribution, temperature, climatic conditions, etc.

The first significant developments in assessing structural performance were based on the use of the USA inspired Benkelman beam and the results of the AASHO and Alconbury Hill experiments. By the early 1970s French and British expertise had produced the deflectograph, essentially in the form in which we recognize it now. Very thorough descriptions of the apparatus and general guidance for its use will be found in the publications identified in the bibliography and in Ref. 8.19.

From the point of view of management, however, it is important to understand practical limitations and the logistic details which can aid or mar the effectiveness of the machine's use.

Early pavement evaluation techniques using the deflectograph tended to be based more on its use for estimating the required thickness of overlay rather than as a management tool in predicting the life available throughout the network. Garrett and Lawrence[8.20] have described the different modes of use as pathological and diagnostic. There is nothing inherently wrong with using the deflectograph as a means of aiding the redesign of a deteriorating pavement so as to determine the thickness of additional bituminous material required to achieve a new required 'life'.

Unfortunately, many such operations in recent years have been associated with its use as an adjunct to CHART surveys, more often than not as a means of confirming (or justifying) decisions already taken. It is arguable that this is not the most effective way of using deflection data for the purposes of management. It is important to understand the difference between the two types of condition survey which can be defined as

(a) *pathological*: an application to road pavements that have already deteriorated or failed and are known to require remedial works — the investigation being carried out to determine the type and extent of the remedial works required on that site

(b) *diagnostic*: an application to road pavements throughout the network or to sections of it, irrespective of their age and/or condition — the survey being carried out to determine the relative maintenance condition of each section and its priority for more detailed investigation and/or remedial works.

Many authorities have been making increasing use of the deflectograph in its diagnostic role, particularly in cases where an embryonic MMS has been established. The cost of surveys while not extravagantly expensive is nevertheless not inconsiderable, often being inflated by resource and logistical problems, e.g. the high cost of traffic control, and the need to discover a great deal of information about the construction, thickness, integrity and type. These problems are discussed in more detail later but when they are compounded by the critical time periods, seasonal and temperature restrictions, it becomes virtually impossible to mount a comprehensive survey covering an entire network in a season.

Obviously this problem does relate to the size of the network, but something of the order of 3000 lane kilometres is a fairly average size for the trunk and principal roads in many authorities. If this is the case some means of spreading the survey load is advisable and it is usual to adopt the procedure of surveying a fixed proportion of the network in a given period of years. Three- to five-year cycles seem to find favour — influenced perhaps by advice given by the Department of Transport earlier in the current decade. It is interesting to note, however, that in many cases the change in frequency preference is changing faster than the completion of the actual cycles! This is often the direct response to restrictions on expenditure which, as argued previously, quickly undermine confidence and credibility.

If full value is to be gained it requires strong-minded management to maintain the strategy for a number of cycles! Some organizations have established and enforced such a policy for the benefits in better strategic planning to become apparent, while in other cases, the strategy was destroyed along with the controlling metropolitan authority.

The operation of deflectograph surveys for motorways and trunk roads has been the subject of detailed instructions and advice from the Department of Transport.[8.21-8.23] Even more important has been the advice regarding the vital back-up pavement investigations needed to determine the support data for deflection interpretation.[8.24] On major works constructed after the mid-1960s these investigations should not be necessary if the as-built drawings have been correctly prepared. Sadly, despite the strictures and pleadings of various writers, this is not the case.[8.25–8.27] Expensive, hazardous and delay inducing investigations will continue to be needed for many years to come to correct the results of earlier minor cost savings. Has that lesson been learnt by present-day managements?

Experiments are continuing to discover whether new developments, such as ground radar and a revival of earlier work involving surface wave propagation, hold the key to uncovering the buried 'secrets' of pavement construction.

It is claimed that correct interpretation of radar signals or other responses can determine construction layer thicknesses, delamination, water table, structural integrity and various other vital or useful parameters to aid deflection interpretation. Although the techniques show promise, as yet extensive correlation with coring is required in order to interpret the signals, a situation somewhat akin to the use of geophysical surveys. British experience has been confined largely to the contact type of ground radar in which travel speed is rather limited. American claims for the contactless type promise much, but have yet to demonstrate the ability to perform satisfactorily in the UK.

The greatest use of deflection measurements is on bituminous or composite pavements for which original research information is readily available. Rigid pavements cannot normally be assessed using these techniques but recently the advent of the long wheel base deflectograph has enabled experiments to be carried out by WDM Ltd, which demonstrated with reasonable success the ability to measure relative movement between adjacent concrete bays. Within the sphere of maintenance management of concrete carriageways, slab movement and joint destruction/deterioration are the principal causes of concern. Any system, which can readily determine the onset of the problem, thus allowing remedial measures to be implemented before extensive damage occurs, obviously has advantages. Not all concrete carriageways are recognized as such, particularly when they are covered by a thin layer of bituminous surfacing — this is particularly true of 'old' roads with no maintenance history. In passing it might be noted that the author has long advocated the need to make constructive use of statutory undertaker's excavations to record what is actually there! Video techniques and powerful databases coupled with Geographic Information Systems (GIS) might well enable this dream to become a reality.

Although deflectograph surveys are now routine operations for many authorities the logistics associated with the survey can be somewhat daunting. The deflections must be measured in a manner that correlates with the original research relating deflection to pavement performance. The thickness of the bituminous materials in the pavement, the associated temperature gradient, the position of the water table and other factors all need to be considered and be reasonably comparable to the original experimental results. Limitations on the extrapolation of such data have been detailed in the relevant TRRL reports (LR 571, 833 and 835). As a result of these restrictions, survey work should be confined to an appropriate temperature range and season. The Department of Transport has established a relationship between the category of the survey (reflecting the data's subsequent use) and the temperature range/time periods considered acceptable. These restrictions are detailed in HD10/83, but essentially confine the preferred periods to spring (April–June) and autumn (September–October). Data being used to support bids for major works have to comply with the regulations concerning number, type and timing of surveys. All machines to be used on trunk road surveys are required to attend and 'pass' the annual calibration 'circus' at TRRL while calibration lengths are *de rigeur* in each area. The net result of these restrictions, aggravated by lack of knowledge concerning temperature gradients and performance of thick pavements, is to concentrate the survey work in a narrow time band. Thick pavements are associated with the heaviest traffic. Although for moderately heavy traffic, deflectograph surveys using 'rolling barrier' traffic safety protection are feasible this is not true on a motorway carrying 120 000/150 000 vehicles per day. The alternative is lane closure, but at these traffic levels daytime restrictions are generally unacceptable. The net result is a classic 'Catch 22' situation: lane closures are unacceptable except at night; deflection surveys at night are not acceptable and cannot be interpreted. Alternative lighter traffic conditions may exist in winter; deflection surveys in winter are not acceptable owing to low temperatures.

Research is still proceeding at the TRRL to broaden the time periods available while details of the temperature gradients used in a deep bituminous mat are to be monitored by West Yorkshire Metropolitan County Council. Unless the problem is resolved in the very near future severe disruption to cyclic monitoring programmes will occur.

Given the logistical problems, some authorities propose to review the ways in which deflectographs are used to see whether surveys could be targeted more accurately. This suggests a reversion to the pathological approach. Research at TRRL has suggested the possibility of using the High Speed Road Monitor (HRM)[8.28,8.29] as an initial screening device, undertaking a high speed survey of the network and using the results to pinpoint sections where more sophisticated analysis is required. By assessing the riding quality and its rate of change with time, pavement deterioration can be detected.

There is a strong argument for the use of some means of rapidly assessing the network condition although if this is to be done successfully it is necessary to ensure that all apparatus, which is supposedly of identical design, does in fact yield comparable results.

Initial consideration of that statement may seem faintly ridiculous but experience has shown repeatedly that the sophisticated devices used in pavement assessment need to be calibrated against each other if there is to be confidence in the data. The inherent problem is that if only one machine is used and its measurements checked as far as possible with traceable standards for the fundamental parameters (e.g. mass, force and time) then the data can be ranked. Hence budgeting proposals formulated on these ranked data can be prepared in a priority order. If two or more devices are used the data can still be ranked, even if the machines differ in absolute values for the same parameter, provided that the data derived are not being used to bid for funds from the same source. If there is only one source of funds the devices must yield identical values when measuring the same section of highway otherwise the results will be biased.

It is more than likely that the machines will be operating in different areas and any biasing of results could result in unfair discrimination in the allocation of funding. In order to mitigate the possibility of this occurring on Department of Transport highways, machines such as the deflectograph and SCRIM are required to undergo comparative calibration trials all together and at the same time each year at TRRL. There is of course no requirement for machines not being used on trunk roads to satisfy the scrutineers or pass this annual examination, but commonsense suggests that there is much merit in all pavement assessment data being related to a common base.

At present there are only two prototype and one production version HRM in operation. If this device is to be used for initial screening (the coarse sieve in PMS terms) and, if the majority of maintenance authorities wish to adopt criteria similar to those of the Department of Transport, more machines are likely to be required and hence more calibration trials.

When considering the use of the HRM it is important to understand that not all machines will be fitted with the full range of measuring apparatus. They are identified as three-function or six-function machines. The three-function machine measures longitudinal profile, macro-texture and rut depth. On the six-function machine the additional parameters measured are cross-slope, gradient and horizontal curvature. It is expected that at some future date advice notes and standards will be issued by the Department of Transport. In the meantime descriptions of the apparatus and its use have been given in TRRL Reports LR 639, 922 and 1037 and SR 443 and 498. Additional information is given in refs 8.28 and 8.29.

The six-function machine by its ability to measure gradient and curvature as well as macro-texture means that it is an ideal complementary device to the use of SCRIM for surface characteristic suveys. The need for a means of deriving gradient and curvature arises because desirable levels of skidding resistance are related to those parameters as well as to traffic intensity, road class, etc.

In some management systems such data may be available, either having been acquired for other purposes or as part of geometric survey data. If this is the case direct correlation with SCRIM readings is viable provided that the geographical referencing system is compatible. This is rarely the case. The difficulties and prospects for improved location reference systems and their relationship to GIS are worthy of a chapter in themselves. For the present, the reader should keep in mind data correlation requirements when considering the following brief description of skidding resistance evaluation.

A fundamental challenge to all highway engineers is to reduce the toll of road accidents by the application of skilled engineering judgement and carefully designed and executed works, together with appropriate management control systems. The factors that make up an accident are extremely numerous and it has been demonstrated that such an event is rare, only occurring when a multiplicity of adverse circumstances coincide. By affecting just one of those factors it is probable that a reduction in accidents will result. A common factor in many accidents is that of skidding by one or more of the vehicles involved and therefore any PMS should have a means of assessing the slipperiness of the highways monitored within the system. It is also important, of course, to scrutinize accidents on roads other than those monitored in the PMS for evidence of undue slipperiness.

The density of traffic, temperate climate and legacy of poorly aligned highways within the UK have focused attention on the problem of wet skidding resistance. The UK's Transport and Road Research Laboratory has had an enviable record in devising ways to mitigate and monitor the problem. The TRRL's success is measured by the adoption of its ideas in many other countries and by the fact that the rise in accidents is less than the growth of traffic. In addition to the improvements in tyres, drainage and surfacings, a major breakthrough was the design of a machine that could be used by any highway authority to monitor skidding resistance. It was hoped that this objective had been achieved with the building in 1973 of the first production machines for the routine monitoring of skid resistance. The acronymic title SCRIM was chosen deliberately to emphasize the routine nature of the operation.

The Marshall Committee rightly welcomed the introduction of SCRIM and made suggestions as to future roles as part of maintenance planning. Unfortunately, at that time their hopes were far in advance of the technological processes available to highway authorities in changing a research tool into an everyday operation. As with so many British inventions the development part of R and D had not been funded. This essential development was undertaken during the next five to seven years by co-operation between the manufacturers and users in particular the GLC, Surrey, West Yorkshire, Greater Manchester Council, Department of the Environment (Northern Ireland), and Department of Transport.[8.30,8.31]

The increasing use of SCRIM as a routine tool was not helped by the attitude of the legal and insurance professions in using the opportunity of such monitoring to further claims against highway authorities. Inevitably this led to a situation where an authority was often in a better position by not knowing the state of slipperiness on its highways.

Nevertheless, development has continued and a modern SCRIM (Fig. 8.7) is a formidable weapon in the fight to reduce accidents. Co-operation between the Department of Transport and the County Surveyors' Society PASV SAG has resulted in the formulation of proposals for the routine monitoring of highways. In the case of trunk roads, early in 1988 the Department of Transport published Standards and Advice notes,[8.13] which explain in considerable detail how and when SCRIM surveys should be undertaken and give guidance on interpretation of the data. In addition, by taking cognizance of the considerable experience gained by local authority users, in particular their developments of appropriate software,

*Fig. 8.7. Modern
SCRIM with automatic
(laser) location
referencing*

the Department of Transport has been able to initiate the first phase of a comprehensive software design study, which will enable the Standard to be fully implemented. When the improved software is available it will of course form part of the routine MMS and any other highway MMS involving trunk roads.

The monitoring of motorways and many trunk roads for skidding resistance is relatively straightforward, e.g. motorway surfaces are often of one consistent type for many miles, there are no statutory undertakers' trenches, changes in speed limit are few and roadside development is prohibited. The majority of roads under local authority management are, however, thronged with features that affect both the actual skidding resistance and the monitoring operation. It is not practicable to apply exactly the same procedures or standards on ordinary roads as those used on trunk roads. Amendments to the LAA Code of Good Practice (first edition),[8.11] as prepared by the County Surveyors' Society PASV SAG, give precise guidance as to methods of operation and factors to be taken into consideration in the interpretation of skidding resistance.

A guide to the operation of SCRIM by Hosking and Woodford,[8.34] and given in TRRL leaflets[8.35] will provide the reader with an elementary understanding of the process, but extensive study of the writings listed in the bibliography is recommended before attempting to manipulate data as recorded by the machine. Usually, however, it is not necessary for engineers using SCRIM as part of a MMS to possess that level of understanding provided that the recorded values have been correctly interpreted before entry in the MMS.

Among the traps for the unwary are: mismatching of data by location reference error; transient response or 'lost' SCRIM messages within a section; data aligned in the 'wrong' direction or to the 'wrong' carriageway on a dual carriageway; statutory undertakers' trenches in and out of wheel tracks; incorrect tracking calibration or correction, merging of incompatible readings in multi-surveys; improper wheel response on sinusoidal bends of small radii; incorrect tyre or tyre pressure, etc.

As an example of typical problems consider the Department of Transport's requirement to use the Mean Summer SCRIM Coefficient (MSSC) for assessment purposes. This means that three runs over the same section of highway are required in the SCRIM season April–September. If the same system is adopted by local highway authorities on their roads the likelihood of unwittingly merging incompatible data is considerable. This problem arises because the road network is dynamic; statutory undertakers and other works are prolific, often of short duration and unrecorded in any format that allows automatic recognition of their presence. Hence, in a three-run survey the first two may traverse a totally different surface from the third. If the third run is actually recording the value of a longitudinal trench (perhaps surfaced with limestone aggregate) it is incorrect to merge this with the first two. In terms of accident potential, however, it should be noted that the third run is probably the most critical. Very few organizations have the ability to recognize and cope with this type of situation.

Figure 8.8 illustrates another common type of problem with longitudinal trenches. In this case, SCRIM data suggested that all was well with the highway surface. Residents of the adjacent houses, however, were making continuing complaints that vehicles, particularly sports cars, were skid-

Fig. 8.8. Offset statutory undertaker's trench

ding off the road into their properties. The carriageway surface was shown
to be of good quality while the trench had been filled with cold fine asphalt
limestone aggregate. Nearside wheels of vehicles (and the SCRIM measuring wheel) ran on the HRA of SFC 0·58, but the offside wheels of any
rapidly accelerating cars encountered a trench with SFC of 0·17. The
results were as stated by the residents!

This case is an excellent illustration of the need to correlate incident as
well as accident data with skidding resistance measurements. As the vast
majority of incidents only involved one vehicle and no personal injury the
accident records indicated nothing unusual. Records of 'incidents' in the
Area Surveyor's office told a completely different story!

The guiding principle in all interpretation of SCRIM and similar data
is *beware*. As with so much human endeavour that which is true is not
necessarily obvious and that which is obvious is not necessarily true.

In the earlier stages of this discussion concerning objective systems,
attention was drawn to the large array of supporting systems required to
enable the three primary information sources, viz. the deflectograph,
SCRIM and HRM, to function effectively. Some of the appropriate
devices have received a brief mention in passing but there are many more.
Perhaps the easiest way to understand the supporting element is to list
their existence grouped under the three primary devices. The listing is not
exclusive and any supporting item may well have a role other than with the
primary devices and even outside the PMS. Indeed coring, although an
essential support element to deflection analysis, is also a vital ingredient in
the MMS itself, e.g. as part of bridges and other structure inspection
programmes.

Considering the deflectograph the auxiliary items may well include

(*a*) Benkelman beam — used for *ad hoc* surveys or localized follow-up
studies of the pathological type, where it would be uneconomic to
re-engage a deflectograph operation

(*b*) coring — used to evaluate pavement structure thickness/
condition/coating and possible core samples for measurement of
related parameters, e.g. density scan (nuclear) voids, overall
density, wheel tracking, binder recovery, delamination studies and
binder/aggregate affinity

(*c*) ground radar — used to establish thickness, water table position
and relevant geotechnical data, delamination and voids

(*d*) video and visual inspection for crack distribution and propagation, surface distress and deformation

(*e*) rolling straightedge and straightedge and wedge or topographical
surveying — localized surveys of pavement distress and monitoring of changes in profile

(*f*) Falling Weight Deflectometer (FWD) — detailed pathological
investigations where knowledge of the deflection bowl is required
to assess strain conditions in its own right or as a follow-up to
HRM

(*g*) wave propagation — used to derive thickness and elastic properties of the pavement.

An associated device (Instrumental Delamination Device) is claimed to be able to detect delaminations or voids in concrete road pavement or the seriousness of visible cracks.

For the assessment of surface characteristics the primary condition indicator is SCRIM measuring the skidding resistance. Associated devices that are valuable in aiding interpretation are

(a) texture meters — the high speed type, for measuring sensor-measured texture depth (SMTD) can travel at traffic speeds and hence can match the daily output expected from a SCRIM

(b) mini texture meters — these measure average SMTD and are intended at present for quality control checks on new hot rolled asphalt surfaces; their use as an adjunct for PMS requires considerable further work. It is important that each machine is checked when in use for its sensitivity, using additional equipment

(c) portable skid-resistance testers (pendulum testers) — which are not recommended for the routine assessment of skidding resistance despite attempts by many organizations so to do. There are no national standards for assessing skidding resistance in terms of SRV, and co-operative work within the County Surveyors' Society has shown that there are often grave discrepancies between machine/operator performance. Primarily it should be considered as a comparison tool to be used where SCRIM cannot (even in its low (20 km/h) configuration) and, until revised, for assessing road marking materials as required by Department of Transport Specification (1200 series)

(d) griptester friction trailers — these measure friction by the slipping (retarding by 14·5%) wheel method. They are currently under development and may become a useful replacement for the pendulum. At present they have no proven correlation with SCRIM over the full speed range neither is there any accident statistic correlation. Again they should be considered as a comparative tool, which may have distinct advantages in measurements of pedestrian areas, walkways, ramps, underpasses, etc.

(e) contactless wheeltrack rut meters and transverse profilometers — these provide the engineer with measurements that may be significant in assessing skid-related accidents. Ruts which allow ponding water (particularly on the approach to signal controlled junctions where traffic is channelled) or flat spots in sag vertical curves at the 'roll-over' of super elevation can create hazards that are not necessarily 'seen' by SCRIM.

To a large extent the supporting devices for the six-function HRM have already been mentioned (e.g. the rolling straightedge or topographic survey as a follow up to HRM determinations), but in addition to the rut meter and transverse profilometer two other devices are worthy of consideration.

(a) the Bump Integrator (BI)

(b) the SWE Road Tester.

The Bump Integrator — is one of the oldest mobile data collection devices still in existence having commenced operation in 1946. Modern machines have much improved data handling systems for what is essentially a response type road-roughness measuring system. Guidelines for conducting and calibrating road roughness measurements were published by the World Bank in 1986.[8.36] This work followed on the International Road Roughness Experiment in Brazil in 1982. Throughout the world there are many versions of road roughness measurement systems. They are defined in four groups of which the response-type (RTRRMS) is the most widely used, practical and fast. The International Roughness Index (IRI) is based on the simulation of the roughness response of a car travelling at 80 km/hour. The reference gives details of calibration and calculation procedures to determine IRI from different types of RTRRMS. The BI surveys at speeds in the range 24–48 km/hour. It is thought that by comparing the unevenness index as measured by the machine on successive surveys, the rate of change with time could provide an indication of pavement deterioration.

The SWE Road Tester is used elsewhere in Europe and has been utilized by some highway authorities in the UK (Fig. 8.9). Fundamentally, the machine as used during UK visits measures tranverse profile, rutting and the near-side edge geometry of the highway. It is claimed that it can measure texture and cracking equally successfully.

Fig. 8.9. SWE Road Tester — transverse lasers arrangement

Included within any PMS there is an absolute need for reliable traffic flow data. The data need to be reasonably comprehensive but more importantly they need to contain details about the axle loading distribution and damaging power of the heavy goods vehicle spectrum. The national census figures published by the Department of Transport are a useful starting point for any pavement evaluation and in the absence of more precise data are used widely. In local conditions of demographic change, however, serious under-design can result. Work is currently in hand to develop satisfactory weighing devices that can be installed easily, economically and which have appropriate and sufficiently accurate responses over a whole range of 'attack' speeds and axle loadings. In addition the apparatus needs to be 'camouflaged' to prevent undue avoidance by heavy vehicles. Methods of obtaining Vehicle Damage Factors were published by the County Surveyors' Society in 1983.[8.37]

If the PMS is to include extensive data about surface dressed roads it is likely that there will be need for regular Road Surface Hardness data. This information has to be obtained using a standard probe which yields 'spot' data.[8.38]

Having completed a review of the objective systems currently available and noting that primarily these relate to PMS, attention may now be re-directed to the overall MMS. The first and fundamental requirement is to bring all the data together and present it in useable form.

8.8. Other measurement information in HMMS

In addition to PMS data, there will be considerable amounts of other condition and inventory data, e.g. bridge and structure inspections including data from half-cell and corrosion surveys; geometric and design data; lighting, street furniture, etc. held within the MMS. Details of job costings, treatment proposals, estimates, accidents, winter maintenance data — thermal mapping, planned improvements and other information such as available assets (e.g. land), together with details of undertakers' services, are also likely to be required either in the system or easily accessed by it.

8.9. Data presentations and location referencing

The amount of data collected by a comprehensive PMS is extremely large. Considering data strings at 10 m intervals on an average 3000 lane-kilometre network it is quickly apparent that each year some hundreds of megabytes will require to be stored and accessed. The only sensible way to cope with this amount of data is by means of a relational database. Displaying the data in a useful format requires that there is a common referencing system for all the data and that the system is equally usable by all evaluation devices at whatever collection speed is appropriate.[8.39]

Compatibility between systems is required if data are to be gathered from diverse sources. The initial development of MMS was confounded by such problems, many of which persist but hopefully will be reduced in future. Most new software is structured in accordance with SSADM and the 'Gateway' concept.[8.40]

End users of data are served best by presentation against a map background or at least some diagrammatic representation of the highway network. In order to achieve this ideal, digitizations of Ordnance Survey mapping is essential, but unfortunately it will not be available throughout the UK until 2000 AD or later. The Chorley Committee's work[8.41–8.43] is evidence of industry's need for GIS. There are about a dozen organizations developing or offering various forms of GIS map digitizing, raster scanning and satellite imagery.

In the future it is likely that satellite location referencing will become the dominant method with the ability to fix any point on the earth's surface at acceptable levels of accuracy. French sources claim an accuracy better than 5 metres while military technology is expected to yield even better results, although still not available for civil use.

Of the existing systems many survey devices still rely on the keyboard entry of network reference code which, while satisfactory at slow speed, is not ideal for the next generation of devices. In an attempt to mitigate this problem use of pre-loaded 'string' entries requiring only one key stroke to enter on passing a reference point have been developed. A mistaken node reference point, however, is likely to disrupt a whole series of entries and require extensive editing. Reflective light patches overcome the human response time problem leaving a 'blip' on the recording trace, which is assumed to be a genuine marker if it appears somewhere near its expected position but such systems are not self-checking. Dead reckoning systems based on magnetometer displacement or the Ferranti Navigational System (FIRS) and the laser bar-code systems are self-checking, leading to significant advantages where more complex networks are involved. Experimental work at TRRL with Surrey's laser system has demonstrated satisfactory decoding at 96 km/h.

Although many of the data are alpha-numeric, with the increasing use of video and photographic recording the need for image data storage is growing. One way of tackling this problem is by use of the video disc but other alternatives are CAD and graphics facilities linked to call-back procedures using video tape. The GIS approach probably provides the best means of data store access for the developments likely to occur during the next decade or two.

8.10. Staffing

When considering the staffing levels needed for a comprehensive MMS it is important to bear in mind the way the system is to be managed. Is the work to be direct, is it to be contractor services, or consultant services, or is it to be a combination of these?

For many public authorities the answer is most likely to be a combination of all three. The highway authority is usually the user of the MMS and probably controls the mainframe computer on which the bulk of the data is stored but may not provide or control the staff running the system. In the case of an average size network as discussed previously, likely staff requirements are: a controller; a network co-ordinator, who controls all amendments to the computer model of the highway network; a systems analyst, responsible for overseeing all developments, preventing data corruption and helping users. In addition, programmers and operators will be required from time to time.

The vital need for data security might be provided by the controller, but in a large system it could be a separate post.

In respect of the actual surveying, inventory data and condition data can on some occasions be collected at the same time. This procedure makes the most cost-effective use of staff but is not always practicable. Decisions must also be taken as to the frequency of up-dating inventory data — as explained previously this can often be at a lower frequency than condition data. Most mobile data collection devices need a team of two and it is usual within the larger authorities for the team responsible for pavement assessment to consist of four to five persons competent to use a whole range of equipment. The utilization of much equipment tends to be unexacting because of time restrictions, preferred periods of operation, etc. Hence with careful programming the same personnel can cope with a variety of tasks.

Specialist contractors tend to concentrate on only one or two aspects of the work and seek a higher utilization rate of the machines by moving rapidly between different projects. When making use of such services, therefore, the actual number of persons involved at a given time may be five to ten times greater than a permanently employed team. There are, however, no absolute advantages in either system, as usually the most crucial factor is not the efficiency with which one item of data can be collected but the time required to process all the data, carry out the interpretation and enter the validated data into the common user database. It is by accessing these data that the end user begins to gain the benefit of the systematic approach and make cost saving decisions.

Interpretation of data has to be undertaken by engineers with a wide range of experience if maximum benefit is to be gained. A thorough understanding of the costs, constraints, logistic requirements of all the treatment options derived from the data is necessary for those allocating financial resources to the works commitment. For those undertaking the interpretation of pavement assessment data it is vital to have an extensive knowledge of the apparatus involved, machine capability recording and electronic system response, machine limitations, and calibration procedures, together with a fundamental understanding of the geotechnical/material processes involved in pavement design and construction.

In-house teams of engineers to cope with these problems will probably number from two to six and would be expected to have at least 75 years' experience between them. Where appropriate skills are lacking the use of consultants is a very cost-effective procedure as time constraints on data acquisition and interpretation to meet budget preparation deadlines are often severe.

8.11. Costings

Assuming at 1988 prices a mean salary of £16 000 p.a. for the personnel involved, numbering 10–18 full-time annual equivalents and with 100%

Table 8.2. Approximate 1989 prices for
pavement assessment operations

Deflectograph	£1200 per day plus processing
FWD	£1500 per day
SCRIM	£1200 per day plus processing
HRM	£2000 per day
BI	£750 per day
Ground radar	£1000 per day plus processing
Inventory	£450 per day

on-costs it will be seen that the running costs will be of the order of 1·5–3·5% for an average £18 million p.a. maintenance budget.

The cost of individual items of survey depend obviously on complexity, quality and timing. A guide for typical pavement assessment operations is given in Table 8.2. By using this information and the answers to the fundamental questions (Table 8.1), cost models can be constructed for various strategies, e.g. it could be decided by the highway authority that 80% of the available funds will be concentrated on those highways carrying more than 65% of the area's total traffic and with heavy goods vehicles flows greater than 2500 per day. From these data, the lane kilometre length of the highways involved could be established together with other demand attributes and a survey strategy determined. By costing this strategy, comparing it against the asset value and estimating the risk of accidents, delays, etc., arising from unplanned and uncoordinated maintenance works, the cost effectiveness of the proposed system can be evaluated. The process can of course be iterative to find the optimum solutions.

8.12. Future development and additional information

During the next decade it is anticipated that there will be an explosive growth of sophisticated management information systems of which HMMS are typical examples. It could be argued that highway management has been the poor relation in the civil engineering industry for far too long. It is over 20 years since Marshall collected his evidence and critics would say that there has been a criminal waste of time and resources in moving towards a proper system.

The House of Commons Expenditure Committee, when reviewing the evidence put before it in the early 1980s said

> The Marshall Committee's finding that 'virtually nothing is known at present about the optimum level of maintenance from the point of view of its value to the community' remained true today

and

> This was in spite of the Marshall Report's conclusion that 'this is the only approach which offers a prospect of arriving at standards which will be acceptable as objectively suitable'.

Similar observations were made to and by the House of Commons Transport Committee prior to the 1987 election and subsequently the Audit Commission was asked to undertake a special study of highway maintenance. Mustow[8.44] reported in 1987 that there was no consistent use of condition surveys, still only limited trend information available either within or between highway authorities and that

> Management system development
> needs some coordination . . . .
> needs to be considered in a total systems context . . . .

As the work of the Commission is continuing it is quite possible that recommendations for further action will draw heavily on the success or otherwise of the Department of Transport/LAA initiative in respect of PMS, and pay increasing attention to the integration of such systems into total management.

Guidelines have been prepared for the specification of a logical design for PMS systems, and tenders invited from selected contractors. These guidelines resulted in a specification based on a modular approach because it was considered that with a number of systems in existence users may already have a particular version relevant to an individual module which they would wish to retain. Hence, the PMS is split into well-defined modules all of which will be prepared in accordance with Structured Systems Analysis and Design Methodology (SSADM). The essential elements of the PMS are: data dictionary and common glossary of terms; locational referencing; item inventory; condition inventory; visual inspections; machine inspections; budget preparation, allocation and outturns; inquiry and report monitor of network condition trends; treatment identification and selection (both conditioned and economics based); estimates; rating and scheme priorities; projection of network condition trends; projection of pavement performance; construction data as a database; monitoring treatment performance; works order interface; and archiving. It is proposed that the performance of the PMS design is to be assessed by using the prototype in three environments, namely a county council, a metropolitan district and a London borough.

The arguments for and against integrated transport policies, infrastructure plans, etc. versus an unfettered free market approach are being debated with increasing regularity. Developments in Europe are bound to affect longer term strategic options after 1992 as irrespective of central government's decisions, industry will have to decide on locations for expansion, transport modes, warehousing/transfer facilities and a host of similarly demanding questions. The answers to these questions will have a profound influence on future highway utilization, planning and maintenance requirements. Failure to invest in proper management and maintenance of the existing assets can have only one result — a continuing decline of the UK's competitiveness. Given these external demands the will to develop HMMS now seems to be acceptable policy for very many highway authorities. The challenges for management in bringing such policies to a successful conclusion are numerous and should not be underestimated. Inevitably the systems require quite substantial investment in computer technology and despite the continuous improvement in electronics hardware, the sheer size of the data stores involved, once successive years' records are on file, will create many problems. In order to provide security of data, back-up systems are vital and as these require even more storage, management and support, the demand for improved facilities will grow. Mention has already been made of laser disc technology but proven long-term capability has yet to be demonstrated. Bubble memories and similar devices are as yet too limited in capacity although they have undoubted advantages in some forms of data capture.

The future of associated data presentation techniques is likely to be greatly influenced by video mapping, satellite and thermal imagery, interaction graphics and CAD. However sophisticated data capture and manipulation may be, the end user requires information in an easily understood form that relates to the real world as perceived by the person who has to carry out remedial work on the highway. Consequently, improvements that translate meaningless tabulations, referenced to 9 or 15 digit spatial locations, into a picture of named and recognizable features will always be welcomed. Most of the technology required is available now, it only remains for managements to implement the systems they need and can use effectively.

Acknowledgements

Many colleagues within the County Surveyors' Society, The TRRL and Department of Transport, together with a number of private consultants, have by stimulating debate contributed to the formulation of the views expressed in this chapter. The numbers are too large to list on an individual basis, but their help and advice extending over three decades is acknowledged with grateful thanks. In addition, the advice of Jeff Stansfield in respect of the Pavement Management Study and permission to quote from this document is much appreciated, as is that of the County Surveyors's Society PASV SAG and to that Group's present and previous Chairmen. Thanks are also expressed to the author's wife, Ms Angela Milne and Cora Brooks for typing the manuscript.

References

8.1. NATIONAL ECONOMIC DEVELOPMENT OFFICE. *Contracting in civil engineering since Banwell.* Her Majesty's Stationery Office, London, 1968, 4.14 *et. seq.*

8.2. MARSHALL A.H. *Report of the Commitee on Highway Maintenance.* Her Majesty's Stationery Office, London, 1970.

8.3. DEPARTMENT OF TRANSPORT. *Review of structural maintenance of motorways and all-purpose trunk roads* (Gaffney Report). Her Majesty's Stationery Office, London, 1986.

8.4. DEPARTMENT OF TRANSPORT. *Code of practice for routine maintenance.* Her Majesty's Stationery Office, London, 1984.

8.5. RENDEL PALMER AND TRITTON and HERTFORDSHIRE COUNTY COUNCIL. *Feasibility study of PMS reported to PMS Management Group.* November, 1988.

8.6. TAPIO R. The evaluation of maintenance and reconstruction needs of roads in the long term planning. *Proc. 2nd Int. Conf. Bearing Capacity of Roads and Airfields*, Plymouth, 1986.

8.7. COTTELL M.N. County Surveyors' Society Presidential Address. Association of County Councils' Annual Conference, Bournemouth, 1988.

8.8. INSTITUTION OF CIVIL ENGINEERS. *Pavement management technology. How does UK compare?* Thomas Telford, London, 1988.

8.9. KERALI H.G.R. and SNAITH M.S. A system for assigning priorities and maintenance projects in developing countries. *Proc. 2nd Int. Conf. Bearing Capacity of Roads and Airfields*, Plymouth, 1986.

8.10. BLAKEY F.W. *Maintenance options and standards PTRC Autumn 1984.* PTRC Education and Research Services, London.

8.11. LOCAL AUTHORITY ASSOCIATION. *LAA highway maintenance — a code of good practice.* Asociation of County Councils, Association of Metropolitan Authorities, Association of District Councils, London, 1983.

8.12. DEPARTMENT OF TRANSPORT. *Code of practice for routine maintenance.* Newsletter No. 4, Her Majesty's Stationery Office, London, September, 1988.

8.13. DEPARTMENT OF TRANSPORT. *Skidding resistance of in-service trunk roads.* Departmental Standard HD 15/87 and Advice Note HA 36/87, DoE/DTp, London, 1987.

8.14. GARRETT C. Whole-life costing of roads. *Mun. Engr*, 1985, **2**, No. 4, 223–232.

8.15. COTTELL M.N.T. Future developments as seen by a county surveyor. *Institution of Highways and Transportation Presidential Conference*, York, 1986.

8.16. BUDDEN M.J. *Microbus Seminar*, Berkshire County Council, Shire Hall, Reading, June, 1985.

8.17. CHILDS S.M. *Pavement assessment in maintenance management IHT.* Premium Paper Award, January, 1988.

8.18. MILLARD R.S. and LISTER N.W. The assessment of maintenance needs for road pavements. *Proc. Instn Civ. Engrs*, 1971, **48**, February, 223–244.

8.19. KENNEDY C.K. *et al. Pavement deflection: equipment for measurement in the United Kingdom.* Transport and Road Research Laboratory, Crowthorne, 1978, Report 834.

8.20. GARRETT C. and LAWRENCE E.D. Structural road maintenance assessment in Kent. *Proc. 2nd Int. Conf. Bearing Capacity of Roads and Airfields*, Plymouth, 1986.

8.21. DEPARTMENT OF TRANSPORT. *Strength of flexible pavements by deflection measurement.* Departmental Standard HD/10/83, DTp, London, 1983.

8.22. DEPARTMENT OF TRANSPORT. *Operational practice for the deflection beam and deflectograph.* Departmental Advice Note HA/24/83, DTp, London, 1983.

8.23. DEPARTMENT OF TRANSPORT. *Analysis interpretation and application of deflection measurements.* Departmental Advice Note HA/25/83, DTp, London, 1983.

8.24. DEPARTMENT OF TRANSPORT. *Structural examinations of bituminous pavements.* Departmental Advice Note HA/30/85, DTp, London, 1985.

8.25. GREEN P.A. and PARKER B.L. The economics of ground investigation for major roadworks. *Midlands Soil Mechanics and Foundation Engineering Society Symposium*, University of Birmingham, 1964.

8.26. PARKER B.L. *Laboratory service to engineers. Are you asking the right questions?* Institution of Civil Engineers North Western Association, Preston, 1974.

8.27. HARDY M.F. A look into the future. *Institution of Highways & Transportation Presidential Address.* Cambridge University, September, 1983.

8.28. JORDON P.G. Measurement of road surface shape using a laser sensor. *Sensors in Highway and Civil Engineering*, Thomas Telford, London, 1981, pp. 105–117.

8.29. JORDON P.G. *et al.* An integrated system for the evaluation of road pavements. *Proc. 6th Int. Conf. Struct. Des. Asphalt Pavement.* 1987, vol. 1. University of Michigan, Ann Arbor.

8.30. YOUNG A.W. *The potential for accident reduction by improving urban skid resistance levels.* PhD thesis, Queen Mary College, London, 1985.

8.31. PARKER B.L. Living with the Marshall Report. Sophisticated testing by improved SCRIM. *Institution of Highway Engineers Symposium 'A Southern Aspct'.* University of Southampton, 1979.

8.32. HATHERLY L.W. Deflectograph and SCRIM: Is the struggle worth the while? *Surveyor*, April, 1974.

8.33. PARKER B.L. *The use of SCRIM and applied laboratory facilities.* Institution of Highway Engineers, Southern Branch, December, 1981.

8.34. HOSKING J.R. and WOODFORD G.C. *Measurement of skidding resistance. Part 1. Guide to the use of SCRIM.* TRRL Laboratory Report 737, Crowthorne, 1976.

8.35. TRANSPORT AND ROAD RESEARCH LABORATORY. Leaflet (original version) LF 915 (HM 41), Crowthorne, November, 1982; Leaflet 983.

8.36. SAYERS M.W. *et al. Guidelines for conducting and calibrating road roughness measurements.* World Bank Technical Paper No. 46, Washington, DC, 1986.

8.37. COUNTY SURVEYORS' SOCIETY. *Vehicle damage factors. Present, past and future values.* Kent County Council, Maidstone, 1983.

8.38. WRIGHT N. *Surface dressing: assessment of road surface hardness.* Transport and Road Research Laboratory, Crowthorne, 1980, Supplementary Report SR 573.

8.39. PARKER B.L. Location referencing and its value in high speed mobile data acquisition. *Proc. 2nd Int. Conf. Bearing Capacity of Roads and Airfields*, Plymouth, 1986.

8.40. COUNTY SURVEYORS' SOCIETY. Highway management systems. *The Gateway Concept Seminar*, Reading, 1987.

8.41. COUNTY SURVEYORS' SOCIETY. Submission to the *Chorley Committee of Enquiry Into the Handling of Geographical Information.* Report 2/2, Cheshire County Council, Feb. 1986.

8.42. DEPARTMENT OF THE ENVIRONMENT. Handling geographic information. *Report of the Committee of Enquiry*, chaired by Lord Chorley. Her Majesty's Stationery Office, London, 1987.

8.43. DEPARTMENT OF THE ENVIRONMENT. Handling geographic information. *The Government's Response to the Report of the Committee of Enquiry*, chaired by Lord Chorley. Her Majesty's Stationery Office, London, 1988.

8.44. MUSTOW S.N. Institution of Highways and Transportation. *Presidential Conference*, University of Nottingham, 1987.

Bibliography

General

A directory of pavement assessment equipment. County Surveyors' Society Report No. 5/10, December, 1988. Devon County Council. (This 35 page document gives a brief résumé of the majority of PA equipment available in the UK listing, *inter alia*, costs, sources and equipment description.)

County Surveyors' Society. *Highway maintenance data: collection, storage, retrieval and use*. Papers by C. Meadon, M. Hatt, B.L. Parker, C. Garrett, D.S. Priest, D. Goldsmith, R. Biggs and D. Pearson. Guildhall, London, May 1985, and County Hall, Manchester, October 1985.

Department of Transport. *ICE detection system, thermal mapping and road weather forecasting*. TRMM 4/88, London.

FIRS (Ferranti Inertial Road Survey Descriptions and Definitions). Navigation Systems Department, Ferranti, Edinburgh, 1982.

MacKenzie N.B. Maintenance management information systems. *PTRC Autumn 1984*. PTRC, London, Lecture 6. (Contains examples of data sheets used by Scottish Development Department in their CHIPS DATA-BASE.) see also FIRS.

MacKenzie N.B. and McCullum D.G. Locationally-referenced highway management information system — the CHIPS database in Scotland. In *Traff. Engng Control*, October 1985.

Maintenance management. *PTRC Spring Courses 1984*. British Institute of Management, PTRC, London.

Sensors in highway and civil engineering. Thomas Telford, London, 1981.

Soussain G. *et al.* and Charles R. *PTRC Summer 1988*. University of Bath, PTRC, London.

Thomas Telford Ltd. *Pavement management technology. How does the UK compare?* TTL, London, 1988.

Standards, strategy, feedback and finance

Hardy M.F. *Presidential Address to the Institution of Highways and Transportation*. University of Cambridge, September, 1983.

Institution of Highway Engineers. *National Workshop on Feedback for Construction and Maintenance*. Leamington Spa, 1983.

Leech G.A. Highway maintenance standards. A County Surveyor's view. *IHT Presidential Symposium on Maintenance Standards*. University of Cambridge, 1983.

Porter J. and Abell R. Analysis of maintenance options. *Institution of Highways and Transportation National Workshop of Highway Maintenance Initiative*. Leamington Spa, April, 1985.

Powell W.D. Failure investigations and designs for strengthening. *Institution of Highways and Transportation National Workshop*. Leamington Spa, 1988.

Richardson P.W. Financial control. *PTRC Autumn 1984*. PTRC, London, Lecture 15.

Smith A.D.W. Highway reconstruction and maintenance. *The Beijing Papers*. Institution of Highways and Transportation, 1986.

Taylor D.A. Maintenance management systems. *Present Practice in an English County. Institution of Highways and Transportation National Workshop on Highway Maintenance Initiatives*. Leamington Spa, April 1985.

Deflection measurement and evaluation

Geotechnical investigation for highway design. Investigation and testing: the material engineer's viewpoint. Case Study 2 in a paper by B.L. Parker, *PTRC Autumn Course 1982*. PTRC, London.

Institution of Highways and Transportation. *The Beijing Papers*, Papers H17, H18, H19 and H20. IHT, London, 1986.

Kennedy C.K. and Butler I.C. Validation of the existing deflection and performance relationships for use on lightly trafficked roads. *PTRC Summer 1983*. PTRC, London.

LISTER N.W. Strengthening and reconstruction: design criteria for decision making. *Nat. Conf. on Maintenance and Reconstruction of Motorways and Other Heavily Trafficked Roads*, Leamington Spa, Institution of Highways and Transportation and Institution of Civil Engineers, 1980.

Proc. 2nd Int. Conf. Bearing Capacity of Roads and Airfields, Plymouth, 1986; WDM, Bristol, 1986. Papers by Kumar and Kennedy, Butler, Roberts and Catt.

Skidding resistance measurement and evaluation

BULLETT A.W. and GARRETT C. Problems of implementing a skid resistance policy. *The performance of rolled asphalt road surfacings*, pp. 169–179. Institution of Civil Engineers, London, 1980.

CARROLL T.J. Skidding resistance standards for trunk roads in England. *The performance of rolled asphalt road surfacings*, pp. 161–168. Institution of Civil Engineers, London, 1980.

CATT C.A. *An alternative view of TRRL's research into skidding resistance.* Institute of Asphalt Technology.

GARRETT T. A skidding resistance investigation on the national road network. *PTRC 16 Meeting*, Seminar F, 1988.

HATHERLY L.W. and YOUNG A.E. Location and treatment on urban skidding hazard sites. *Proc. 2nd Int. Skid Prevention Conf. Columbus.* Transportation Research Board, Washington, DC, 1977.

Kent procedure for monitoring and control of skidding resistance. Kent County Council, 1987.

SALT G.E. and SZATOWSKI W.S. *A guide to levels of skidding resistance for roads.* Transport and Road Research Laboratory, Crowthorne, 1973, Report LR 510. (This document should be studied together with that of Garrett and the revised Code of Good Practice.)

The influence of the road surface in skidding. *University of Salford Symposium*, 1975.

9

Accident prevention

In less than a century, road transport has come to occupy a central position in the lives of the developed world's population. Not only does it provide the largest contribution to satisfying the demand for personal mobility, but it is also responsible for the movement of the majority of goods that contemporary society produces and consumes. The private motor car potentially offers a level of service to the individual with mass personal flexibility almost undreamt of as little as four or five generations ago. This flexibility, and the right of the individual to exercise it, is not, however, without disadvantages to society. With the development of road transport has come growth in pollution, urban congestion and incidents in the system. The initial use of the word 'incident' is quite intentional since virtually all of what are colloquially known as 'accidents' can, on detailed examination, have one or more causes associated with them. Strictly speaking, therefore, they cannot be described as 'accidents', the Oxford Dictionary definition of which is '...an event without apparent cause...' happening purely by chance. If this were so then there would be no basis on which to seek effective remedial measures, no matter what route was chosen. Lapsing into the generally used terminology, experience gained as the system has developed has shown that carefully chosen measures matched to factors repeatedly involved can prevent the occurrence of accidents, which statistics and trend analyses indicate would otherwise have occurred.

9.1. Scale of the problem

The primary object of this chapter is to explore measures, available in the context of highway maintenance, for improving the safe movement of pedestrians and vehicular traffic without undue negative effects on overall efficiency of movement or personal freedom of choice. Before doing this, however, the scale of the problem implicitly tolerated by society justifies consideration. Only a few years ago the broadcaster Nick Ross presented two TV documentaries dealing with the road accident problem, the first of which was entitled 'The biggest epidemic of our time'[9.1] and the second, 'Still the biggest epidemic of our time'.[9.2] While perhaps some might think that these titles are typical of a media attraction to sensationalism, their use was totally justifiable in this case. In human terms it is estimated[9.3] that the annual toll of road traffic accidents worldwide numbers more than

Fig. 9.1. Department of Transport Stats 19 Accident Report form: accident record — attendant circumstances

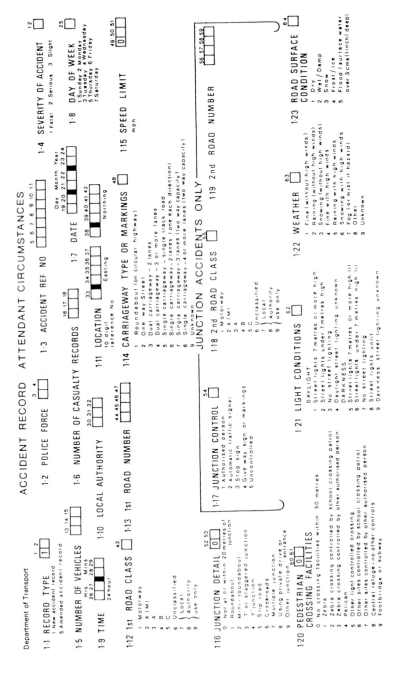

1·24 SPECIAL CONDITIONS AT SITE [65]
0 None
1 Automatic Traffic Signal-out
2 Automatic Traffic Signal partially defective
3 Permanent road signing defective or obscured
4 Road works present
5 Road surface defective

1·25 CARRIAGEWAY HAZARDS [66]
0 None
1 Dislodged vehicle load in carriageway
2 Other object in carriageway
3 Involvement with previous accident
4 Dog in carriageway
5 Other animal in carriageway

1·26 OVERTAKING MANOEUVRE PATTERNS [67]
No longer required by the Department of Transport

1·27 DTp SPECIAL PROJECTS [68 69 70 71]

VEHICLE RECORD

2·1 RECORD TYPE [1 2] [2]
1 New vehicle record
5 Amended vehicle record

2·2 POLICE FORCE [3 4]

2·3 ACCIDENT REF NO [5 6 7 8 9 10 11]

2·4 VEHICLE REF NO [12 13 14]

2·5 TYPE OF VEHICLE [15 16]
01 Pedal cycle
02 Moped
03 Motor scooter
04 Motor cycle
05 Combination
06 Invalid Tricycle
07 Other three-wheeled car
08 Taxi
09 Car (Four wheeled)
10 Minibus/Motor caravan
11 PSV
12 Goods not over 1½ tons UW (1·52 tonnes)
13 Goods over 1½ tons UW (1·52 tonnes)
14 Other motor vehicle
15 Other non motor vehicle

2·6 TOWING AND ARTICULATION [17]
0 No tow/articulation
1 Articulated vehicle
2 Double/multiple trailer
3 Caravan
4 Single trailer
5 Other tow

2·7 MANOEUVRES [18 19]
01 Reversing
02 Parked
03 Waiting to go ahead but held up
04 Stopping
05 Starting
06 U Turn
07 Turning left
08 Waiting to turn left
09 Turning right
10 Waiting to turn right
11 Changing lane to left
12 Changing lane to right
13 Overtaking moving vehicle on its offside
14 Overtaking stationary vehicle on its offside
15 Overtaking on nearside
16 Going ahead left hand bend
17 Going ahead right hand bend
18 Going ahead other

2·8 VEHICLE MOVEMENT COMPASS POINT [20 21] From To
1 N
2 NE
3 E
4 SE
5 S
6 SW
7 W
8 NW
or [0 0] Parked – not at kerb
[0 0] Parked – at kerb

2·9 VEHICLE LOCATION AT TIME OF ACCIDENT [22 23]
01 Leaving the main road
02 Entering the main road
03 On main road
04 On minor road
05 On service road
06 On lay-by or hard shoulder
07 Entering lay-by or hard shoulder
08 Leaving lay-by or hard shoulder
09 On a cycleway
10 Not on carriageway

— continued overleaf

Fig. 9.1 — continued

2·10 JUNCTION LOCATION OF VEHICLE AT FIRST IMPACT [24]
0 Not at junction(or within 20 metres/22 yards)
1 Vehicle approaching junction/ vehicle parked at junction approach
2 Vehicle in middle of junction
3 Vehicle cleared junction/vehicle parked at junction exit
4 Did not impact

2·11 SKIDDING AND OVERTURNING [25]
0 No skidding, jacknifing or overturning
1 Skidding
2 Skidded and overturned
3 Jacknifed
4 Jacknifed and overturned
5 Overturned

2·12 HIT OBJECT IN CARRIAGEWAY [26 27]
00 None
01 Previous accident
02 Road works
03 Parked vehicle - lit
04 Parked vehicle - unlit
05 Bridge(roof)
06 Bridge(side)
07 Bollard/refuge
08 Open door of vehicle
09 Central island of roundabout
10 Kerb
11 Other object

2·13 VEHICLE LEAVING CARRIAGEWAY [28]
0 Did not leave carriageway
1 Left carriageway nearside
2 Left carriageway nearside and rebounded
3 Left carriageway straight ahead at junction
4 Left carriageway offside onto central reservation
5 Left carriageway offside onto central reservation and rebounded
6 Left carriageway offside vehicle crossed central reservation
7 Left carriageway offside
8 Left carriageway offside and rebounded

2·14 HIT OBJECT OFF CARRIAGEWAY [29 30]
00 None
01 Road sign/ Traffic signal
02 Lamp post
03 Telegraph pole/Electricity pole
04 Tree
05 Bus stop/Bus shelter
06 Central crash barrier
07 Nearside or offside crash barrier
08 Submerged in water(completely)
09 Entered ditch
10 Other permanent object

2·15 VEHICLE PREFIX/SUFFIX LETTER [31]
PREFIX/SUFFIX LETTER or one of the following codes –
0 More than twenty years old (at end of year)
1 Unknown/cherished number/ not applicable
2 Foreign/diplomatic
3 Military
4 Trade plates

2·16 FIRST POINT OF IMPACT [32]
0 Did not impact
1 Front
2 Back
3 Offside
4 Nearside

2·17 OTHER VEHICLE HIT (VEH REF NO) [33 34 35]

2·18 PART(S) DAMAGED [36 37 38]
0 None
1 Front
2 Back
3 Offside
4 Nearside
5 Roof
6 Underside
7 All four sides

2·19 NO OF AXLES [39]
0 Not goods vehicle
2 2 axles
3 3 axles   } Goods Vehicles only
4 4 axles
5 5 or more axles

2·20 MAXIMUM PERMISSIBLE GROSS WEIGHT [40 41]
Metric tonnes (Goods vehicle only)

2·21 SEX OF DRIVER [42]
1 Male
2 Female
3 Not traced

2·22 AGE OF DRIVER [43 44]
(Years, estimated if necessary)

2·23 BREATH TEST [45]
0 Not applicable
1 Positive
2 Negative
3 Not requested
4 Failed to provide
5 Driver not contacted at time

2·24 HIT AND RUN [46]
0 Other
1 'Hit and run'
2 Non-stop vehicle not hit

2·25 DTp SPECIAL PROJECTS [47 48 49 50]

Stats 19 (Rev. Nov. 1983)

CASUALTY RECORD

3·1 RECORD TYPE [3] `1 2`
1 New casualty record
5 Amended casualty record

3·2 POLICE FORCE [ ] `3`

3·3 ACCIDENT REF NO. [ ][ ][ ][ ][ ][ ][ ] `5 6 7 8 9 10 11`

3·4 VEHICLE REF NO. [ ][ ][ ] `12 13 14`

3·5 CASUALTY REF NO. [ ][ ][ ] `15 16 17`

3·6 CASUALTY CLASS [ ] `18`
1 Driver or rider
2 Vehicle or pillion passenger
3 Pedestrian

3·7 SEX OF CASUALTY [ ] `19`
1 Male
2 Female

3·8 AGE OF CASUALTY [ ][ ] `20 21`
(Years, estimated if necessary)

3·9 SEVERITY OF CASUALTY [ ] `22`
1 Fatal
2 Serious
3 Slight

3·10 PEDESTRIAN LOCATION [ ][ ] `23 24`
00 Not pedestrian
01 In carriageway crossing on pedestrian crossing
02 In carriageway crossing within zig-zag lines approach to the crossing
03 In carriageway crossing within zig-zag lines exit the crossing
04 In carriageway crossing elsewhere within 50 metres of pedestrian crossing
05 In carriageway crossing elsewhere
06 On footway or verge
07 On refuge or central island or reservation
08 In centre of carriageway not on refuge or central island
09 In carriageway not crossing
10 Unknown

3·11 PEDESTRIAN MOVEMENT [ ] `25`
0 Not pedestrian
1 Crossing from drivers nearside
2 Crossing from drivers nearside-masked by parked or stationary vehicle
3 Crossing from drivers offside
4 Crossing from drivers offside-masked by parked or stationary vehicle
5 In carriageway stationary-not crossing (standing or playing)
6 In carriageway stationary-not crossing (standing or playing)-
  masked by parked or stationary vehicle
7 Walking along in carriageway facing traffic
8 Walking along in carriageway back to traffic
9 Unknown

3·12 PEDESTRIAN DIRECTION [ ] `26`
Compass point bound
1 N
2 NE
3 E
4 SE
5 S
6 SW
7 W
8 NW
or 0 - Pedestrian - standing still

3·13 SCHOOL PUPIL CASUALTY [ ] `27`
0 Not a school pupil
1 Pupil on journey to/from school
2 Pupil NOT on journey to/from school

3·14 SEAT BELT USAGE [ ] `28`
0 Not car or van
1 Safety belt in use
2 Safety belt fitted-not in use
3 Safety belt not fitted
4 Child safety belt/harness fitted-in use
5 Child safety belt/harness fitted-not in use
6 Child safety belt/harness not fitted
7 Unknown

3·15 CAR PASSENGER [ ] `29`
0 Not car passenger
1 Front seat car passenger
2 Rear seat car passenger

3·16 PSV PASSENGER [ ] `30`
0 Not a PSV passenger
1 Boarding
2 Alighting
3 Standing passenger
4 Seated passenger

3·17 DTp SPECIAL PROJECTS [ ][ ][ ][ ] `31 32 33 34`

250 000 fatalities and 10 million personal injuries. Within the member states of the EEC, there are currently some 1·2 million road traffic accidents reported each year in which more than 1·5 million suffer personal injury. At the time of writing the most recent annual statistics available for the UK[9.4] show that there were 5382 fatalities and some 321 000 casualties occurring in 248 000 accidents reported as having involved personal injury. Also, there are approximately 1·5 million non-injury accidents involving property damage reported to insurance companies and an unknown number that do not appear in any statistics. As well as the personal and emotive consequences of this situation there are considerable economic implications for society in general and these are further considered later in the chapter.

9.2 Accident reporting and classification

Alarming though the national statistics are, the full extent of the problem is not revealed. They are based on details of personal injury accidents reported to the police and recorded on the Department of Transport (DTp) form known as Stats 19 (see Fig. 9.1). The information required for the completion of this form is reasonably comprehensive, the current version having evolved over many years. Basically consisting of three sections, it seeks to establish details pertinent to the circumstances, the vehicles involved and the casualties. There is, however, no general requirement in Great Britain for road traffic accidents to be reported to the police. The Road Traffic Act 1972 simply requires that the driver of a motor vehicle involved in an accident should give to any interested party details of himself, his vehicle and, if someone is injured, his insurance. Only when the driver is unable to do this is there a requirement to report the accident to the police.

A comparison by Bull and Roberts[9.5] of hospital and police records estimated that about one-third of slight, and one-sixth of serious injuries had arisen in unreported accidents. This was further supported by the results of an investigation[9.6] of the length of time casualties spent in hospital following a road traffic accident, which revealed that about 30% were in this category and were not therefore included in national statistics. The extent of under-reporting was found to depend on the category of road user involved. Injuries to car occupants were under-reported by about 14%, pedestrians by about 27% and pedal cyclists by about 60%. By definition these findings relate to those injuries classified as 'serious'. It seems probable that there is greater under-reporting of accidents involving slight injury.

Furthermore, the information available for those accidents that are reported is, for a variety of reasons, frequently incomplete. The police officer may not have attended the scene and may be reporting it 'second hand'; the person reporting it may not have details of vehicles or others involved, and may be vague about the location. This last point may be of particular significance in relation to accident remedial measures involving the highway. Data from the Stats 19 form (see section 1.11 of Fig. 9.1) appear to specify location to within 10 m in either direction. Clearly this apparent accuracy will, however, be spurious in many cases. Inaccuracies are most likely in rural areas where the number of identifying features available to assist the description of the accident 'in clear' will generally be far fewer than in a built-up region.

Classification of the severity of the accident is also recorded by the police on the Stats 19 form (see section 1.4 of Fig. 9.1). This is determined by the severity of the most seriously injured casualty involved, either slight, serious or fatal (see section 3.9 of Fig. 9.1), using the following criteria

(a) *slight injury* — an injury of a minor character such as a sprain, bruise, cut or laceration not judged to be severe, or slight shock requiring roadside attention

(b) *serious injury* — an injury for which a person is detained in hospital as an 'in-patient', or any of the following injuries whether or not detention results: fractures, concussion, internal injuries, crushings, severe cuts and lacerations, severe general shock requiring medical treatment, injuries causing death 30 or more days after the accident

(c) *fatal* — death from injuries sustained, resulting less than 30 days after the accident.

An injured casualty is coded by the police as 'seriously' or 'slightly' injured on the basis of information available within a short time of the accident. This generally will not include the results of a medical examination, but may include the fact of being detained in hospital. Death within 30 days will subsequently be notified to the police and the Stats 19 record amended as necessary, but awareness of changes between 'slight' and 'serious' classifications is much less likely.

There is little that the safety practitioner can do to rectify retrospectively these shortcomings in existing basic data. However, sight must never be lost of the fact that these data are the raw material of the accident investigator's trade; its shortcomings and limitations must be clearly borne in mind and allowance made for them wherever possible. Against this background accident-preventative work has to identify those problems most deserving of effort and resource, evaluate them, formulate possible solutions and monitor the effectiveness of that eventually implemented. It is in such a context that the statistics used to illustrate the remainder of this chapter are quoted.

9.3. Accident statistics and trends in Great Britain

Recent decades have witnessed large increases in the number of vehicles on our roads. Over the same period highway development has been contained by both fiscal and environmental considerations. The relatively modest scale of the road-building programme has therefore resulted in large increases in traffic densities.

The changing scale of the problem over the past 60 years is summarized in Fig. 9.2 (from Ref. 9.1). The number of vehicles and the motor traffic index have each shown seven-fold increases over no more than 40 years. Until the early 1960s, fatalities and serious casualties increased year by

Table 9.1. Calendar of events affecting road safety and traffic[9.4]

1964–65. Introduction of trial speed limit of 70 mph (112 km/h) on motorways and other previously derestricted roads — 50 mph (80 km/h) speed limit is introduced on selected roads during the summer period — 'drink and drive' publicity campaign — voluntary registration scheme for driving instructors is introduced

1967. Seat belt fitting is made compulsory for new cars — further 'drink and drive' publicity campaign — it becomes an offence to drive with over 80 mg of alcohol per 100 ml of blood — permanent maximum speed limit of 70 mph (112 km/h) introduced for previously unrestricted roads

1968–69. Introduction of plating and testing of goods vehicles and voluntary HGV driving tests — tyres to have 1 mm of tread for at least 75 per cent of their width — regulations on drivers' working hours are introduced — cars registered in 1965 and 1966 are required to have seat belts fitted — test certificate now required for cars more than three years old — pelican crossings are introduced in London — new enlarged edition of Highway Code is published — a new licence group is introduced for vehicles with automatic transmission

1970. HGV driving test and registration of driving instructors becomes compulsory — new regulations on lorry and PSV drivers' hours of work

1971–72. Zig-Zag markings introduced at zebra crossings — 16 year olds are limited to riding mopeds only — rear markings and long vehicle signs are made compulsory for HGVs — unlit parking in 30 mph (48 km/h) areas allowed for certain vehicles under 1·5 tons — electricity blackouts in February 1972 lead to loss of street lighting and traffic signals, resulting in road casualties

1973–74. Safety helmets are made compulsory for two-wheeled motor vehicle users — 'energy crisis' leads to petrol shortages and large fuel price increases and to 50 mph (80 km/h) national maximum speed limit, later increased to 70 mph (112 km/h) on motorways and 60 mph (96 km/h) on dual carriageways — vehicle lighting regulations

1975. Vehicles now required to be lit when daylight visibility is seriously reduced — unlit parking permitted in marked places where speed limit is 30 mph (km/h) or less — minimum age of trainee HGV drivers reduced to 18 — temporary 50 mph (80 km/h) and 60 mph (96 km/h) limits extended — abolition of front number places on TWMVs

1976. Invalid tricycles phased out and replaced with extended cash mobility allowances — very hot summer increased holiday traffic

1977. New standards for safety helmets — 50 mph (80 km/h) and 60 mph (96 km/h) limits raised to 60 (96) and 70 (112) — mopeds redefined to 30 mph (48 km/h) maximum design speed — extended licensing hours and Sunday drinking permitted in Scotland — 'MOT' test widened to include windscreen wipers and washers and exhaust systems

1978. New edition of the Highway Code — 60 mph (96 km/h) and 70 mph (112 km/h) speed limits are made permanent — new rules on the maximum number of hours which may be worked by goods vehicle drivers are introduced — high intensity rear fog lamps become a mandatory fitment to most vehicles manufactured after 1 October 1979 and used from 1 April 1980

1979. Regulations are introduced to help prevent lorries hitting overhead bridges — code of practice issued on vehicle safety defects (arrangements for recall on new vehicles found to be defective) — use of tachograph accepted by Government

1980. Higher standards for crash helmets manufactured after 1 October — reform of bus licensing and removal of advertising restrictions from private car sharing schemes

1981. Two-part motor cycle test to apply from March 1982 — reduction in minimum driving age to 16 for invalid cars — extremely bad winter depresses traffic

1982. New two-part motorcycle test from 29 March — application of two year limit on provisional motorcycle licence with effect from 1 October — recall code announced for manufacturers to recall potentially defective motorcylces — tougher braking standards for new buses, coaches and lorries from 1 October — tougher written examination for entrants to driving instructor registration scheme

1983. Seat belt wearing becomes law for drivers and front seat passengers of cars and light vans — learner motorcyclists now only allowed to ride machines of up to 125 cc — use of wheel clamps on illegally parked vehicles in central London — tyres must now have 1 mm tread depth across three-quarters of their width and visible tread on the remainder — very hot July and August increases holiday traffic

1984. Stiffer driving tests for entrants of driving instructor registration scheme — tougher internal checks on tuition given by qualified driving instructors — new pedal cycles are required to meet British Standards — Revised Code of Practice on safety of loads on vehicles is issued — regulations introduced requiring spray reducing devices to be fitted to lorries and trailers

1985. Both load and speed performance to be marked on new car tyres — regulations allowing the use of traffic cones, warning lamps and triangles in the event of breakdowns come into force — new safety package (improved audible and visual warnings and minimum pavement widths) for pedestrians at modernized level crossings — pedal cycle traffic declines by 9% and TWMV traffic by 7%, but all motor traffic increased by 3%

1986. Uniform construction standards to apply to minibuses first used from April 1988 — dim-dip headlamp lighting device becomes mandatory on vehicles manufactured from October — measures to reduce accidents to vulnerable road users include publication of the revised Accident Investigation Manual and some relaxation of the Road Hump Regulations — improved braking standards required for motorcycles manufactured from 1 October — the temporary use of spare tyres up to a maximum speed of 50 mph (80 km/h) is permitted — tyres are now required to support maximum axle weights at a vehicle's maximum speed — all new cars manufactured from 1 October to be fitted with rear seat belts — close proximity and wide angle rear view mirrors to become a legal requirement on new HGVs from 1 October 1988 — seat belt legislation is made permanent — European Road Safety Year

year, more or less in proportion to the number of vehicles registered. They have since shown a steady decline and are currently at about the same level as was experienced in the mid-1950s when traffice volumes were little more than 20% of their present levels. With the exception of the ten-year period following the end of World War II, annual fatalities are now at their lowest level since the 1920s. Accidents of all injury severities have also been decreasing over the past 20 years. There are no doubt many interacting reasons for this trend; most other industrialized countries have experienced similar changes over the same period. These include various educational, enforcement and engineering measures besides changes in vehicle ownership, which have tended to reduce the proportions in the most vulnerable sectors of the population as car ownership has risen. A summary of the legislative changes aimed at the road user and introduced over this time is included in Table 9.1.

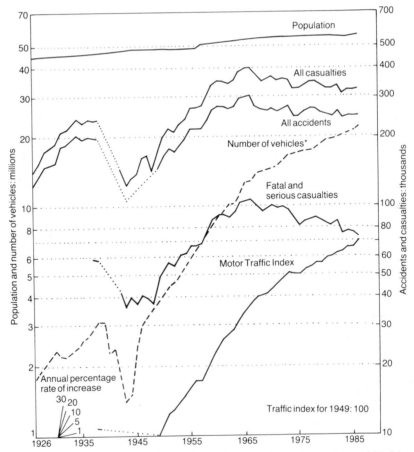

Fig. 9.2. Population, vehicles licensed, accidents, traffic and casualties: 1926–86 (from Ref. 9.4)

Table 9.2. Accidents in Great Britain (1986) by area

Area	Number	Percent of total	Number of licenced vehicles: thousands	Road length: km	Accident density: acc./km
Total	247 854	1050·0	11	339 480	0·7
England	217 515	87·7	11	258 690	0·8
Scotland	19 814	8·0	13	49 450	0·4
Wales	10 525	4·2	10	31 340	0·3
English shire counties	131 571	53·1	9	211 014	0·6
Greater London	43 222	17·4	16	12 851	3·4
Metropolitan counties	42 722	17·2	12	34 829	1·3
Built-up areas	187 818	75·8	—	136 680	1·4
Non-built-up areas	60 022*	24·2	—	202 800	0·3

*Includes all motorway accidents.

Table 9.3. Proportions of accidents by area, road classification and severity (1986)

Road class	Accident rate: per 10^8 veh. km	Percentage of all accidents of a given severity on road of given class			
		Fatal	Serious	Slight	All
Built-up					
A	126	28·5	30·7	36·1	34·7
B	135	6·9	9·3	9·6	9·5
Other	158	16·9	29·5	32·7	31·6
Total of built-up roads excluding motorways		52·3	69·5	78·4	75·8
Non-built-up					
A	37	32·1	17·1	11·9	13·5
B	67	5·0	4·3	2·8	3·2
Other	60	6·5	7·1	4·8	5·4
Total of non-built-up roads excluding motorways		43·6	28·5	19·5	22·1
All speed limits					
Motorways	12	4·1	1·9	2·1	2·1
A	76	60·6	47·9	48·0	48·2
B	107	11·9	13·6	12·4	12·7
Other roads	127	23·4	36·7	37·5	37·0
Total	82	100	100	100	100

Clearly in terms of risk to the individual, road traffic has become safer in recent years. Based on reported accident statistics for 1977, Sabey and Taylor[9.3] showed that there was a risk of being involved about once every nine years in a non-injury accident, every 57 years in one involving injury, and every 2500 years in one involving fatality. Perhaps it is the relatively low frequencies for the measure of exposure involved, familiarity with the road transport system, and an attitude that it always happens to the 'other' person, which leads to society's acceptance of the annual road toll as being an inevitable consequence of our way of life. Whatever the perception of risk to the individual (and whether or not that is an accurate perception), however, it is quite evident that the costs, both social and economic, are unacceptable to the community as a whole. The most recent estimate (1986) of the overall financial cost is £3800 million, or £70 per year for every member of the population. This figure provides a 'feel' for the magnitude of savings that relatively small percentage reductions in accident numbers can produce.

To decide on the most appropriate ways of tackling the problem requires a more detailed insight, *inter alia*, into how road accidents are distributed by area, road classification, vehicle type, road user and severity; some of these issues are considered in the following sections.

9.4. Distribution of accidents by area and road classification

In Great Britain, as in most heavily urbanized countries, road accidents are distributed unevenly between built-up (speed limit of 40 mph (64 km/h) or less) and non-built-up areas. The urban area houses a greater complexity of movement, more frequent junctions, visibility and movement increasingly hindered by parked vehicles, and growing opportunities for conflicts to occur as traffic volumes increase. There is greater use of two-wheeled vehicles and greater pedestrian activity in close proximity to vehicles, two road-user groups having high rates of accident involvement (see section 9.5).

Table 9.2 indicates some features of the distribution in 1986. More than three-quarters of all accidents occurred in built-up areas. The average accident density was correspondingly high (1·4 per km of road compared with 0·3 per km in non-built-up areas[9.7]). Table 9.3 (for the same year) shows the distribution of accident rate by road class, indicating the proportion and rate of occurrence on each, and their relative severities (in terms of the most seriously injured casualty reported). The accident rate on A-class roads in built-up areas is almost four times that on similar

Table 9.4. Proportions of total road length and traffic carried by each road class

Type of road	Road length: % of total	Traffic: % of total
Motorways	0·8	14·0
A	13·5	52·4
B	8·3	9·7
Other roads	77·4	23·9

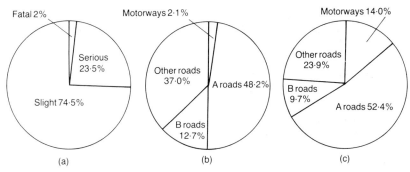

Fig. 9.3. Distribution of total traffic carried and accidents (1986) by class of road, and of accidents by severity: (a) accidents by severity on all classes of road; (b) accidents by class of road (all areas) in Great Britain; (c) percentage of total traffic carried

roads in non-built-up areas. On other classes of road the built-up area rate is higher by a factor of 2 to 2·5. A-class roads constitute 13·5% of the country's total road network (see Table 9.4), carry 52·4% of total traffic and experience 48·2% of all accidents. The length of the B-class network is 8·3% of the total, it carries 9·7% of all traffic and experiences 12·7% of all accidents. Non-classified roads represent more than three-quarters of the total network, carry 23·9% of traffic and experience 37% of accidents. Total length of motorways is less than 1% of the whole network, but they carry 14·0% of traffic and experience 2·1% of all accidents. The accident risk per vehicle km on motorways is less than one-sixth that on A-roads, nine times less than on B-roads, and more than ten times less than on non-classified roads. This situation is summarized in Fig. 9.3.

London's roads constitute less than 4% of the national network but experience 17·4% of the accident total at an average density of 3·6 per km. Within the built-up area, however, the hierarchical road structure and the distribution of traffic it generates can typically result in the majority of accidents occurring on a relatively small proportion of the overall network. Young[9.8] has shown that 63·4% of the accidents that occurred in the Greater London area in 1980 were on trunk and principal roads, the combined lengths of which make up only 12·9% of the network. The corresponding respective densities were 14·0 and 18·1 per km, the combined average of 17·5 per km being an order of magnitude greater than on the remaining 87·1% of the network — made up of local borough roads (average density 1·5 per km). Thus, the accident density on London's trunk and principal road network is 25 times the overall national average (0·7 per km from Table 9.2) and almost 60 times the average for roads in non-built-up areas (0·3 per km).

Furthermore, accidents are not distributed uniformly over a given road network, but tend to cluster at locations such as junctions (particularly on main roads), pedestrian crossings, and shopping or other areas where pedestrian activity is high. Accidents which occurred at, or within 20 m of, a junction (the Stats 19 criterion) are given in Table 9.5. Over the country as a whole 60·1% of all accidents are in this category. In built-up areas more than two-thirds are at, or close to, a junction. More than half of all accidents reported nationally (irrespective of area) occur at, or close to, junctions in built-up areas. By far the most frequently involved type is the T-, or staggered, junction.

Concentration of accidents around junctions is not surprising since this is where by definition there are conflicts in vehicle movements and where pedestrians commonly choose to cross the road. Neither is it surprising that a higher proportion should occur at, and close to, junctions in built-up areas since their density tends to increase with the level of urbanization. Charlesworth[9.9] observed an average density of 5·8 junctions per km on urban roads compared with 1·2 per km on rural roads. On the principal roads of a London borough Young[9.8] found 10·1 per km. Bearing in mind that, in this context, 'junction' includes a distance of 20 m in each direction, this frequency is such that, even if accidents were uniformly distributed, some 50% would be classified as junction accidents. Throughout London in 1980, Young found that 69·8% of all accidents were at, or within 20 m of, a junction.

Some of the accidents involving pedestrians also tend to be located in clusters and this too is of significance to the safety practitioner. Of 60 875 pedestrian casualties during 1986 (19% of all casualties) almost 19% occurred in accidents on, or within 50 m of, a pedestrian crossing facility while in the course of crossing the road. Young[9.8] found that 12·2% of the accidents occurring in London during 1980 were at or within 50 m of a zebra (10·1%) or a pelican (2·1%) crossing.

Such findings are of particular relevance in terms of engineering remedial measures. Optimizing the effectiveness of those which are site-specific depends on being able to apply them to well-defined areas where accidents tend to cluster or on links where average densities are high. The costs of most such measures are broadly the same whether they are applied in areas where the potential accident saving is only one or two, or where

Table 9.5. Accidents (all severities) by junction type and area (1986)

	Built-up roads	Non-built-up roads	All speed limits
Number occurring at junction	128 237	20 842	149 086
Percentage of total	68·3	34·7	60·1
Percentage of junction accidents at			
Roundabout	7·2	13·5	8·1
T- or staggered	56·9	42·7	54·9
Y-junction	2·9	10·9	4·0
Cross roads	21·8	14·6	20·8
Multiple junction	2·1	1·2	2·0
Private drive or entrance	6·2	14·1	7·3
Other junctions	2·9	3·0	2·9
All junctions	100	100	100

it is considerably greater. Consequently, the attainment of cost effectiveness in their implementation depends on the accuracy of appropriate site identification.

9.5. Casualties by class of road user and vehicle(s) involved

As road users, some individuals are more vulnerable than others. In some respects this situation arises because of behavioural or psychological characteristics that lead to accident 'proneness'. Accidents in this category cannot be readily identified from aggregated data. However, the national statistics clearly indicate widely differing rates of casualty involvement for different types of road user in different age groups.

Table 9.6 shows the casualty rate by age, severity and class of road user based on the 1986 data.[9.4] Those most involved in total are the 15–19 year old age group. However, involvement varies significantly with road-user group.

9.5.1. Pedestrians

The pedestrian is one of the most vulnerable road users of all, generally being totally unprotected when struck by any type of vehicle. More than one third of all fatalities on our roads are pedestrians (of 5382 fatalities in 1986, 1841 were pedestrians), and a very high proportion of accidents involving injury to a pedestrian occurs in urban areas (more than 95% of the 60 875 casualties experienced by this class of road user in 1986). Casualty rates are highest for children (5–14 year olds). They decrease with increasing age, being at their lowest in middle age (30–59) then increasing again to relatively high levels for the elderly (70 +). The inexperience of youth and decreasing agility, perception and resilience in old age, result in these groups being the most vulnerable. One out of every 30 pedestrian casualties is killed compared with one in 100 pedal cyclists, one in 60 riders or passengers on motorcycles or scooters, and a little over one in 70 car occupants.

9.5.2. Pedal cyclists

Again the young are the most vulnerable. Other than walking, the bicycle is the only mode of transport independently available to those below 16. Relatively high use in this age range, both for play as well as for purposeful transport, coupled with inexperience, results in high casualty rates.

9.5.3. Two-wheeled motor vehicle users

More than 1 in 6 fatalities and 1 in 4 casualties in road traffic accidents during 1986 involved users (riders or passengers) of two-wheeled motor vehicles despite the fact that they represent less than 1 in 20 vehicle registrations and less than 2% of total vehicle kilometres travelled (see Table 9.7). As Table 9.6 shows, the most vulnerable age group by far is that containing the 15–19 year olds (and, to a lesser extent, the 20–29 year olds). To many, particularly males, a motorcycle or similar machine is the first experience of being in charge of a motorized vehicle on the road.

Table 9.6. Casualty rates (per 10^5 population) by age, road user type and severity: 1986[94]

Age group	Pedestrians		Pedal cyclists		Two-wheeled motor vehicle users		Car users		Bus, coach, goods vehicle users		All road users[†]	
	KSI*	All	KSI	All	KSI	All	KSI	All	KSI	All	KSI	All
0–4	24	88	1	4	—	—	11	90	—	13	37	196
5–9	73	260	10	50	—	—	13	111	1	11	98	434
10–14	76	278	29	147	2	3	14	111	2	22	124	564
15–19	51	179	24	139	268	468	117	579	9	44	360	1455
20–29	26	92	11	61	70	216	110	566	11	57	228	995
30–39	16	56	7	34	21	65	57	328	7	45	109	530
40–49	17	53	6	27	12	40	45	268	7	44	87	434
50–59	20	58	7	24	10	31	39	216	6	37	81	366
60–69	29	71	5	15	5	13	35	167	3	36	77	304
70	55	120	4	11	2	4	30	120	4	35	97	292
All ages[‡]	35	110	10	47	31	95	54	288	6	39	134	582

*KSI: killed or seriously injured.
[†]Includes other road users.
[‡]Includes casualties whose age was not reported.

Table 9.7. Vehicle population and usage: 1986[9.4]

Vehicle type	Number of vehicles licensed $\times$ 10^3	Traffic: x 10^8 veh. km
Pedal cycles	—	42
Two-wheeled motor vehicles	1 065	54
Private cars	16 981	2 424*
Light goods/others	1 771	247
Buses and coaches	125	31
Heavy goods vehicles	593	221
All[†]	21 699	3 018

*Includes taxis.
[†]Includes others not classified elsewhere.

Inexperience, exuberance, and an incomplete realization of the dangers involved contribute to a high incidence of death and serious injury among this age group. Head and neck injuries are common and serious injury causing permanent disability and total change in quality of life is, unfortunately, not unusual. Not only is there a high total casualty rate for this group, but the proportion of all injuries that are fatal or serious is also high (see Table 9.6). Consistently about half of the casualties in this category result from accidents in which cars are also involved. About a quarter involve no other vehicle[9.10] When mixed with traffic containing vehicles of all sizes, the smallness of motorcycle and rider leads to problems of perception by other road users and an increased likelihood of it being masked by other vehicles or objects near the edge of the carriageway. The daytime use of headlights has helped to increase its conspicuity, but casualty rates remain a major cause of concern.

Besides the greater vulnerability (because of lack of protection) of the rider or passenger, the likelihood of maintaining control of a two-wheeled machine under emergency conditions is much less than in a car or larger vehicle. Whitaker[9.11] has found that about a quarter of the single vehicle accidents involve collisions with parked vehicles and a further third while negotiating bends or corners at junctions. Other contributory factors include loss of control on uneven or slippery road surfaces, and hitting kerbs or animals running into the roadway.

9.5.4. Car users

High casualty rates to car users reflect the high proportion of cars (78·2%) in total vehicle registrations and of their use (0·3% of all vehicle kilometres). As a function of age, casualty rates (of all severities) for the 15–29 year old group are virtually double the overall average for this class of road user.

9.5.5. Buses, coaches and heavy goods vehicles

Casualty rates to users are relatively low (compared with the overall average), but the severity of injury to pedestrians or occupants of smaller vehicles with which they collide is relatively high because of the disparity

Table 9.8. Effects of lighting and road surface conditions on accidents: 1986[9.4]

| Road class | Road surface condition | | | | | | | | | | | |
| | Daylight | | | | Darkness | | | | All* (daylight or darkness) | Fog | |
	Dry	Wet or flood	Snow or ice	All*	Dry	Wet or flood	Snow or ice	All*		Light	Dark
Built-up											
Fatal and serious	19 762	7 319	422	27 503	8 068	6 961	508	15 537	43 049	75	77
All severities	93 387	35 842	2 659	131 888	28 477	25 161	2 236	55 874	187 762	414	281
Non-built-up (excluding motorways)											
Fatal and serious	7 475	3 994	666	12 135	3 101	2 932	562	6 595	18 730	180	129
All severities	22 024	13 083	2 387	37 500	7 620	7 956	1 775	17 355	54 860	554	319
Motorways											
Fatal and serious	565	226	31	822	254	187	32	473	1 295	15	10
All severities	2 331	1 105	112	3 548	840	665	106	1 611	5 159	67	26
All speed limits†											
Fatal and serious	27 803	11 539	1 119	40 461	11 423	10 080	1 102	22 605	63 066	270	216
All severities	117 755	50 030	5 158	172 943	36 937	33 783	4 117	74 837	247 780	1 035	626

*Includes road surface condition not reported.

†Includes speed limit not reported.

of scale. While the drivers of such vehicles generally enjoy high seating positions, which allow good forward visibility, their turning geometry (frontal overhang or nearside cut-in) can give rise to hazardous situations. The nearside of the cab is a particularly vulnerable area since a pedestrian, bicycle or small vehicle can be excluded from the field of view, either by direct line of sight or in the nearside mirror. Buses appear to have a disproportionately large involvement in accidents (particularly fatal and serious) involving pedestrians and this is probably attributable to their routes tending to concentrate in areas of high pedestrian activity (e.g. shopping streets). Also, occasionally it is found that casualties arise from standing passengers falling over while the bus is in motion or falling from it while getting on or off.

9.6. Lighting, road surface and weather conditions

Accident occurrence is affected by lighting (daylight or darkness), weather, and the resulting road surface condition. Year-to-year fluctuations may be anticipated, particularly in relation to the weather and the variability in the British climate.

A summary for 1986 is given in Table 9.8 from which some general conclusions may be drawn which are, broadly speaking, maintained year by year. First, almost half of all accidents occur in daylight when the road surface is dry and a little under a quarter of these involve fatality or serious injury. The degree of severity is similar for other road and weather conditions during daylight (wet or flood, 23·1%; snow or ice, 21·7%; fog, 26·1%; overall, 23·4%). More than two-thirds of all accidents occur during daylight. A little under a third of these occur when the road is wet (3·0% when snow or ice is present and 0·6% in fog). Corresponding figures during the hours of darkness are 43·9% when the road is dry, 45·1% when wet, 5·5% with snow or ice, and 0·8% in fog. It can be seen that a substantially greater proportion of accidents occur in inclement weather, during the hours of darkness, than would occur under otherwise similar, daylight conditions. Also, in all cases the degree of severity is increased during darkness (dry, 30·9%; wet or flood, 29·8%; snow or ice, 26·8%; fog, 34·5%; overall, 30·2%). While adverse conditions of snow, ice or fog are generally well acknowledged (and to some extent because of it) their contribution to the overall accident total is relatively small. They generally have relatively short duration, occur at times of the year when monthly traffic flows are at their lowest and tend to restrain many non-essential trips or at least cause them to be rescheduled when weather and/or road conditions have improved.

A particularly noticeable feature is the combination of wet roads and darkness when almost as many accidents occur as when the roads are dry. (This compares with a corresponding figure of 42·5% during daylight.) Besides the effect of rain on impairing visibility (e.g. of road surface condition and road markings) roads stay wet for longer during the hours of darkness because of lower evaporation rates.

It is therefore necessary to exercise caution when these figures are being compared.

9.7. Contributory and causative factors in traffic accidents

While statistics such as those included in the previous section identify features that recur frequently in the aggregated data and can thus indicate priorities for investigation, considered alone they do not establish specific causative or contributory factors. To do this requires more detailed accident investigation on a local scale. Once a problem area has been identified the requirement is then to provide a diagnosis of the factors repeatedly involved, after which potential countermeasures must be found and evaluated.

9.8. Accident investigations

At the local level, the understanding provided by a numerical or statistical analysis of Stats 19 data can be extended by further investigation of individual accidents. This will typically include observation of site features, physical evidence recorded by the police and a study of witness statements. The role of the highway engineer at this level is to identify hazardous road locations, to diagnose the problem and, where appropriate, to formulate cost-effective engineering improvements. Comprehensive guidance is provided by the DTp's Accident Investigation Manual[9.12] and a distillation of international experience is reported in Ref. 9.13.

Serious accidents may also be studied in detail by specialized police accident investigation units and these studies may be pursued if a traffic offence is suspected, which might result in a criminal prosecution. Police investigation has the advantage of access to the physical evidence immediately after the accident so more information is potentially available than can be obtained by direct observation at a later stage by a civilian investigator. (This is not universally so; in some European countries the prosecutor may visit the locus very shortly after the accident and may then call a civilian investigator to the scene.) For this reason police accident reports are an extremely useful source of information both to those who might, generally at a much later stage, become involved in civil proceedings and to the safety practitioner concerned with accident remedial measures, though their disclosure is at the discretion of the Chief Constable. The reporting police officer is in the prime position for the collection of information directly pertinent to the accident, and the report is the most substantial input to our data bank and knowledge of the factors involved, no matter for what purpose(s) it is eventually used. While many police forces now have accident investigation units with full-time manning by specially trained officers, the majority of accidents are reported by officers not specializing in this way. Because of the social and economic scale of the road traffic accident problem, it is important that the data bank is as accurate and comprehensive as justifiable resources will allow, and that police officers receive detailed instruction of accident reporting requirements in their basic training. This should convey the importance of the function as well as providing a basic understanding of the information of relevance, the reasons, and ways in which it can be collected.

In addition to routine investigations as performed by the police or highway engineers, special investigations by multidisciplinary teams have been undertaken primarily by the Transport and Road Research Laboratory (TRRL). The objective is to obtain a comprehensive understanding of how and why traffic accidents occur by in-depth assessments of factors associated with road user, vehicle and environment. Detailed team appraisal of each accident studied leads to a determination of the primary causative factor(s) and interaction between the three groups. The most comprehensive study[9.14,9.15] in this country was carried out between 1970 and 1974 by a team from TRRL. It examined 2130 accidents in the area readily accessible to the Laboratory, supplementing evidence collected at the scene by vehicle examination and interviews with those involved. While to some extent such assessments are inevitably subjective, the team reached agreement on the attribution of contributory factors and blame in more than 95% of the accidents studied. A summary of their findings is presented in Fig. 9.4. Single causative factors were responsible for 70% of accidents and, of these, the road user (65%) was by far the most common. Double causative factors were held to be involved in a little under 29% and treble factors in just over 1%. In total it was found that the human factor contributed to some 95% of all accidents, road environment to 28%, and vehicle features to 8·5%. These results were in close agreement

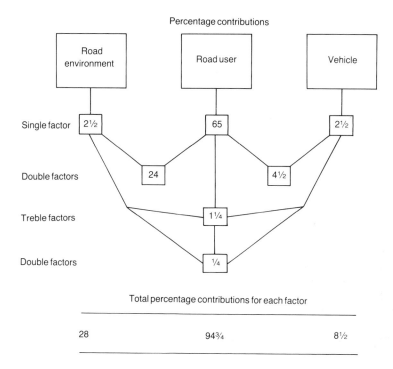

Fig. 9.4. Factors contributing to road accidents (from Ref. 9.3)

with a study[9.16] carried out independently in the USA and have since been generally confirmed by a further study[9.17] at TRRL.

On the face of such assessments it would at first seem that the most justifiable avenue for channelling resources into accident prevention would be in measures aimed at the road user, human factors contributing with three to four times the frequency of those associated with the road environment and more than eleven times the frequency of vehicle factors. Measures available are often broadly described as the '3-Es' (Education, Enforcement and Engineering). Since all vehicles are driven by human beings and, by definition, all reported accidents involve injury to a road user, then it might seem reasonable to suppose that educative measures have the greatest potential for savings. Unfortunately, however, these are some of the most difficult to realize due to the complexities of human behaviour and they may be less cost effective than engineering (or enforcement) measures. Indeed, these other measures will frequently need to be designed to compensate for human shortcomings and fallibility, and a more detailed examination of each set of contributory factors is worthwhile.

9.9. Road user factors

Road user behaviour depends on perceptual ability, skill acquired from previous experience in making judgements and taking decisions, then in executing them. The gaining of experience is, by definition, an on-going, 'hands-on' activity. Increased experience is only gained by using the roads while relatively inexperienced. Young children are taught by parents or teachers how to cross a road safely, then how to ride a bicycle. All too frequently when the advice has become totally familiar the lessons learnt are forgotten, particularly when at play with others. For instance the introduction of the Green Cross Code and the publicity given to it in the media caused an 11% decrease in the pedestrian accident rate (mainly in the 5–9 year age group) but this improvement was short lived. Organized schemes of cycle training for school children (by the Royal Society for the Prevention of Accidents or Local Authority Road Safety Officers) have been found to result in much improved cyclist behaviour but have a lesser effect in reducing accidents. In many areas Road Safety Officers also organize courses for young learner motorcyclists and some motorcycle dealers require their customers to register for such a course when purchasing the machine. Initial experience in riding a motorcycle is for many at a time in their lives when the exuberance and inexperience of youth far outweighs the realization of the harm which can arise.

For the driver initial familiarization with traffic and highway conditions, and with vehicle control can be achieved in off-road driving schools, in vehicle simulators[9.18] and with the benefit of supervision from an experienced driver up to the time when the driving test is passed. Experience and road sense continue to be gained for many years thereafter. Unfortunately, however, the judgement and performance even of experienced road users can be temporarily impaired by a variety of factors such as fatigue, ill health, and effects of alcohol or drugs. The

Table 9.9. Road user factors contributing to accidents[9.14]

Factors	Drivers	Pedestrians
Perceptual errors: looked but failed to see, distraction or lack of attention, misjudgement of speed or distance	1090	53
Lack of skill: inexperience, lack of judgement, wrong action or decision	462	—

Manner of execution
  Deficiency in actions: too fast, improper overtaking, failed to look, following too closely, wrong path
  Deficiency in behaviour: irresponsible or reckless, frustrated, aggressive
	1153
	
	94
		107
		
		—

Impairment: alcohol, fatigue, drugs, illness, emotional distress	632	7
Total factors	3431	167

*Total accidents in which a road user factor was a main contributor: 1942.
Total accidents assessed: 2042.

overall pattern of life of an individual can clearly have a bearing on their likelihood of being involved in an accident. The rich variation in events and activities, which constitute our individual lifestyles underlines the complexities of the situation and the difficulties in assessing relative risk in terms of human characteristics and behaviour. Nevertheless, the in-depth TRRL study[9.14] identified a range of human factors and quantified their involvement, as shown in Table 9.9. On average, there are at most two road user factors involved in every accident in which this class is either the main, or a contributory factor. Those occurring most frequently are perceptual errors (looked but failed to see) and, in terms of manner of execution, deficiencies in actions. The next highest contribution is from alcohol-induced impairment followed by lack of skill attributed to inexperience. A full discussion of the role of human characteristics and behaviour is outside the context of this book. The interested reader can refer to more comprehensive treatments elsewhere.[9.19-9.21] However, in terms of accident prevention, education and enforcement complement engineering measures.

Enforcement is necessary to ensure compliance with road traffic laws if these are to make a meaningful contribution to enhanced safety. The association of personal traits or circumstances with the road user breaking traffic laws, generally remains a matter of speculation though some observations have been made in the literature.[9.22] There is reasonably good compliance with some laws (e.g. the wearing of seat belts by motor vehicle occupants or helmets by motorcyclists), but much poorer observance of others (e.g. speed limits, parking regulations). It has been suggested that the degree of compliance reflects the perceived usefulness of a law, in which case education can play a complementary role in informing road users of the increased risk in, for example, travelling significantly faster than average or parking in an inappropriate position (e.g. at a junction). There remains a small minority who object to the imposition of almost any law on the grounds that it restricts the 'rights' of the individual. Education can fulfil a useful function here in disseminating information about the net benefits of such laws and the potential non-compliance cost to the community (in terms of increased accident likelihood or increased injury severity).

9.10. Vehicle factors

Despite the not uncommon occurrence of an involved driver claiming that control of the vehicle had been affected by mechanical failure, Fig. 9.4 indicates that vehicle factors are of relevance in only about 1 accident in 12. Mechanical 'failure' was found to be a causative factor in only about 1% of accidents. Defects were mainly of the type brought on in a relatively short space of time due to inadequate regular maintenance or inspection of the vehicle. Two-thirds of these involved defective tyres or brakes (see Table 9.10). It is probable that since the initial study[9.14] more stringent vehicle inspection procedures and the law governing minimum tyre tread depth (a feature significantly affecting wet road skid resistance) have reduced the contribution from mechanical defects. In fact the later study[9.17] found that vehicle factors then contributed to only 5% of accidents.

9.11. Road environment factors

Reference has already been made in earlier sections to accident rate and injury severity, varying with area and class of road. There are many reasons for such variation, e.g. widely differing traffic volumes and compositions, operating speeds and design standards. The influence of basic design quantities such as the number of lanes and their width were studied

Table 9.10. Vehicle factors contributing to accidents*[10.14]

Factors — defects	Number
Tyres	67
Brakes	65
Steering	7
Lights	10
Mechanical failure	22
Electrical failure	4
Defective load	10
Windscreen	4
Poor visibility	4
Overall poor condition	5
Unsuitable design	9
Total	207

*Total accidents in which a vehicle factor was a main contributor: 173.
Total accidents assessed: 2042.

many years ago.[9.18] Three-lane roads were found to be safer than two-lane when traffic volumes were relatively low, but as these increased to above 10 000 vehicles/day accident rates increased. For high flows, four-lane roads are safer, but special attention needs to be paid to intersection arrangements when these are designed as dual carriageways. On two-lane roads accident rates decrease with increasing lane width.[9.23]

Other features of the cross-section also influence safety. Rates decrease with increasing widths of shoulder and median. The latter separates opposing traffic, no matter how small its width but, in the absence of crash-barriers it has been found[9.24] that a width of at least 15 m is necessary if cross-over accidents are to be prevented. Design of horizontal and vertical alignment also has a bearing. On rural roads accidents tend to cluster on bends and generally to increase as the degree of horizontal curvature increases although this can be alleviated by building-in aids to perception of the bend's severity. However, care must be exercised in the design of re-alignment schemes. While these can produce substantial reductions in accident rates at isolated bends, safety can be adversely affected if significantly higher speeds result. Isolated bends in what are otherwise long straight roads have been found[9.24] to produce higher accident rates than on road with more bends. Vertical alignment is also of significance, crests and dips at the bottom of downgrades tending to be associated with accident occurrence. Sight distances can be restricted and speed differentials exaggerated by changing gradient. Simultaneous vertical and horizontal curvature can produce visually deceptive conditions and it is not uncommon for such locations or those where accesses are sited on sharp curves to experience increased rates.[9.25–9.27]

Intersections and access points are of particular concern. It was shown in Table 9.5 that some 60% of all injury accidents occur at these design elements, over half of which are of T- or staggered junctions. By their very nature these areas are individually localized and, having high accident densities, can offer potentially high rates of return for investment in remedial measures. Studies[9.28,9.29] of accident occurrence at three-way intersections have resulted in a number of conclusions.

(a) Right-turn movements have a much higher risk than left turns.
(b) Slight right-hand splayed junctions are safer than either a left-hand splay or a square layout (see Fig. 9.5).
(c) Accident frequency is proportional to the square root of the product of the flows involved.

Four-way junctions (crossroads) are more dangerous than three-way. Where past performance justifies it, redesigning a four-way intersection as a pair of three-way staggered junctions (see Fig. 9.6) is claimed[9.30] to achieve an average reduction of 60% in accidents, the recommendation being that the offset should be about 36 m. (There is evidence that crossroads that are only slightly offset are less safe than the straight cross-over type unless an offset island can be incorporated in the main road.) On single carriageway roads a 'right–left' stagger (Fig. 9.6(a)) has been found to be safer than the 'left–right' (Fig. 9.6(b)).

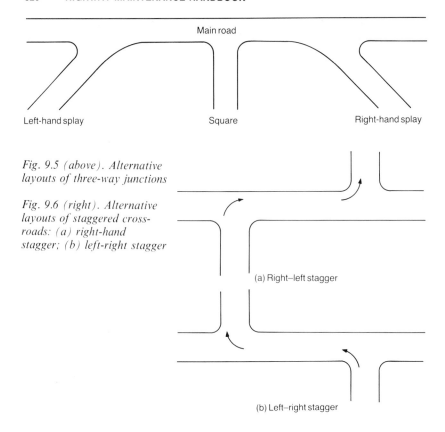

Main road

Left-hand splay   Square   Right-hand splay

Fig. 9.5 (above). Alternative layouts of three-way junctions

Fig. 9.6 (right). Alternative layouts of staggered crossroads: (a) right-hand stagger; (b) left-right stagger

(a) Right–left stagger

(b) Left–right stagger

More generally it has been found that the type of junction control influences accident rates, the safest being achieved with grade separation where traffic volumes justify it. However, some at-grade types have been found to be significantly safer than others. Roundabouts with priority rules have been found[9.31] to be advantageous in this respect, and the advent of the mini-roundabout has enabled this form of control to replace others in situations where space restrictions would otherwise have prevented it.

While the uniqueness of each situation prevents the formulation of all-embracing design rules, nevertheless some general principles have emerged from prolonged experience of junction operation. These include the provision of adequate kerb radii at both entry and exit, and an island warning of its presence, which can also reduce entry speeds when offset,[9.32] measures to enhance sight distances from the minor road, such as bringing forward the give-way lines at entry to the major road, and removal of hills or crests. Almost any measure that reduces conflicts is likely to be beneficial. These arise when one vehicle crosses or merges with the path of another or when a vehicle in a stream is caused to decelerate suddenly resulting in the following vehicle colliding with it.[9.33] Detailed illustration of these principles is included in Ref. 9.

Deceleration lanes and extra space for right turning traffic can both be provided in conjunction with the central island, thus reducing the risk of head-on or head-to-tail collisions. This is readily achieved in dual carriageway layouts, but local widening of single carriageways can allow the same junction design principles to be applied.

While roundabouts are generally safer than other at-grade junction types, the requirement to negotiate relatively small radius turns can present difficulties to vehicles with high centres of gravity unless measures are taken to ensure appropriate speed adjustment. These include clear signing and road markings, and adequate illumination for night-time visibility since studies[9.35] have indicated that a higher than expected proportion of accidents at roundabouts occurred during the hours of darkness and were probably due to difficulties in fully perceiving the extent of the hazard as it was approached.

This brief consideration of roundabouts has also served to illustrate the more general importance of such features as road markings, traffic signs and standards of night-time illumination. The Traffic Signs Manual[9.36] contains detailed information and guidance on the design and siting of signs (various chapters) and on road markings (Chapter 5). A comprehensive treatment of the whole subject of road lighting is given in the nine parts of BS 5489[9.37] and in a Departmental Advice Note.[9.38] Objectives and ways of achieving them are discussed[9.39] and there have been many evaluations[9.40,9.41] of the accident-reducing effects of improvements.

Sabey and Johnson's analysis[9.40] of the before-and-after effects on 19 trunk road sites indicated that fatal and serious accidents were reduced by 60% and all injury accidents by about 50%, where road lighting was installed where none had been before. Scott[9.41] examined the effect of improvements in lighting and found that for average values of road surface luminance L within the range 0·5–2·0 candela/m^2, the ratio of accidents occurring in the dark to those in the light could be expressed as

$$0·66 \exp(-0·42\ L)$$

which indicates a reduction of 35% in night-time accident ratio for an

Table 9.11. Road environment factors contributing to accidents*[10.14]

Adverse road design: unsuitable layout, junction design, poor visibility due to layout	316
Adverse environment: slippery road, flooded surface, lack of maintenance, weather conditions, dazzle	281
Inadequate furniture or markings: road signs, markings, street lighting	157
Obstructions: road works, parked vehicle, other objects	129
Total	883

*Total accidents in which a road environment factor was a main contributor: 569.
Total accidents assessed: 2042.

increase of 1 candela/m^2 in surface luminance. The accident-reducing effect of improved road lighting has become accepted as a realizable return and is used in cost-benefit analysis to establish priorities amongst other highway improvement proposals.

Accident rates are also dependent on whether the road surface is wet or dry. Rainfall affects the visibility of drivers because of spray thrown up by other vehicles and this can be a particular problem when passing or being passed. During the hours of darkness it also increases the glare from the road surface caused by both street and vehicle lighting. It also has a very significant effect on the levels of skid resistance available to vehicle tyres on almost all surfaces and thus considerably reduces their limiting braking and cornering capabilities. Unless speeds are reduced accordingly to compensate both for poorer vision and increased stopping distances, accident risk will increase. The effect of wet weather on average traffic speeds is generally small and, as has been demonstrated in section 9.6, there is a significant increase in accident risk observed. Chapter 8 (section 8.7) contains an in-depth appraisal of wet road skid resistance and it will not be considered further here.

Table 9.11 shows the contribution of road environment factors to the 2042 accidents examined in the study reported in Ref 9.14. Some aspect of the road environment was considered to be a main contributory factor in 569 (27·9%) of these. A total of 883 road environment factors were identified and, of these, adverse road design (35·8%) was the most prominent. This category relates primarily to unsatisfactory layout and its safety consequences. Next highest came adverse environment (31·8%), which included the effects of insufficient highway maintenance, then inadequate signs, markings or street lighting (17·8%), with obstructions produced by roadworks, parked vehicles or other objects in the carriageway constituting the smallest (14·6%), though still sizeable, category. The highway maintenance function impinges on each of the sections within this category and obviously has a significant role to play in contributing towards accident reduction.

9.12. Potential and means for accident reduction

Taken at face value the relative frequencies of occurrence of contributory factors described in section 9.8 would indicate that the highest potential for accident reduction is in influencing human behaviour and that this is where major effort and resources should be applied. Consideration of remedial measures, however, must recognize that the most effective treatment from a number of alternatives may only be indirectly related to the main contributory factor. It may be both easier and more cost effective to change the indirect factor if that then beneficially influences the other. Such an approach is very pertinent in bringing about reductions in that group of accidents in which the primary cause is some failing in human behaviour or lack of skill. Engineering improvements to the highway environment may compensate for such deficiencies at much lower cost than the additional training or enforcement otherwise required if, in fact, such remedies could be formulated. In many situations the causes of certain human errors may not be understood so that no direct remedy can be specified.

An assessment of achievable accident savings in Great Britain by the use of proven remedies has been made by Sabey and Taylor.[9.3] Savings from individual measures were quantified and the target group amenable to each measure was identified. The estimated savings were then applied to the target group and the resulting savings related to the total accident situation. Options for countermeasures have been classified as being designed to influence road environment, vehicle or road user. Potential savings estimated by adopting this approach (see Table 9.12) indicate that 20% of all accidents could be prevented by the adoption of low-cost road engineering measures, 25% by vehicle safety measures and 33% by measures applicable to the road user. The options are not mutually exclusive so that these benefits are not cumulative. However, the combined effect has indicated a potential overall saving of 60% when all known options in each area have been implemented. This represents a potential monetary saving of some £2 billion p.a. (based on 1986 costs).

Table 9.12. Potential for accident and injury reduction in road accidents (based on 1977 data)[9.3]

Options	Potential savings*: (%)
Road environment (low cost remedies)	
Geometrical design, especially junction design and control	10·5 (11·5)
Road surfaces in relation to inclement weather and poor visibility	5·5
Road lighting	3 (1·5)
Changes in land use, road design, and traffic management in urban areas	5–10 (7·5–16·5)
Overall	One-fifth of accidents
Primary vehicle safety measures	
Vehicle maintenance, especially tyres and brakes	2
Anti-lock brakes and safety tyres	7 (6)
Conspicuity of motorcycles	3·5 (3)
Secondary vehicle safety measures	
Seat belt wearing	7 (10)
Other vehicle occupant protection measures	5–10
Overall	One-quarter of casualties
Road user and road usage	
Restrictions on drinking and driving	10
More appropriate use of speed limits	5
Propaganda and information	Up to 5
Enforcement and police presence	Up to 5
Education and training	Up to 5
Other legislation (e.g. restrictions on parking)	Up to 5
Overall	One-third of accidents

*Figures in brackets indicate earlier values based on 1973 data — where different from latest estimates.

Table 9.13. *Potential accident savings from improvements in road environment by low cost remedial measures*[9.3.9.12]

Feature	Improvement	Target group of accidents (B)	Benefit (A): %	Potential savings (A × B) (at 1977 levels)	Number of accidents: % of total
Geometrical design: junctions	Control and design: mini-roundabouts, traffic islands, speed control, visibility	Uncontrolled junction accidents on class A and B roads in urban areas: 63 000	40	25 000	$10\frac{1}{2}$
		Rural junctions on class A and B roads: 15 100	20	3 000	
Surface	Rougher texture	Excess of accidents due to wet weather Slippery roads: 13 000	75	10 000	$5\frac{1}{2}$
		Impaired visibility in the dark: 5 000	40	2 000	
		Splash and spray: 7 000	33	2 000	
Lighting	Installation of new lighting and guard rails	A proportion of dark accidents on unlit roads Urban: 1 600 Rural: 8 000	30 50	500 4 000	3
	Improvement on lit roads	Half of accidents on lit roads: 25 000	20	5 000	
Urban areas: arterial roads and residential roads	Area application of low cost measures	Accidents on arterial roads and residential areas: two-thirds of total in urban areas: 138 000	10–20	14 000–28 000	5–10%

In aiming to achieve the most cost-effective utilization of resources, every potential improvement has a common requirement, this being to identify those sites to which the treatment can be most beneficially applied. A fundamental prerequisite is the availability of comprehensive information on past accident history. However, there still remain problems in the selection of treatable sites and in the evaluation of a treatment's effectiveness due, *inter alia*, to chance variation in the occurrence of rare events. There has been detailed consideration of such statistical phenomena as the 'regression-to-mean' effect and accident migration and these are extensively reported in the literature,[9.42–9.45] to which the reader is referred for further information.

Given that sites can be efficiently identified, Table 9.13 gives a breakdown of the potential savings from low-cost remedial measures applied to the road, and illustrates the basis on which they are estimated. Improvements in geometric design (particularly in junction layout) and urban area-wide application of a range of low-cost measures can each produce up to 10% savings (in the accident total) while improvements to pavement surfaces and in lighting standards are capable of smaller, but nonetheless significant savings. Clearly there is wide scope for the application of such safety-enhancing measures within the context of highway maintenance. With the wide choice of options available it is important to assess the relative costs of implementation and probable returns. Table 9.14 is based on experience of the performance of remedial measures implemented in London in the late 1970s and reported by Landles.[9.46] The overall average cost of such schemes at then-current prices was £2340. The data show that all adopted measures, irrespective of cost, produced worthwhile accident savings (14–48%), that typical first-year rates of return ranged from 180% (for lighting improvements) to 3660% for one of the cheapest measures (signing improvements).

Comprehensive guidelines for achieving accident reduction by engineering measures are set out in Ref. 9.47. It is estimated that of those accidents preventable by low-cost road engineering measures, roughly half can be achieved by 'single site' treatments and half from more widespread approaches. Experience from a variety of authorities indicates that, on average, a first year rate of return of at least 50% may be expected from site-specific treatments while that from others (such as mass application of particular remedies, route schemes and area approach to application of measures) is likely to average about 25%. The operational objectives recommended in the strategy developed in the Guidelines are summarized in Table 9.15.

In general site-specific, mass action and route action schemes concentrate attention and resources on specific parts of the network that are known to experience higher-than-average concentrations of accidents. When such sites have been treated the remaining accidents are more scattered and further reductions require a broader, area-wide approach. Such an approach, intended to provide the basis for a generally applicable management system and to demonstrate the likely benefits in accident reduction, has been developed in TRRL's Urban Safety Project. The design and implementation of five different schemes developed for the towns of Reading, Sheffield, Nelson, Bradford and Bristol have been described in Ref. 9.48. Scheme designs were developed in four stages

(a) analysis of road hierarchy and traffic patterns
(b) analysis of accident patterns
(c) definition of safety objectives for each part of the network
(d) proposal of measures to meet these objectives.

Schemes were agreed via public meetings and exhibitions, and discussions with local groups and members of local transport committees. The procedures developed have produced schemes gaining general support from the community and from a wide range of professional interests. The schemes (average cost about £250 000 at 1985 prices) were implemented in areas of average accident risk such that any benefits demonstrated should be generally obtainable in all other similar areas. Objectives and measures introduced in the Reading scheme are shown in Fig. 9.7. Interim results from four of the schemes have been published in a complementary report[9.49] and compared with accident records from specially selected areas of similar urban form. Combined data from the four towns indicate a reduction of 13% (two years before, one or two years after) in the study area and of 3% in the comparison areas indicating that there were 10%

Table 9.14. Performance of accident remedial measures in London (after Landles[9.46])

	Percentage of all measures	Average cost of scheme (overall average)	Accident savings: %	Typical first year rate of return: %
Traffic signals	14	1·28	28	400
Lighting	2	0·85	14	180
Pedestrian facilities	8	0·64	17	320
Signing	2	0·13	30	3660
Parking restrictions	2	0·13	27	2530
Vehicle channelization	6	0·43	20	640
Carriageway surface	19	1·71	24	200
Traffic management	4	0·85	39	790
Miscellaneous	1	0·43	48	1250
Combinations	42	0·85	25	420

Table 9.15. Operational objectives for accident reconstruction by low-cost engineering measures[9.47]

Objectives	Type of approach			
	Single site	Mass action	Route action	Area action
Average accident reduction: %	33	15	15	10
First year of return: %	50	40	40	25

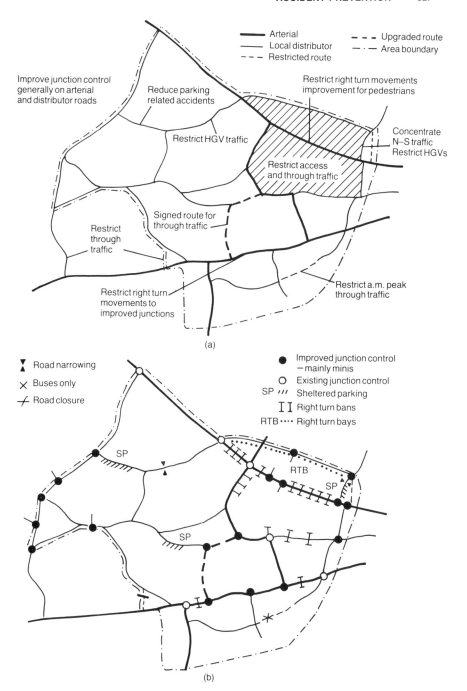

Fig. 9.7. *Safety objectives and measures in Reading — TRRL Urban Safety Project (from Ref. 9.48)*

fewer accidents than would have been expected without the schemes. This suggests that the 10% accident-saving objective (see Table 9.15) is attainable for this type of measure. The report examines the effects of the schemes on different road user groups and shows that the benefits have been mainly to pedestrians (particularly children) and to pedal cyclists. Perhaps this is symptomatic of the more widespread nature of accidents generally observed to these classes of road user, a factor which renders them more difficult to treatment by other strategies. Many of the measures employed in such schemes can be readily incorporated into, or combined with, more general highway maintenance programmes. Schemes primarily having environmental objectives and which reduce the amount of traffic in residential areas have been shown[9.50] to produce accident reductions of 30% within the treated area without detectable accident migration. It has also been observed[9.51] that the introduction of properly designed speed control humps ('sleeping policemen') can reduce accidents on the roads to which they are applied but the partial traffic re-routing which they produce may increase the number on surrounding roads resulting in no overall benefit.

Before concluding this section a cautionary note is justified. There are now many examples of significant accident reduction having been produced by well-formulated schemes appropriately implemented. Other instances can be found where the application of unjustified measures, perhaps applied because of political or emotive pressures not substantiated by statistics of accident occurrence, have actually led to an increase in numbers. Despite the increasingly wide application of engineering remedial measures there remain countless sites where accident rates remain unacceptably high. The success of this type of approach rests squarely in their identification. If the rate at a specific site is low then it is better to 'leave well alone' and to use those resources in an alternative application where they are capable of producing higher returns. It is axiomatic of course that, other factors remaining stable, as more sites with poor records are improved by remedial measures then the economic potential of those remaining will decrease so that investment in future years of long-term programmes can be expected to produce decreasing rates of return. As the highest accident rates are reduced so the overall average of all similar sites will decrease. Whatever level is pursued there will always remain sites having a performance worse than the current average.

To what level we should go on applying remedial measures is inextricably linked to the public's attitude to levels of risk and the perceived 'break-even' point between expenditure on road safety measures and an 'acceptable' accident total. This implies a valuation of accident costs including such consequences as pain, injury, grief, suffering, permanent disability and death. While there are obvious difficulties, it is necessary to 'cost' accidents in this way if economic justification for expenditure on remedial measures is required. Much of the original work on estimating the community costs of road accidents in Great Britain is contained in Refs 9.52 and 9.53. The notional amounts for the suffering and grief involved were subsequently increased on the recommendation of the Leitch Committee.[9.54] Such estimates are updated annually by the Department of Transport[9.55] with the production of average cost figures for accidents involving

(a) damage only
(b) all injury
(c) slight injury
(d) serious injury
(e) fatality

subdivided by road category

(a) all roads
(b) urban roads
(c) rural roads
(d) motorways.

Current costings and the projection of trends established in recent years indicate that there will remain ample scope for highly cost-effective investment in accident remedial measures for the foreseeable future.

9.13. Legal aspects

The responsibilities of highway authorities in administering and maintaining their roads are governed by the provisions of numerous pieces of legislation. It is well outside the scope of this book to attempt any sort of comprehensive treatment of this subject. The aim of this section is to indicate some elements of the legislative framework that have contributed to the current position in relation to highway maintenance and/or safety.

Our system of law is evolutionary so that, to some extent, an historical approach is inevitable. One of the first Acts to be concerned with maintenance matters potentially affecting safety was the Road Improvements Act of 1925. This gave authorities the power to prescribe building lines along roads and, at bends and corners, to control the height and character of roadside structures so as to maintain adequate sight distances. The Road Traffic Act 1930 removed all speed limits for motor cars and motor cycles, making it necessary for highway design standards to accommodate high vehicle speeds. However, the 1934 Road Traffic Act imposed an overall speed limit of 48 km/h (30 mph) in all built-up areas and introduced the requirement for those not already holding a driving licence to take a test.

The approach of war time resulted in preoccupation with other matters. However, in the post-war era, the Special Roads Act of 1949 introduced the concept of a new category of road (motorway) having access prohibited to certain classes of traffic. In conjunction with design standards subsequently developed this had a major impact on road safety as statistics included in Table 9.3 have indicated. The 1956 Road Traffic Act introduced compulsory annual testing for roadworthiness for vehicles more than ten years old. Other provisions aimed at improving road safety included increased penalties for dangerous driving, stricter regulations on the renewal of driving licences and an obligation on pedestrians to obey the directions of police officers on traffic duties.

The Highways Act of 1959 and the Road Traffic Act of 1960 had the effect of bringing together many of the earlier laws dealing with the creation, management and use of highways and bridges. Earlier relevant legislation is conveniently summarized in Ref. 9.56.

The right to bring a civil action against an authority for failure to adequately maintain a highway in its charge was established by the Highway (Miscellaneous Provisions) Act of 1961. The number of such actions continues to grow, perhaps partly due to the tight restrictions on maintenance expenditure in recent years, resulting in continuing deterioration of some categories of road, and partly to greater public awareness. In parallel with the growth in numbers of such actions their size has increased to the extent that six-figure claims are now commonplace and the occasional claim is an order of magnitude higher. The potential scale of such claims is a further incentive to authorities to ensure a comprehensive awareness of legal obligations and the highest professional standards in satisfying them within the limits of resources made available to them.

Road safety was also the primary concerns of the Road Traffic Act of 1962, which granted more flexible powers to impose speed limits and of the 1967 Act which dealt with drinking and driving, making it an offence to drive if the blood alchohol level exceeded 80 mg/100 ml. It also gave the police the power to impose selective roadside breath tests and increased powers for making roadside checks on commercial vehicles.

One of the most far-reaching legal provisions affecting the duty of local authorities to promote road safety was contained in section 8 of chapter 50 of the Road Traffic Act 1974, which increased the powers granted two years earlier in connection with the giving of road safety information and training. It stated that

> Each local authority shall prepare and carry out a programme of measures designed to promote road safety and shall have power to make contributions towards the cost of measures for promoting road safety taken by other authorities or bodies.
>
> Without prejudice to the generality of subsection 2 (above), in pursuance of their duty under that subsection each local authority —
>
> (*a*)   shall carry out studies into accidents arising out of the use of vehicles on roads or parts of roads, other than trunk roads, within their area
>
> (*b*)   shall, in the light of those studies, take such measures as appear to the authority to be appropriate to prevent such accidents, including the dissemination of information and advice relating to the use of roads, the giving of practical training to road users or any class or description of road users, the construction, improvement, maintenance or repair of roads for which they are the highway authority and other measures taken in the exercise of their powers for controlling, protecting or assisting the movement of traffic on roads
>
> (*c*)   in constructing new roads, shall take such measures as appear to the authority to be appropriate to reduce the possibilities of such accidents when the road comes into use.

Guidance on the duties of highway authorities in England and Wales is outlined in Ref 9.57. Possible limitations (and ways in which they may be reduced) imposed by the terms of the act are discussed in Ref. 9.47.

The 1974 Act also included provision for increased fines for various traffic offences, the installation of road humps to control speeds and to make the renewal of driving licences generally unnecessary before the age of 70.

Section 41 of the Highways Act 1980 established that the authority has a duty to maintain the highway, the duty being defined by inference in Section 58(1) as to take such care as in all the circumstances is reasonably required to secure that the part of the highway in question is not dangerous to traffic having regard to five factors listed in that section. The duty is not subject to qualification.

A further range of regulations imposed on some categories of road user were introduced in the Transport Act of 1981. These included measures to encourage proper training for riders of two-wheeled vehicles and compulsory wearing of seat belts for front-seat occupants of cars and light vans. In a more recent year (1986), visibility problems encountered by the drivers of heavy goods vehicles have been recognized by the introduction of a legal requirement for the fitting of close proximity and wide angle rear-view mirrors (on vehicles registered from October 1, 1988). Accident studies have indicated that a particularly vulnerable area for other road users has been close to the nearside (particularly alongside the cab) of such vehicles where they can easily be concealed by the higher waistline and/or be outside the field of view of conventional exterior mirrors.

Of particular note in relation to the routine maintenance of trunk and principal roads has been the recent introduction[9.58] of statutory investigatory levels of skidding resistance. The policy established is that all such roads must now be subjected to SCRIM monitoring and at, or below, the specified investigatory level of Mean Summer SCRIM Coefficient (MSSC), the engineer shall undertake a site examination to determine whether the existing skidding resistance is causing, or is likely to cause, an unacceptable accident problem. If so, then the site must be listed for remedial treatment; otherwise it must be kept under close observation so that any developing problem does not remain undetected. A further recent provision to increase safety at roadworks is to make legally enforceable the temporary speed limits, which have previously been advisory.

Clearly, compliance with all relevant aspects of legislation is an essential requirement for a highway authority and any employee, for each of whom it is vicariously liable. All concerned have a duty to make themselves fully conversant with the current situation by reference to relevant source material wherever appropriate.

9.14. Future developments

This chapter has given an indication of the wide range of factors that have been shown to influence the occurrence of road accidents. Comprehensive and systematic study of the accident situation has grown considerably over the last 20 years, but there are still many areas where our understanding is incomplete. Undoubtedly, there will be further developments in the foreseeable future which will influence society's capacity to deal with the problem. The first point which has to be made is that there is continuing annual growth in the number of vehicle-kilometres travelled on our roads. The number of vehicles is growing at a faster rate than the provision of additional road space and we will need to continue to make significant progress in accident prevention even to ensure that the present status quo is maintained.

Section 9.13 has given an indication of the development of that part of the legislation having a bearing on traffic safety. The law constantly evolves and there will be further changes regulating the management of our highway system, the vehicles that use it and the people that drive them. There will be increasing harmonization with the legislation of other European countries not only in recognition of the effects of the Channel tunnel but more generally in the drive to create a more fully integrated Europe. In the shorter term there will be significant national changes. In relation to the road user, implementation of some of the recommendations of the Road Traffic Law Review[9.59] will aim to produce a system which is both more understandable and acceptable to the individual and therefore creates a greater respect for the provisions of the law. No matter what the potential effectiveness of legislation, however, its actual regulating effect rests in the degree to which it can be enforced. The effect of a conspicuous presence of law-enforcement agencies in speed restricted areas bears ample testimony to that. There must be recognition of the resource implications of enhancing the benefits to be derived from whatever laws we have if they are to be effectively enforced. The public must be made aware that contravention is accompanied by a significant chance of being caught, so that respect for them is increased.

Increasing assistance in enforcement will be derived from developments in the field of electronics and telecommunications. Already police forces are using video techniques to detect speed limit violations and red-light infringements and this form of evidence is being accepted by the courts. There is considerable scope for automating much of the procedure and, although in a different context, the recent Hong Kong pilot study of the use of electronic number plates has demonstrated that the type of hardware required already exists and is capable of reliable operation. More generally, information technology has much to offer in the management and operation of our highway and traffic system. Considerable resources are being devoted to developments in this area. On a European scale the PROMETHEUS and DRIVE programs are notable examples having far-ranging safety implications. Some probable developments are specifically safety orientated (e.g. aids to safer driving, collision avoidance devices) while others (e.g. route guidance systems) have safety implications, the possible side effects of which will require further study. Totally automated control of specially designed vehicles is already technically possible, but such systems will have to demonstrate high standards of safety if they are to gain the degree of public acceptance necessary for their viability. More readily realizable are the improvements which technology offers by developments such as in-vehicle information systems, automatic incident detection and signing, fog detection, congestion and traffic monitoring systems. These latter areas impinge directly on highway operation and maintenance as too do the possibilities provided for improved forecasting. Already there exist early-warning systems for advising on the build-up of adverse weather conditions. The information provided is valuable to winter maintenance programmes, increasing the confidence with which decisions can be taken as to whether or not gritting is necessary.

In the all-important area of site identification there is considerable scope for integrating accident data storage and retrieval software with parallel records of highway inventories, condition monitoring surveys and traffic counts. Much of the manual correlation of data could thereby be eliminated and the determination of sites appropriate for remedial treatment could be further enhanced.

More efficient maintenance of our highway network developing from systematic monitoring aided by new technology should result in a reduction of the type of condition (e.g. pothole, low skid resistance associated with overseal banding), which specifically affects the stability of two-wheeled vehicles. More road building, particularly of by-passes, will reduce traffic densities in built-up areas where accident risks are relatively high by removing through traffic to much safer roads. Wider segregation of different classes of road user in town and city redevelopment will have beneficial effects on accidents to pedestrians and nose-to-tail collisions. Improvements in street lighting will reduce the number of accidents occurring during the hours of darkness. Increasing compliance with the provisions of HD 15/87[9.58] has the potential for significantly reducing the wet road accident rate.

Improvements to the safety performance of vehicles will continue. Some accidents will be prevented, and the severity of others will be reduced, by the wider introduction of anti-lock braking systems, which not only dramatically shorten emergency stopping distances on wet roads, but also enable a degree of steering control to be retained. Further development of commercial vehicle tyres will hopefully produce wet-road braking capability approaching that of the motor car. (At present under some circumstances the minimum stopping distance of a heavy goods vehicle can be twice that of a car.) Developments in both tyre tread design and the road surface can reduce the problem of spray. Wider use of pervious macadams in resurfacing work can largely eliminate the surface-water problem. A maintainable macro-texture criterion is likely to be introduced to ensure that there is less fall-off in skidding resistance with increasing speed than occurs on many roads at present.

There will be further refinements in vehicle body engineering to optimize crash performance in terms of minimizing injury to occupants or pedestrians. While notable advances have been made in energy absorption capabilities of vehicle structures in frontal and rear-end collisions, there is considerable scope for improvements in crashworthiness in side impacts. Stricter vehicle testing may make further small, but worthwhile, improvements.

In bringing the chapter to a close it must be reiterated that while the human factor is the major contributor to road accidents, there is much that the engineer can do to compensate for some of these shortcomings as well as reducing the direct contribution of engineering factors themselves. Our overall ability to improve road safety ultimately rests with society's perception of the scale of the problem and its acceptance of the complex compromise between a desire for mobility, the unwelcome side effects, and the will to commit increased financial resources to reduce them. It might be anticipated that in the same way that environmental awareness has grown in recent years, so increased media attention and education to the scale and effects of road accidents will lead to changing attitudes. Increasing prosperity may then be accompanied by a greater willingness to devote more resources to this important area of public health. Given the means, the highway engineer has a significant contribution to make in reducing, if not eliminating, the 'biggest epidemic of our time'.

References

9.1.   *The biggest epidemic of our time.* BBC TV, 1982.

9.2.   *Still the biggest epidemic of our time.* BBC TV, 1984.

9.3.   SABEY B.E. and TAYLOR H. *The known risks we run: the highway.* Report SR567, Transport and Road Research Laboratory, Crowthorne, 1980.

9.4.   DEPARTMENT OF TRANSPORT. *Road accidents Great Britain 1986: the casualty report.* Her Majesty's Stationery Office, London, 1987.

9.5.   BULL J.P. and ROBERTS B.J. Road accident statistics — a comparison of police and hospital information. *Accident Analysis and Prevention*, 1974, **5**, 45–53.

9.6.   HOBBS C.A. *et al. Classification of injury severity by length of stay in hospital.* Report LR871, Transport and Road Research Laboratory, Crowthorne, 1979.

9.7.   POWELL D.G. The contribution of pavement skidding resistance to traffic accident prevention. *IATSS Research*, 1988, **12**, 2.

9.8.   YOUNG A.E. *The potential for accident reduction by improving urban skid resistance levels.* PhD thesis, Queen Mary College, University of London, 1985.

9.9.   CHARLESWORTH, G. Design for safety. *Proc. Conf. Engineering for Traffic*, Printerhall, London, 1963.

9.10. WILLIAMS M.C. *Tabulations of 1977 road casualties indicating risks of injury to road users in relation to vehicles involved.* Report SR 576, Transport and Road Research Laboratory, Crowthorne, 1980.

9.11. WHITAKER J. *A survey of motorcycle accidents.* Report LR 913, Transport and Road Research Laboratory, Crowthorne, 1980.

9.12. DEPARTMENT OF TRANSPORT. *Accident investigation manual.* Royal Society for the Prevention of Accidents, London, 1986.

9.13. SCIENTIFIC EXPERTS GROUP. *Road accidents: on-site investigations.* Organisation for Economic Co-operation and Development, Paris, 1978.

9.14. SABEY B.E. and STAUGHTON G.C. Interacting roles of road environment, vehicle and road user in accidents. *5th Int. Conf. Int. Assn Accid. Traff. medicine*, London, 1975.

9.15. STAUGHTON G.C. and STORIE V.J. *Methodology of an in-depth accident investigation survey.* Report LR 762, Transport and Road Research Laboratory, Crowthorne, 1977.

9.16. ANON. *Tri-level study of the causes of traffic accidents.* Final report DOT-HS-034-3-535-77-TAC, Washington, DC, 1977.

9.17. SABEY B.E. Recent developments and research in road safety remedial measures. *Symp. Road Safety in the 80s*, University of Salford, 1983.

9.18. ANON. *Simulators for driver training*, Leaflet LF 251, Transport and Road Research Laboratory, Crowthorne, 1971.

9.19. *Research on road safety*. Her Majesty's Stationery Office, London, 1963.

9.20. GRIME G. *Handbook of Road Safety Research*, Butterworths, London, 1987.

9.21. O'FLAHERTY C.A. *Traff. plann. engng*, Arnold, 1987, vol. 1, 3, ch. 7.

9.22. SHEPPARD D. Why do drivers break traffic laws? *Police Rev.*, 1981, April.

9.23. ROAD RESEARCH GROUP. *Hazardous road locations; identification and countermeasures*. Organisation for Economic Co-operation and Development, Paris, 1976.

9.24. *Research on road traffic*. Her Majesty's Stationery Office, London, 1965.

9.25. MINISTRY OF TRANSPORT. *Layout of roads in rural areas*. Her Majesty's Stationery Office, London, 1968.

9.26. DEPARTMENT OF TRANSPORT. *Layout of roads in rural areas — a guide to revisions*. Departmental Advice Note TA 28/82, 1982.

9.27. DEPARTMENT OF TRANSPORT. *Road layout and geometry: highway link design*. Departmental Standard TD 9/81, DTp, London, 1981.

9.28. TANNER J.C. Accidents at rural three-way intersections. *J. Instn Highw. Engrs*, 1953, **2**, No. 11, 56–57.

9.29. COLGATE M.G. and TANNER, J.C. *Accidents at rural three-way junctions*. Report LR 87, Transport and Road Research Laboratory, Crowthorne, 1967.

9.30. DEPARTMENT OF TRANSPORT. *Design of major/minor priority intersections*. Tech. Memo. H11/76, DTp, London, 1976.

9.31. GREEN H. *Accidents at off-side priority roundabouts with mini- or small islands*. Report LR 774, Transport and Road Research Laboratory, Crowthorne, 1977.

9.32. FAULKNER C.R. and EATON J.E. *Accident investigation and prevention by applying the location sampling technique to rural crossroads*. Report LR 780, Transport and Road Research Laboratory, Crowthorne, 1977.

9.33. RUSSAM K. and SABEY B.E. *Accidents and traffic conflicts at junctions*. Report LR 514, Transport and Road Research Laboratory, Crowthorne, 1972.

9.34. DEPARTMENT OF TRANSPORT. *Junctions and accesses: determination of size of roundabouts and major/minor junctions*. Advice Note TA 23/81, DTp, London, 1981.

9.35. WEBSTER F.V. and NEWBY R.F. Research into relative merits of roundabouts and traffic signal controlled intersections. *Proc. Inst. Civ. Engrs*, 1964, **27**, 47–75.

9.36. *Traffic Signs Manual*. Her Majesty's Stationery Office, London, ch. 1–14, (various dates.)

9.37. BRITISH STRANDARDS INSTITUTION. *Road lighting*. BS 5489: 1987: Parts 1–9.

9.38. DEPARTMENT OF TRANSPORT. *Appraisal of new and replacement lighting on trunk roads and motorways*. Advice Note TA 49/86, DTp, London, 1986.

9.39. RUSTON B. Street lighting. *J. Instn Highw. Transpn*, 1987, **34**, No. 11, 29–32.

9.40. SABEY B.E. and JOHNSON H.D. *Road lighting and accidents: before and after studies on trunk road sites*. Report LR 586, Transport and Road Research Laboratory, Crowthorne, 1973.

9.41. SCOTT P.P. *The relationship between road lighting quality and accident frequency*. Report LR 929, Transport and Road Research Laboratory, Crowthorne, Berks, 1980.

9.42. HAUER E. Selection for treatment as a source of bias in before-and-after studies. *Traff. Engng Control*, 1980, **21**, No. 8/9, 419–421.

9.43. WRIGHT C.C. Some technical issues in accident remedial work. *PTRC Summer Annual Meeting*, Paper No. J1, University of Warwick, July 1981.

9.44. ABBESS C. *et al.* Accidents at blackspots: estimating the effectiveness of remedial treatment with special reference to the "regression-to-mean" effect. *Traff. Engng Control*, 1981, **22**, No. 10, 535–542.

9.45. WRIGHT C.C. Road accident data for engineering remedial work. *J. Instn Highw. Transpn*, 1983, **30**, No. 8/9, 14–17.

9.46. LANDLES J.R. Accident remedial measures. *PTRC Summer Annual Meeting*, University of Warwick, July 1980.

9.47. INSTITUTION OF HIGHWAY ENGINEERS. *Guidelines for accident reduction and prevention in highway engineering.* IHE, London, 1986.

9.48. LYNAM D.A. *et al. Urban safety project: 1. Design and implementation of schemes.* Research Report RR153, Transport and Road Research Laboratory, Crowthorne, 1988.

9.49. MACKIE A.M. *et al. Urban safety project: 2. Interim results for area-wide schemes.* Research Report RR154, Transport and Road Research Laboratory, Crowthorne, 1988.

9.50. BROWNFIELD D.J. Environmental areas — interim report on a before-and-after study. *Traff. Engng Control*, 1980, **21**, 278–282.

9.51. SUMNER R. and BAGULEY C. *Speed control humps on residential roads.* Report LR878, Transport and Road Research Laboratory, Crowthorne, 1979.

9.52. DAWSON R.F.F. *Cost of road accidents in Great Britain.* Report LR79, Transport and Road Research Laboratory, Crowthorne, 1967.

9.53. DAWSON R.F.F. *Current costs of road accidents in Great Britain.* Report LR 396, Transport and Road Research Laboratory, Crowthorne, 1971.

9.54. DEPARTMENT OF THE ENVIRONMENT. *Report of the Advisory Committee (Leitch Committee) on Trunk Road Assessment.* Her Majesty's Stationery Office, London, 1978.

9.55. DEPARTMENT OF TRANSPORT. Road accident costs. *Highway Economics Notes* series, annually.

9.56. HYDE W.S. Highway legislation. *J. Instn Mun. engrs*, 1961, **88**, No. 5, 169–174.

9.57. DEPARTMENT OF THE ENVIRONMENT. *Duty of local authorities to promote road safety.* Circular Roads 12/75, London, 1975.

9.58. DEPARTMENT OF TRANSPORT. *Skidding resistance of in-service roads.* Departmental Standard HD 15/87, DTp, London, 1988.

9.59. DEPARTMENT OF TRANSPORT. *Road traffic law review.* Her Majesty's Stationery Office, London, 1988.

10

Winter maintenance

10.1. Introduction

Winter maintenance is the most misunderstood service provided by the highway authority as it is the most difficult for which defined standards can be consistently achieved. There is much criticism from various bodies, not least the Audit Commission, about the costs of provision and the service provided. Before looking at the subject in detail, an understanding of the variability of the problem being dealt with may clarify some of the difficulties. Thornes[10.1] has suggested a Temporal Winter Index comprising a series of factors as a way of monitoring the relative severity of a winter. The variability of the conditions can be seen in Fig. 10.1

This clearly illustrates the problem of providing a flexible, responsive service, which can also be seen to be economic. Because of a series of mild winters the motorist has come to expect a consistent, delay free road network, and consequently any delay results in vocife rous criticism. It is interesting to contrast this with the precautions and preparations needed by the motorist in some countries where the use of snow tyres is obligatory between defined dates. The varying faces of winter can be seen from the photographs shown in Figs 10.2 and 10.3.

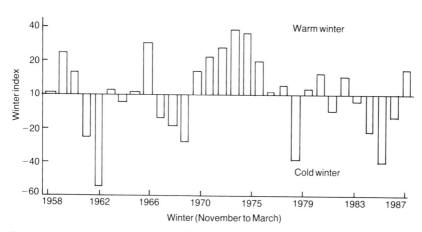

Fig. 10.1. Temporal Winter Index:[10.1] Manchester Winter Index (1958–59 to 1987–88) (NIPS, April 1988)

Fig. 10.2. A pleasant winter scene

Fig. 10.3. A serious winter problem

From Fig. 10.1, great variability in conditions can be seen, which indicates the extent of the funding problem. Analysis of spending records suggests a variance of 1 : 3·5 between minimum and maximum spends, but in the exceptional years of 1962–63 and 1978–79 this was, in some areas, as high as 1 : 4·5. In a county with a large proportion of urban roads, when heavy continuous snowfall prevails and round-the-clock working is necessary, it is possible to reach a spending rate of £150 000 per day.

Traditional regional variation was overturned in the winter of 1987–88 when the south east of England faced very severe continuous blizzard conditions while many more northerly areas experienced a relatively mild winter.

There are several pragmatic solutions to the funding of winter maintenance, since to try to contain it within an annual maintenance allocation is not sensible, because expenditure occurs too late in the financial year to allow meaningful virement to or from other programmes. Two of these are

(a) to have separate highways and winter maintenance budgets, and absorb any variance in the authority's overall contingency reserves

(b) to provide funding for a normal/hard winter and transfer any surplus or deficit to a winter maintenance suspense account, such that a mild winter subsidizes the cost of a severe winter and vice versa. The account should balance over a five-year period.

An increasing number of authorities are moving towards this second option.

The cost of providing for winter maintenance is significant and is estimated by the Audit Commission[10.2] to be 8·5% of the total spending, as shown in Fig. 10.4.

Despite the responsive character of winter maintenance, it can be organized in a manner similar to routine maintenance by considering gritting and snow clearance separately, and by examining in detail the various elements of the management cycle as set out in Fig. 10.5.

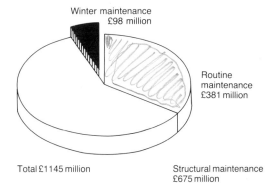

Winter maintenance
£98 million

Routine
maintenance
£381 million

Total £1145 million

Structural maintenance
£675 million

Fig. 10.4. National winter maintenance costs (1986–87)[10.2]

LEGALLY BOUND,

10.2. Legal position

Highway authorities have a duty, under Section 150 of the Highways Act 1980, to clear obstructions from the highway, including the removal of snow and ice, or to take such action as will render the highway safe for use by vehicles and pedestrians in bad weather. This duty also extends to private roads and streets, subject to a Section 38 Agreement.

There is also an obligation, under Section 41 of this Act, to ensure safety. At present, however, case law indicates that there is no statutory duty to undertake winter maintenance, other than snow clearance, where snow forms an obstruction. This difficulty is further emphasized in the case of footways, where the removal of snow by an adjacent owner can involve a legal obligation to take reasonable care in so doing. In the absence of clear guidance, it is necessary to adopt a sensible level of action aimed at minimizing the risks to each user category and supported by a well-defined plan of priorities.

A user of the highway can complain to a magistrates court that the highway authority has failed to remove an obstruction (snow). The magistrate can require the highway authority to act within a reasonable period (not less than 24 hours). There are those who would argue that if the complainant interprets the presence of snow on the highway as being a 'dangerous state' the defence would be that the highway authority has not caused the nuisance. It would be relevant for the highway authority to consider its public profile before being prepared to go to court on this issue.

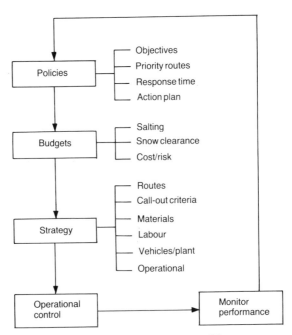

Fig. 10.5. Management cycle for winter maintenance[10.3]

RECORDS OF SALTING etc , for use of GIS/gps. — salting runs, how much etc.

WINTER MAINTENANCE 341

There have been a number of out of court settlements following injuries sustained in accidents which when analysed would require the highway authority to be able to show much more clearly how, when, and why it had acted.

10.3. Policies

10.3.1. Objectives of winter maintenance

To provide an effective and economic service, which will minimize hazards and assist traffic mobility at all important locations on the road network, by a graduated and time related procedure. Ideally the result will be to maintain a bare wet surface for the duration of adverse weather conditions. Rock salt in conjunction with snowploughs remain the most economic and effective method of keeping roads clear of ice and snow.[10.4]

10.3.2. Priority routes

The order of priorities currently recommended by the Department of Transport for their roads and by many highway authorities is as follows

A. Pre-salting
First priority
(a) Motorways and certain primary routes as defined by the Department of Transport.
(b) Other primary routes, principal roads, roads leading to important industrial or military establishments, hospitals, ambulance stations, fire stations, bus garages, important bus routes, important commuter routes (i.e. more than 3000 vehicles/day), slip roads, approaches to interchanges and known trouble spots.
Second priority
Known trouble and accident spots not included in the first priority, all other bus routes (including school buses), other commuter routes, main feeder routes and shopping centres.
B. Snow clearance (in priority order)
1. Motorways and selected primary routes.
2. Other primary routes and principal roads.
3. Highways leading to essential industrial and military establishments, hospitals, ambulance and fire stations, bus garages, bus routes, important commuter routes.
4. Highways serving shopping centres, slip roads, single accesses to villages, schools, farms.
5. All remaining roads including urban streets.

Variations in the above advice may be necessary to suit local conditions and the economic planning of treatment routes.

Response time is sometimes referred to as the tie between the decision to salt and the vehicles' return to the depot. Typically this may be three hours. It may, however, be more reasonable to segment this into

(a) *Response time*: from decision to grit to the first vehicle leaving the depot — 1 hour
(b) *Treatment time*: time to complete the route — 2 hours.

three hours in 1990

NB
Now 1 → 2 hours

Consider that there are to be four levels of action with the priority and timing basis as shown in Table 10.1, and the treatment objectives as shown in Table 10.2.

As part of the definition of policy, it is normal to prepare an 'action plan' which, in addition to setting down the previously mentioned objectives, considers a framework for action. As no one knows the circum stances in which they are likely to be operating, it is not possible to plan for a particular emergency, but rather to establish a framework within which to operate during the emergency. This document will not only advise all interested parties of the plan, but will also ensure consistency of operation where control is decentralized. The typical contents of the action plan are as shown in Table 10.3.

Table 10.1. Treatment time objectives

Action	Priorities dealt with*	Time: h
1. Precautionary	1,2	2
gritting	3	4
2. Anticipated	1,2	2
snowfall	3	4
	4	6
3. Falling	1,2	2
snow	3,4	4
4. Settling and/or	1,2	2
drifting snow	3,4	4
	5	24

*Priorities are as defined in section 10.3.2. B.

Table 10.2. Treatment objectives

1.	Motorways and selected primary routes should never become impassable to heavy vehicle traffic unless there are exceptional weather conditions and when snow is drifting
2.	Other primary routes and principal roads shall not remain impassable to heavy vehicle traffic for more than 3 hours, unless exceptional
3.	Essential access roads shall not remain impassable to heavy vehicle traffic for more than 6 hours, unless exceptional
4.	Other access roads shall not remain impassable to heavy vehicle traffic for more than 12 hours, unless exceptional
5.	All remaining roads including urban streets shall not remain impassable to heavy vehicle traffic for more than 24 hours, unless exceptional

In preparing an action plan and particularly the route structure, the many variables affecting each locality have to be considered, among which are

(a) climatic variations
(b) traffic variations
(c) the importance and sensitivity of the route
(d) available resources
(e) geographic location
(f) gradient
(g) surfacing.

Local knowledge of trouble spots and the needs of the community will play a vital part in the decision-making process. The resulting plan will feature a graduated level of response triggered from a control centre reacting to weather information, and in an order of priority determined in advance.

10.4. Budgets

A prior estimate of the cost of winter maintenance is not possible and it is normal to make a provision based on historic data. The preferred method is to provide for a moderate to severe winter and transfer any money not spent to a holding account to provide the extra for a severe winter. The variance between a mild and severe winter is of the order of 1:3·5.

The Audit Commission recommend that a funding provision be calculated for the activity over a 3–5 year period, making separate allowances

Table 10.3. Action plan contents

1.	Policies
2.	Description of how system is intended to work
3.	Control location and method
4.	Specific procedure — who does what by when
5.	Treatment decision process
6.	Resource locations: depots, salt, plant, emergency plant
7.	Presalting route structure
8.	Snow clearing procedure
9.	Records to be kept
10.	Manning, drivers, hours, driving licences
11.	Contact list
12.	Appendices
	(a) boundary arrangement
	(b) gritting routes (maps — possibly separate volume)
	(c) location of hospitals, fire stations, etc.
	(d) radio call signs
	(e) record format
	(f) snow fencing
	(g) equipment maintenance
	(h) agreed working procedures and controls

for salting and snow clearing. It can be seen from Figs 10.1 and 10.7(c) that this period is too short to get a realistic average. It may be more relevant to look at a moving average cost over the longest period for which data are available, to examine in detail the recommended efficiency criteria, to maintain explicit records and to review the situation annually. Whichever method an authority chooses, some system of providing a contingency for a severe winter must be considered.

Typical records that may assist in making an estimate are shown in Table 10.4 and Figs 10.6 and 10.7, although it must be appreciated that this example relates to a particular geographical area.

Using this information it is possible to attempt an 'average winter' needs based budget along the following lines.

(*a*) Precautionary gritting

average turnouts × primary routes length treated × unit rate

(*b*) Snow clearance

average turnouts (length cleared × unit rate + length salted × unit rate)

The realistic minimum budget provision is then the sum of these two amounts. Caution should, however, be exercised before using this simplistic analysis, as the variance in number of turnouts (Table 10.4) is in the range 1–2·3 whereas the snow on the ground (Fig. 10.7(c)) is in the range 1–10. It will be necessary to maintain more specific records of the actual work involved in snow clearing and to attempt to correlate cost incurred

*Table 10.4. Call-out records (based on meteorological forecasts received) for Barnsley, South Yorkshire (figures in brackets are for Sheffield, South Yorkshire)**

Year	Dates		Number in year	
	Earliest	Latest	After 1 April	Total
1974–75	23.10	10.4	9	80
1975–76	11.10	7.4	2	60
1976–77	2.11	15.4	4	68
1977–78	25.10	14.4	8	72
1978–79	17.10	4.5	10	105
1979–80	1.11	9.4	2	73
1980–81	14.10	1.5	8	72
1981–82	14.10	8.4	1	88
1982–83	14.11	19.4	7	73
1983–84	21.10	12.4	5	93
1984–85	4.11	26.4	3	73
1985–86	3.11	19.4	(8)	(94)
1986–87	24.11	2.4	(1)	(61)
1987–88	22.11	16.3	—	(46)

*Variance 2·3:1. Average: 75.

with this information. A very relevant additional record may be the incidence of wind above a certain speed as, in rural areas, wind can cause a continuous ploughing problem as snow is blown from fields over walls and particularly through gates on to the road.

As funds become scarcer and must be more competitively sought, this form of assessment becomes more relevant. In the short term, the practical way forward may be to attempt to predict a 'precautionary gritting budget' and to add to this a provision for snow clearance based on average year costs. An allowance for the variability in snow clearing should be made in some form of contingency account.

The Audit Commission have developed a format for examining the efficiency of various elements of the process such that the costs which are incurred, within the vagaries of the prevailing conditions, can be seen to be reasonable. The various factors considered are

(*a*) route coverage — ratio of priority routes to total network

		Average: %	Range: %
All roads excluding motorways	Counties	31	24–38
	Metropolitan counties	55	—
All roads excluding motorways, trunk principal	Counties	19	12–25
	Metropolitan counties	48	—

Road geometry in urban areas may require two-way running, which is not allowed for in these figures

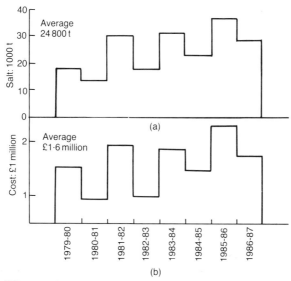

Fig. 10.6. Winter maintenance statistics: (a) salt used; (b) cost (1986 base)

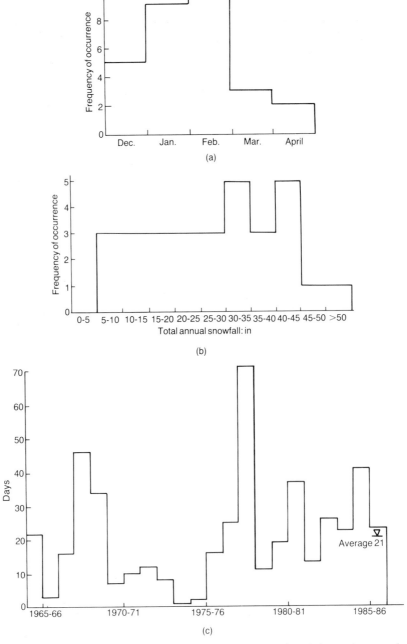

Fig. 10.7. Snowfall records (from Clayton 29 year records): (a) snowiest month;
(b) total annual snowfall (Holmfirth, W. Yorks); (c) total days snow on ground
(Weston park, Sheffield)

(*b*) unit cost indicators — total cost related to workload (1986–87 base)

Coverage: %	< 15	15/20	20/25	25/30	30/40	> 40
Unit cost: £/mile	40	33	27	24	21	20

A deduction of £0·15/mile is made for each turnout and an addition of £1·00/mile is made for each day of snow clearance, e.g. cover factor 27%, number of turnouts 58, days of snow clearance 6, therefore

$$\text{target unit cost} = \pounds24\!\cdot\!00 - (\pounds0\!\cdot\!15 \times 58) + (6 \times \pounds1\!\cdot\!00)$$
$$= \pounds21\!\cdot\!30/\text{mile}$$

(*c*) routeing efficiency — ratio of total treatment route mileage to salting mileage. A target efficiency of 75% is recommended and route redesign should be considered is < 65%

(*d*) call-out index — relates turnouts to weather — with target range 80–120

$$\frac{\text{number of turnouts}}{0\!\cdot\!6 \times \text{days of air frost} + 1\!\cdot\!25 \text{ days of snow clearing}}$$

(*e*) labour efficiency — relates hours booked to total miles gritted. The suggested target is represented by the sloping line below and the range of route mileage and typical times taken forms the rectangle. A satisfactory result is where majority of the rectangle is below the line

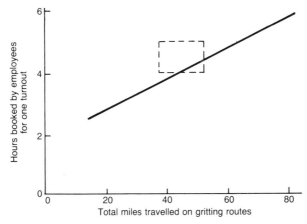

(*f*) fleet size and capacity — based on 100 salting miles of primary route and units per route

	Unit per priority route	Carrying capacity: m^3/100 miles (160 km)
Good	< 1·3	< 25
Typical	1·3–1·45	25–35
Poor	> 1·45	> 35

(g)   actual rate of spread — g/m^2 achieved — with targets of $10\,g/m^2$ for precautionary salting, $20–40\,g/m^2$ immediately prior or during snow and $40–60\,g/m^2$ for snow removal.

In examining the budget provision, consideration must be given to the overall economic implications of the service, i.e. the cost of failure to provide an adequate service. As attempts are made to reduce the cost of the service, there will inevitably be a point at which the risk of failure increases and it is relevant to try to establish this point.

The incidence of road traffic accidents, which can be attributed to freezing conditions can be monitored. Equally, it is also relevant to consider the effects of delays due to snowfall. One attempt may be to consider the simple delay model incorporated in the Pavement Management System Design Study Report[10.5]

user delay cost £ $= K\,[3 \cdot 35 ADT - 16\,500]$

where K is road length (km), ADT is two-way annual average daily flow, cost is per week (in the PMS this is limited to a maximum of £75 000) and delay cost per hour is

$$K\,[3 \cdot 35\ ADT - 16\,500] \times \frac{1}{168}$$

Taken over the total length of the priority gritting network, this can be seen to be a significant figure.

Analysis along these lines may be relevant in describing the economic benefits of winter maintenance to counteract the various claims that it represents, at its worst, profligate spending.

10.5. Routes

Treatment routes should systematically cover all roads in the area set out in a priority hierarchy as defined in section 10.3.2. The practical length of routes is governed by a series of factors, some of which are the required response time, the equipment available, the location of the salt stock, the shape of area maintained, the topography of the area, whether the area is urban or rural and the spread rates required. All roads should be covered once and dead running should be minimized.

Ideally, routes should be capable of being completed in no more than two hours for precautionary gritting with a target efficiency of 75% (ratio of whole route to gritted length). This efficiency will, however, depend on the shape and layout of the area being treated and the road geometry, as islands and one-way systems will clearly affect this.

Where possible, routes should loop out from a depot and return to complete at the depot. As road layouts have not, usually, been laid down with winter maintenance in mind, an element of dead running (travelling not gritting) is inevitable. Only in extreme circumstances should a road be treated in both directions. In an urban area there is a clear conflict, as roads tend to be wider and for this reason it may not always be practical to grit the full width due to the greater probability of damage being caused as salt is thrown longer distances by the spinner. In these circumstances it may be relevant to consider a spread width less than the carriageway. For example, in some European countries it is standard practice to leave a 1 m wide strip at each side untreated as the salt will be distributed over this area by passing traffic.

Care should be taken in planning routes to ensure that all sections of the network are systematically covered, both for pre-salting, and for snow clearance. In the latter case this will usually require a separate set of routes. Typical maximum lengths for presalting are 30 miles (48 km) for urban roads and 40 miles (64 km) for rural roads.

With the demand for more efficient routes, it may be necessary to establish an independent check to see that continuous treatment has been successful and chute blockage or undetected mechanical malfunction has not occurred. In some areas this is allowed for by out and back routing, where salting takes place on the out run and inspection on the return. The maximum efficiency with this, however, is only 50%.

The search for increased efficiency may require the crossing of operational boundaries, both divisional, and adjacent authorities, and a pragmatic operational approach should be maintained at all times. Where a major traffic flow crosses an area, and is covered by more than one route,

GOOD TO HAVE IN REPORT FROM RCS / NEATH L.C.

DEPOT: Bentley	VEHICLE NO: DL394		
ROUTE: 7	PRECAUTIONARY GRIT		
LOAD: Spotbrough (neat salt)	GRIT	24·6	
	DEAD RUNNING	3·3	
	TOTAL	27·9	
ROUTE		GRITTING	MILEAGE
Commence A19/A638 grit to North Yorkshire Boundary		On	10·0
Return on A19 to C53 Askern		Off	2·0
Left on C53 to C97		On	3·0
Right on C97 to C25 at Barnby Dun		On	5·5
Left on C25 through Barnby Dun to Church Road		Off	0·5
Grit Church Road and Madam Lane back to C97		On	0·3
Return on C97 to Farstead Lane unclassified 54		Off	0·8
Grit unclassified 54, Farstead Lane and Almholme Road –		On	4·5
Arskey Lane to A19			
Right on A19 and left on to Cooke Street			
Grit Cooke St. and Watch House Lane to A638 and finish		On	1·3

Fig. 10.8. Typical gritting route format

treatment co-ordination will be required to ensure a consistent standard of service.

In some areas it may be relevant, particularly with the advent of better forecasting and sensors, to plan some routes based on elevation, say, all above a certain contour, although care must be taken to look at overall efficiency.

Once routes have been drafted and trial run to ensure the correct coverage, the necessary direction should be clear and unambiguous. One way is to set out the route instructions as in Fig. 10.8 on one side of a sheet (Fig. 10.8) with a map on the reverse. This can either be sealed into a waterproof cover or simply pasted on to hardboard and sealed with a clear varnish. In either case it can conveniently be used by the drivers concerned. The information given in Table 10.5 may be of assistance in route planning.

The recent availability of computerized route scheduling techniques allows existing routes to be examined to achieve optimal efficiency. Routes should be reviewed annually to allow for any changes to the road network due to improvement or traffic patterns (e.g. changed bus routes).

In urban areas, it will also be necessary to consider the removal of snow from footways and other areas. Work on some of these areas may be rechargeable to other committees and organizations. In some cases it will be necessary to agree policies and standard of service with clients. When preparing route lists for footways, special attention must be given to steps, footbridges, bus stops and pedestrian crossings.

10.6. Weather information and forecasting

The Meteorological Office provides a detailed and extensive information service to its customers, which also include highway authorities. As highway authorities invest in sensors and monitoring equipment, which are progressively being linked to the Meteorological Office, the accuracy of local forecasting is improving.

The standard service available by Prestel is a general five-day forecast. Highway authorities have usually subscribed to a more detailed service,

Table 10.5. Length of road in kilometres treated by 1 tonne and 1 m³ of salt*

Salt used	Spread rate: g/m²	Spread width		
		6 m	7·3 m	9 m
1 tonne	10	16·7	13·7	9·1
	20	8·3	6·8	4·5
	30	5·6	4·6	3·0
	40	4·2	3·4	3·5
1 m³	10	24	19·7	13·1
	20	12	9·9	6·5
	30	8	6·6	4·4
	40	6	4·9	3·3

*For all practical purposes, a density of 0·7 m³/t can be used.

which has been helpful in timing the response to potentially hazardous conditions. These forecasts are received on a daily basis.

At an additional cost, highway authorities can receive a Road Danger Warning, which gives warnings of the development of potentially hazardous conditions on a 24-hour basis, and is passed to whatever contact system has been established. The Meteorological Office also provides a consultancy service whereby nominated personnel can contact the duty weather forecaster to gain direct information.

In 1986 the Meteorological Office provided its 'Open Road' service specifically designed to meet the needs of highway authorities. 'Open Road' is a detailed prediction for the next 24 hours, with guidance on surface temperatures and wetness, and an opinion on the likelihood of ice formation. It is also possible to have a five-day forecast based on weather radar, together with a hard copy of the relevant data. An example of this

The Met. Office Open Road
For Sheffield

FORECAST FROM 1200HRS TODAY UNTIL 1200HRS TOMORROW.
ISSUED 1200HRS 29TH NOVEMBER 1988.

HAZARDS: NIL.

WEATHER: PERIODS OF RAIN BECOMING SHOWERY AFTER MIDNIGHT.

TEMPERATURES: MAXIMUM 10C MINIMUM 8C THOUGH ON HIGH LEVELS MINIMUM 5C.

ROAD SURFACE TEMPERATURE: NOT BELOW FREEZING.

FREEZING LEVEL [FREE AIR] 8000FT.

WIND: VARIABLE 07MPH BECOMING SOUTHEAST 15MPH AND SOUTHERLY 08MPH
      TOMORROW.
FORECASTER
ISSUED BY LEEDS WEATHER CENTRE

                THE EXTENDED OUTLOOK......

TOMORROW AFTERNOON: SCATTERED SHOWERS, NO ROAD HAZARDS.
WEDNESDAY NIGHT: SHOWERS, NO ROAD SURFACE HAZARDS.
THURSDAY: SUNNY INTERVALS, SCATTERED SHOWERS, NO ROAD SURFACE HAZARDS.
THURSDAY NIGHT: RAIN, DRY AND COLDER TOWARDS DAWN BUT NO ROAD SURFACE
                HAZARDS.
FRIDAY: SUNNY INTERVALS AND SCATTERED BLUSTERY SHOWERS. NO ROAD SURFACE
                HAZARDS.
FRIDAY NIGHT: SCATTERED SHOWERS FALLING AS SLEET ON THE HILLS. BUT ROAD
                SURFACE HAZARDS UNLIKELY.
ISSUED BY LEEDS WEATHER CENTRE.

Fig. 10.9. Open road weather forecast (from Leeds Weather Centre)

is shown in Fig. 10.9. The typical cost of this service for a highway authority in 1986–87 was £3000 + VAT per season (November–April).

The 'Open Road' information can also be presented in graphical format (Fig. 10.10), which gives a pessimistic and realistic forecast of road surface temperatures for a specific location. This is very helpful in planning when to take action.

The cost of the precautionary element of winter maintenance depends on the accuracy of the forecast and more particularly how it is interpreted and acted upon. In a county area where the cost of a single gritting

The Met. Office Open Road
For Sheffield

```
ROAD TEMPERATURE (DEGREES CELSIUS) AND ICE PREDICTION FROM  1200 29/11/88
_ _ _ _ _ _MOSCART....................A57 _ _ _ _ _ _ _ _ _
+22I..I..I..I..I..I..I..I..I..I..I..I..I..+..I..I..I..I..I..I..I..I..I..I..I+22
+21I..I..I..I..I..I..I..I..I..I..I..I..I..+..I..I..I..I..I..I..I..I..I..I..I+21
+20I..I..I..I..I..I..I..I..I..I..I..I..I..+..I..I..I..I..I..I..I..I..I..I..I+20
+19I..I..I..I..I..I..I..I..I..I..I..I..I..+..I..I..I..I..I..I..I..I..I..I..I+19
+18I..I..I..I..I..I..I..I..I..I..I..I..I..+..I..I..I..I..I..I..I..I..I..I..I+18
+17I..I..I..I..I..I..I..I..I..I..I..I..I..+..I..I..I..I..I..I..I..I..I..I..I+17
+16I..I..I..I..I..I..I..I..I..I..I..I..I..+..I..I..I..I..I..I..I..I..I..I..I+16
+15I..I..I..I..I..I..I..I..I..I..I..I..I..+..I..I..I..I..I..I..I..I..I..I..I+15
+14I..I..I..I..I..I..I..I..I..I..I..I..I..+..I..I..I..I..I..I..I..I..I..I..I+14
+13I..I..I..I..I..I..I..I..I..I..I..I..I..+..I..I..I..I..I..I..I..I..I..I..I+13
+12I..I..I..I..I..I..I..I..I..I..I..I..I..+..I..I..I..I..I..I..I..I..I..I..I+12
+11I..I..I..I..I..I..I..I..I..I..I..I..I..+..I..I..I..I..I..I..I..I..I..I..I+11
+10I..I..I..I..I..I..I..I..I..I..I..I..I..+..I..I..I..I..I..I..I..I..I..I..I+10
+ 9I..I..I..I..I..I..I..I..I..I..I..I..I..+..I..I..I..I..I..I..I..I..I..I..I+ 9
+ 8I..I..I..I..I..I..I..I..I..I..I..I..I..+..I..I..I..I..I..I..I..I..I..I..I+ 8
+ 7IEEEEEEEEI..I..I..I..I..I..I..I..I..I..+..I..I..I..I..I..I..I..I..IREE+ 7
+ 6E..I..I..EEEEEEEEEEEEEEEEEEEEEEEEEEEEEEEEEEEEEER..I..I..I..I..I..IREEP.I+ 6
+ 5I..I..I..I..I..I..I..I..I..I..I..I..+..I..I..PEEEERRRRRRI..I..IRRRP.I..I+ 5
+ 4I..I..I..I..I..I..I..I..I..I..I..I..+..I..I..I..I..PPPPPP.RRRRRRR.PP..I..I+ 4
+ 3I..I..I..I..I..I..I..I..I..I..I..I..+..I..I..I..I..I..PPPPPPPPP.I..I..I+ 3
+ 2I..I..I..I..I..I..I..I..I..I..I..I..+..I..I..I..I..I..I..PPPPPPPP.I..I..I+ 2
    +++++++++++++++++++++++++++++++++++++++++++++++++++++++++++++++++++++++++++++
    12 13 14 15 16 17 18 19 20 21 22 23 0  1  2  3  4  5  6  7  8  9 10 11 12
REL ........PPPPPPPPPPPPPPPPPPPPPPPPPPPPPPPPPPPPPPPPPPPPPPPPWWWWWWWWWWWWWWWWW WET
PES ........PPPPPPPPPPPPPPPPPPPPPPPPPPPPPPPPPPPPPPPPPWWWWWWWWWWWWWWWWWWWWWWWW WET
```

PERIOD OF FREEZING ROAD TEMPERATURES	REL NONE	PES NONE	
MINIMUM ROAD TEMPERATURES	REL ·4.2	PES 2.6	

KEY: ..dry light(d)ew heavy(D)ew light(f)rost heavy(F)rost (W)et (I)ce
     (P)recipitation   (R)ealistic (P)essimistic (E)qual
     ISSUED BY THE MET OFFICE AT 1225 29 NOVEMBER 1988

PESSIMISTIC INDICATES LOW WIND SPEEDS AND LARGER CLOUD BREAKS.

Fig. 10.10. Predictive graph of road surface temperatures (from Leeds Weather Centre)

operation may be £15 000, any reduction in the number of turnouts can lead to significant savings.

The decision to turn out has traditionally been left to local managements who have a good knowledge of the local problem areas and weather patterns, and first consideration is usually based on the Meteorological Office normal weather forecast.

The advent of local sensors placed in the road has allowed comparisons to be made between freezing road surface temperatures forecast and those measured. Ponting[10.6] suggests an accuracy of 57%; records maintained by the author over a four-year period indicate a range of 47%–70%. From this very limited information, the potential scale of savings can be judged as operational management err on the safe side and grit when there is a forecast of icy conditions.

Ice detection systems have been available for some years, and Fig. 10.11 shows a passive Icelert system that was installed in Sheffield in 1968. This was based on a map of the city indicating the position of each of eleven sensors against which were three coloured lights; under normal circumstances, the lights showed green, but this changed through amber at one degree above freezing point, to red when road surface temperatures reached 0°C. When this system was operational, action was taken on amber readings with the onset of nightfall or during the night. A major

Fig. 10.11. Early ice prediction system (Icelert) — Sheffield

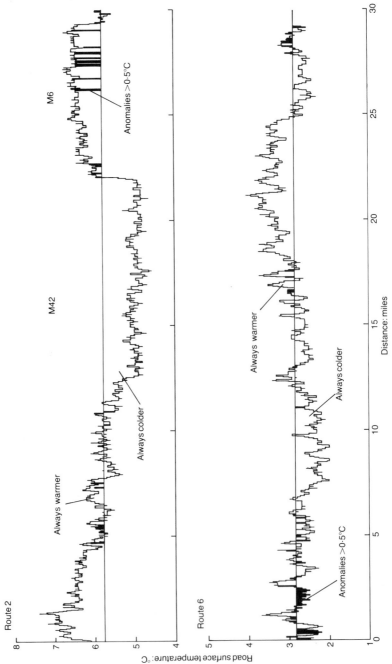

Fig. 10.12. Typical thermal map: County of West Midlands thermal mapping survey

advantage of this type of system is that it allows geographically specific treatment in areas of varying topography.

As technology progressed, a subsequent generation of this type of system allowed for more information to be available on temperatures, moisture and salinity on the road surface. This was again a passive system whereby a recorded message could be interrogated. On telephoning, the sensors were able, via a system of relays, to trigger the appropriate report which was in four basic parts

(*a*)   road surface temperature above or below $+2°C$
(*b*)   road surface temperature above or below $0°C$
(*c*)   whether moisture was present on the road surface
(*d*)   whether salt solution was present on the road surface.

Later systems were developed to send a recorded message by telephone when preset conditions were reached and this meant that periodic interrogation was not necessary, although the latter was still available in the event of doubt.

The latest version of this system can now be linked to the Meteorological Office to give forecasters specific local information and this is leading to savings in treatment costs. Additionally, at local level the sensor can be connected to a VDU and the temperature trend periodically monitored, covering either the last 12 hours or 1 hour; the latter being useful when treatment is imminent. Those sensors that are linked to the Meteorological Office give continuous information on air, road surface and sub-soil temperatures. The benefit of this broader information is gained from being able to predict the road surface temperature from a knowledge of the sub-soil temperature, which is indicative of the heat stored in the ground.

This has a counterbalancing influence on the air temperature and it has been possible on several occasions to determine no treatment when a predicted road surface temperature based on air temperature would have led to a different course of action. When a sensor of this type, usually known as a deep probe, is linked to the Meteorological Office, it is possible to get a more accurate predictive graph, as shown in Fig. 10.10, than that available under the normal Open Road Service. When this information is used in conjunction with the monitoring from an individual sensor, it is possible to restrain treatment as long as possible and in some cases take a finely balanced decision not to grit.

To maximize on a sensor installation requires a thermal map to be produced of the various routes. By this process it is possible to find how the road surface temperature varies along a route and from this information to optimally site the sensor. Using this knowledge of the temperature profile, it is possible to correlate what is happening over the network and organize treatment accordingly. The process of producing thermal maps was described by Parmenter and Thornes,[10.7] and a typical example relating to routes in the West Midlands is shown in Fig. 10.12.

There are four facets to the use of weather prediction systems, the first two deal with the installation and detailed sensor positions, which are decided using local knowledge and a thermal map and from a survey of the availability of a power source and Telecom lines, respectively.

Cost and benefits are the next consideration. As a yardstick, an installation will cost about £10 000 times the number of sensors used with a typical total of £80–100 000 being normal. Although limited benefit information has been described by Ponting[10.8] and Chorlton,[10.9] this leads to the conclusion that a typical payback period is five years. Information collated in Sheffield over one winter's experience of a nine station system installed in 1987 has considered what would have previously been done, with the action taken, and a comparison of costs indicated a saving of £12 000 on salt alone. In that first winter a depot based shift was in place; this is now being examined, such that the potential saving may be higher. From this it is concluded that a five year pay back period is realistic, if not pessimistic.

The final facet is the development of the selective prediction of ice formation on the highway network based on ice detection sensors, thermal maps and a knowledge of how fundamentally different weather patterns may affect the thermal map. Some packages are available to do this, although there is a need for some fundamental research on the effect of different weather patterns. A further development being researched is the computer generation of treatment routes to deal with a partial or localized turnout and effect further savings.

An authority considering an installation, particularly if trunk roads are involved, is advised to consult the Department of Transport specification

Fig. 10.13. Winter maintenance control room

for a National Ice Prediction Network (number MCE 2020F) published in August 1987.

The room shown in Fig. 10.13 is specially set aside for winter maintenance and is used only for that purpose. It contains: a large scale map of the area with priority routes, status boards, a master station for an ice prediction system, two-way radio, two normal telephone extensions, one ex-directory telephone, route boards, a counter for issuing route boards and desk space for recording personnel. An ice detection installation is shown in Fig. 10.14.

(a) (b)

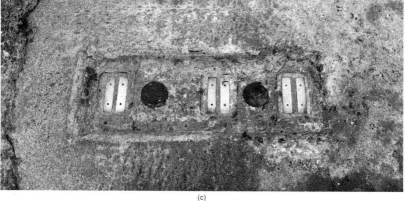

(c)

Fig. 10.14. Ice detection installation: (a) general view of installation; (b) details of cabinet; (c) road mounted sensor

10.7. Materials

As mentioned in section 10.3.1, rock salt in conjunction with snowploughs remains the most economic and effective method of keeping roads clear of ice and snow. In addition to the variants on rock salt, there are other materials which, albeit more expensive, have specialist uses and these are briefly reviewed.

Salt dissolves in water and lowers the freezing point; it will also melt ice which has already formed. Chemically, sodium chloride (salt) will melt ice and snow at temperatures as low as $-21°C$. However, below $-10°C$ the quantities of salt required increase to a point where it becomes environmentally and economically undesirable. In Britain, with rare exceptions, the temperature during periods of icing or snowfall is usually above $-3°C$. Recommended application rates are $10\,g/m^2$ for precautionary salting, $20–40\,g/m^2$ for heavy frost or falling snow, and $40–60\,g/m^2$ for snow removal. The use of salt has increased significantly since 1960 (see Fig. 10.15) and current sales are running at £40 million/year. All salt from UK sources is from the ICI mine at Winsford in Chesire and is supplied in accordance with BS 3247.[10.11] While there is no competition in the supply, delivery is predominantly by road and it remains a huge logistic problem. Costs are kept down by utilizing return loads wherever possible. While very cost effective in keeping roads ice free, salt has derogatory effects on vegetation, watercourses, concrete and vehicles.

A strong solution of salt in soil water can affect the properties of soils and prevent plants from taking up moisture through their roots. Dehydration results, making the death of plants almost certain. A typical example being the first 2–3 ft of a grass verge which abuts the carriageway on a busy road, where spray of salt solution kills the grass.

The sodium ferrocyanide added to rock salt as an anti-caking inhibitor is not toxic. Toxicity results from conversion of ferrocyanide, by sunlight, into cyanide, although tests indicate this to be unlikely in this country.

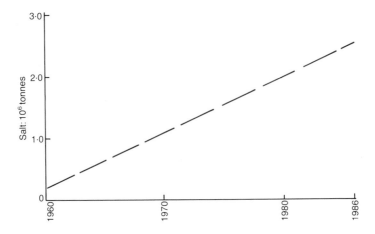

Fig. 10.15. Trend in salt purchases (1960–86)[10.10]

Run off from salt piles should not, however, be allowed to drain into watercourses containing fish or to which livestock have access.

Concentrated dried salt solution can have a serious affect on concrete, causing spalling and progressive deterioration, particularly if reinforced. The long-term effects on concrete bridges are now becoming a problem particularly where the waterproofing membrane breaks down.

Salt solution is corrosive to metal and has a derogatory effect on road vehicles. Those particularly at risk are associated with winter maintenance, and regular and careful washing and maintenance is required.

The price of salt varies around £20/tonne throughout the year, and highway authorities can minimize their cost by up to £1/tonne by ordering and taking delivery out of season. As funds become scarcer, few authorities maintain the sizes of stockpiles they did previously. In a bad winter this can be a problem, and a supply co-ordination system is run by Lancashire County Council on behalf of the County Surveyors' Society to minimize any hardship.

In times of shortage, it has been normal to restrict salt to primary routes and to use sharp sand and salt mixed in the ratio 1:2, respectively. This, however, causes problems of blocked gullies and requires extra expenditure on sweeping, but has the advantage that the general public can see when treatment has occurred. There are various alternatives to natural rock salt: imported salt, urea, polyglycol, calcium chloride and single sized grit.

Salt is imported from either Mediterranean countries or East Germany. It is usually white, possibly with a high content of anti-caking agent, which is prone to leaching, and may not conform to BS 3247.[10,11]

Urea does not affect steel but costs £130–£140/tonne. It must be used carefully and requires a spread rate of about twice that of salt to have the same effect. It is available in light granule form and for practical handling requires application in solution. It has specialist uses on long suspension bridges and airfields where lowest initial cost is not critical.

Polyglycol is used by the RAF and British Airports Authority and is applied in solution from a spray tanker. Its use on highways is limited although trials were carried out on the Erskine bridge in Scotland prior to 1979. There is little information on costs other than that it is very expensive, and it would not be used where salt or a cheaper alternative would suffice.

Calcium chloride will melt ice at considerably lower temperatures than rock salt, but such temperatures are rarely encountered in the UK. It costs approximately £100/tonne, is very hygroscopic, and has a serious effect on poor quality reinforced concrete.

Single size grit (6 mm) can be mixed with rock salt when roads, especially those with steep gradients, are covered with hard packed snow. In some countries, where salt is not used, it is normal practice to allow the snow to compact and then spread grit to provide traction.

No substitute is seen for salt as a primary de-icing agent on highways in the UK, and its use is likely to continue with improved application control and more attention paid to storage.

The majority of salt stocks are outside, and subject to the weather. While a heap will be self thatching, there will be an amount of leaching. Salt should be stored on a hard base, ideally air-entrained concrete, summitted in the centre and falling gently towards the edges of the pile to allow drainage. Positive drainage should be provided around the edges of the pile.

The salt should be stored in heaps with a convex surface to ensure free surface drainage and the height of the heap should be minimized and preferably lower than 4·5 m. A large heap should be formed of a series of parallel clamps with some form of dividing wall so that they can be regularly and systematically replaced. Experience indicates that, in a large conical pile that is never completely used, the edges degenerate to marl and are ineffective for winter maintenance.

To get good spreading properties and overall effectiveness, salt should be as dry as possible. The Transport and Road Research Laboratory estimate[10.12] that 0·125% of the initial weight of a pile is lost for each inch (2·54 cm) of rainfall. Consequently, as a minimum, all salt piles should be sheeted with black polythene sheeting (0·2–0·3 mm thick) or black butyl rubber (0·7–0·8 mm thick) held down by netting and suitable weights, and the economics of investing in a salt barn should be examined. The Audit Commission have concluded that a positive benefit results and the majority of Department of Transport owned compounds feature barns. In the latter case, it is also normal to provide a hopper to facilitate an easy, rapid, single-man loading operation. The construction of a salt barn should be simple and robust, incorporating timber sleeper walls, A major problem is the necessary height to facilitate discharge within the barn by articulated tipping lorries, which require some 12 m of headroom. The

Fig. 10.16. Typical modern salt barn

alternative to this is to tip outside, and stack using a conveyor elevator, which adds a perpetual annual cost to the restocking. A typical, recently constructed salt barn is shown in Fig. 10.16.

To be most effective, the salt should be spread on a damp road, otherwise it will quickly blow into the channels. In the case of forecast snow, it is essential to complete operations before snowfall starts to ensure a wet surface, which, with the assistance of passing tyres, will break up and melt any standing snow. If this wet surface is not present, the snow will compact to ice and become both dangerous and difficult to remove.

Regular testing in accordance with BS 3247[10.11] should take place, particular attention being paid to particle size, because oversized particles can be dangerous and can cause extensive damage to passing vehicles and to property adjacent to the highway.

10.8. Personnel

Personnel involved in winter maintenance are the most critical part of the plan, for it is they who will have to cope with adverse conditions and long unsociable hours in the event of need. At one extreme, it might be the odd night gritting, at the other it may involve several weeks of continuous 24 hour working.

Competent direction and supervision, operating within a flexible framework, is a vital part of the plan. Once the plan has been reviewed and updated annually a comprehensive training exercise should begin. This will consist of a combination of formal classroom lectures and discussion periods together with practical training on all equipment to be used. At these sessions, the learning experience will be two-way and may cause management to review previous ideas — which it must be seen to be sufficiently flexible to do. Training should cover:

(*a*) the organization
(*b*) details of the winter maintenance plans: to ensure that each person knows exactly what is expected and how it might be achieved
(*c*) the individual responsibilities of the personnel involved
(*d*) working hours, shift schedules, standby rotas, call-out procedures, how and where to report
(*e*) the importance and completion of the relevant paperwork and records
(*f*) the use, limitations and operating characteristics of all snow removal and gritting vehicles and equipment
(*g*) communications procedures
(*h*) knowledge of routes
(*i*) first line field maintenance procedures
(*j*) instructions on the individual's scope for independent action
(*k*) available back-up service
(*l*) safety of the travelling public.

Safety of the winter maintenance operations is not only related to operatives employed on them, but also to members of the public, as much of the work is carried out on roads open to normal traffic. Operatives must, therefore, be made aware of their responsibilities to other road users.

In any operation involving manual labour, health and safety is a prime consideration, which is particularly relevant to winter maintenance where the work is frequently carried out in poor visibility on roads subject to hazardous surface conditions. The following factors should be borne in mind.

(a) Operatives work less efficiently and less safely after long hours on duty; shift systems should be set up when emergencies are prolonged.

(b) Operatives will work less safely outside normal workings hours and inexperienced operatives should not be employed at these times.

(c) When a hazardous operation of work in a remote location is undertaken, double manning should be employed.

Several systems of providing personnel are used in different authorities

(a) *voluntary call-out system* — where volunteer personnel are called when the need arises; payment is only made when volunteers are involved in work. This system relies heavily on goodwill.

(b) *standby system* — where personnel volunteer to be available for a payment to compensate for constraining their normal out-of-work activities. Nationally agreed payment structures are available.

(c) *shift* — where personnel are depot based and are paid accordingly

(d) *stand to systems* — which involves no standby payment but employees report to the depot at 5.30 a.m. each morning regardless of the weather and are paid whether they turn out or not.

Standby periods vary from one authority to another, although for Department of Transport Agencies, the following winter maintenance periods are defined for operational purposes[10.13]

(a) high — December, January and February, when severe conditions might reasonably be expected

(b) low — November and March, when severe conditions may occur

(c) marginal — October and April, when severe conditions are not expected.

Those authorities that operate this type of system usually have half resources available for low and marginal periods and full for the high period. Where a shift is used, there is a need to achieve an agreement on the willingness of the operatives to be involved in alternative work when no winter maintenance is taking place.

The payment of a bonus while engaged on winter maintenance is an issue of some contention, particularly for drivers, since to complete routes above a recommended speed increases likely damage to passing motorists and properties. This is especially relevant when snowploughing in an urban area. Some years ago the author had to deal with the aftermath when the front room of a terraced house adjacent to a main road was damaged by a large volume of wet snow which gained access through a closed window, due to over-vigorous snowploughing during night-time operations. The Audit Commission recommend that a bonus, if paid at all, should be at a predetermined fixed percentage, or the average paid for other work in the relevant period.

The regulations governing drivers' hours embodied in the Road Transport Act 1968 Part IV and subsequently amended in Drivers' Hours (Goods Vehicles) (Modifications) Order 1986, allow for no maximum number of hours a driver can drive in an emergency, which includes winter maintenance, although when the emergency is past, the driver must have the relevant rest period. The definition of what constitutes emergency requires consideration; for example, involvement in first line salting and snow clearing causes no problems, but transporting a specialist piece of plant to another location, say on a low loader might. There are, in some areas, records of prosecution for work remote from the front line.

Care must also be taken during the preseason training to document and explain the legislation governing the various forms of licence required and the age limits that apply. In the teeth of an emergency, it is very easy to take operationally pragmatic decisions, which cause people to operate illegally. While in many cases it has been known for the police to take a similar view, this cannot be done in the event of an accident.

Arrangements must be clear, against a defined plan, for the employment of labour available from a number of council departments, other than those immediately concerned with highways, for the clearance of snow from footways. Supervision is best undertaken by the department providing the labour, and as such it is important that departments are instructed

Fig. 10.17. Demountable gritter

in advance of what work will be required of them, and for which locations they are responsible.

10.9. Vehicles and plant

The vehicles and plant used in winter maintenance comprise a diverse collection from purpose-designed and -built equipment to ad hoc converted semi-pensioned off items of transport, and comes in all shapes, sizes, and drive configurations. The geographical area to be treated has a considerable influence on what is required or desirable. A relatively level urban area is best served by small manoeuverable items probably in a second career. On the other hand, rural, and hilly large urban areas, are better suited by larger, more powerful items. The equipment used falls, primarily, into three categories, viz. gritters, snowploughs and snowblowers.

Spreaders, more commonly known as gritters, have their origin in agricultural equipment, originally designed to spread lime. The design consisted of a hopper, usually on a trailer pulled behind a tractor. Early gritters were basically modified limespreaders mounted on lorries. The hopper, usually of 3 or 4 m^3 capacity, was emptied using a moving chain grate, running over sprockets driven by an independent power unit, to transport the salt via a variable feed gate to a chute and hence on to one or two rotating discs for distribution. The abrasive and aggressive nature of the salt led to the use of a rubber conveyor belt to move the salt and, as technology progressed, a single rotating disc became normal.

Early equipment had closed chutes that were susceptible to blockage. European experience related to auger screw feed of salt rather than to belt,

Fig. 10.18. Small fixed gritter

(a)

(b)

(c)

(d)

Fig. 10.19. Large purpose-built gritter:
(a) general view; (b) spreader disc;
(c) controls; (d) plough blade

but this required much drier salt than was normal in the UK. Peitch in Germany developed the use of stainless steel and open chutes, which has progressively become normal in the UK.

The present day gritter in the UK is often demountable, an example being shown in Fig. 10.17, which is also independently power operated by a small donkey engine driving both the feed belt and distribution spinner. The advantage with demountable units is that the host vehicle can be used for normal work. Mounting and securing takes about 20 minutes and this form of unit is the mainstay of many authorities. A recent development of this has been the replacement of the donkey engine by hydraulic power driven from a pump on the host vehicle. This has allowed the development of speed related distribution, whereby a relatively constant spread rate of salt can be achieved on the ground (BS 1622: 1976[10.14] covers the distribution performance of this equipment).

A large number of authorities have older lorries on to which gritter bodies have been mounted on a permanent basis, and which can be used on the shorter tighter routes in an urban area. An example is shown in Fig. 10.18. An advantage of this arrangement is that no road fund licence is necessary as the unit can be classed as plant and operated on rebated fuel oil in accordance with S4(1)(1) or S7(3) of the Vehicle (Excise) Act 1971. Some authorities have found it economical to untax part of their normal lorry fleet in the winter and permanently mount gritters to take advantage of these economies.

Hopper capacity varies from 3–9 m^3, although above 6 m^3 they will be permanently mounted. Typical of the larger purpose built or permanently mounted units are those operated by the Department of Transport, shown in Fig. 10.19(a–d). These vehicles are built to an extremely high specification with respect to corrosion, and are 6 × 4 drive and capable of one-man operation. The spreader arrangement, which is hydraulically driven, can be seen in Fig. 10.19(b), the small probe being a sensor to monitor whether the salt is distributing correctly, as this cannot be seen by the driver under normal operating conditions. The drilled quadrant on the right of the vehicle controls the delivery gate to the chute, the salt being transported to the gate by a rubber conveyor belt. As previously mentioned, all vehicles should be fitted with two-way radios, which can be seen alongside the cab mounted controls shown in Fig. 10.19(c). Later versions of this control are based around micro-electronics and remote servo-motors rather than the cable arrangement shown here. Details of the plough blade arrangement are shown in Fig. 10.19(d). This blade is specifically for motorways, having a large top cowl to permit ploughing at much faster speeds than would be sensible on non-motorway roads. The blade can be raised and lowered hydraulically, runs on jockey wheels and can be angled to either side, contact with the road being made by a rubber runner on the bottom of the blade.

Snowploughing on non-motorway roads is carried out by specialist heavy plough vehicles, an example being shown in Fig. 10.20. This vehicle is a 6 × 6 drive ex-World War II American Mack, which is ballasted with concrete blocks and can either be equipped with an angled blade, as

Fig. 10.20. Specialist heavy snowplough

shown, or a vee blade for serious first pass work. Once off the motorway it is usual for plough blades to have the rubber tips in short sections of about 500 mm long mounted on a springback arrangement such that on contacting street furniture a section of blade will yield and, once passed over the projecting item, will return.

A more recent vehicle now being used extensively to fulfil both the large gritter and heavy plough role is shown in Fig. 10.21. It is purpose built, and features 6 × 6 drive, which is so necessary in upland serious conditions. Equipped with the latest micro-electronic controlled hydraulic speed related spreader and plough control, and fitted with either angled or vee blade, this type of vehicle is now replacing the previous generation of Department of Transport vehicles bought second hand by highway authorities some years ago and now generally unserviceable.

It is normal with spreaders to be able to alter the spread pattern to allow for differing road configurations. Later vehicles have cab mounted controls; older ones required a physical adjustment of the spreader disc, easily accomplished on a pin and bar system.

Loading screens are commonly fitted to bulk gritters to prevent the ingress of large objects, which could jam the feed belt or block the delivery gate. They are made of metal mesh and not well liked by drivers as they significantly increase loading time.

Trailer gritters essentially have a hopper and spinner on a single axle. Normally driven by the direct drive of their wheels or by power take off from the towing vehicle, they have a small hopper capacity, which is capable of being replenished from the towing lorry. On straightforward estate roads they can be used to good effect, but are not very manoeuverable, particularly in culs-de-sac.

Fig. 10.21. Heavy all-purpose vehicle

Many urban authorities have, in the past, used a side spinner arrangement on smaller lorries. A rubber or metal rotating disc, hydraulically driven, is slung under the lorry within the wheelbase. Salt is fed down a chute mounted under a removable plate in the lorry floor. The salt is shovelled into the chute by two men in the lorry back. A more recent development of this, designed and manufactured by Sheffield City Council, is shown in Fig. 10.22. Adaptation of a lorry takes a matter of minutes. The spinner arrangement is hydraulically driven and the salt is again fed manually.

A most versatile item of plant is a tractor plough, due to its manoeuverability. In rural areas, where there is an availability of farm tractors, particularly the more recent larger four-wheel drive types, they are almost unstoppable and capable of considerable output.

In most authorities it is not normal to run with plough blades, when only gritting operations are in progress, but it is essential that they can be fitted quickly and easily. Consequently, they must be easily accessible and Fig. 10.23 shows how they might be stored in a depot.

Snowploughing operations begin when there is 40–50 mm of snow and it is recommended that an immediate application of salt at a rate of 10 g/m² is given. With purpose-built ploughing vehicles, this requires the use of a separate gritter. For this reason it is economic to use an all-purpose vehicle, although when conditions are bad, the range may be reduced by the need to keep the vehicle ballasted.

In rural areas the use of a large vehicle with a vee blade (Fig. 10.24) can be most effective and fast for charging a way through, the deep snow being subsequently widened out by an angled plough, or where this is too deep by a snow cutter or blower. These are specialist, very expensive, vehicles

Fig. 10.22 (left). Modern trailboard gritter

Fig. 10.23 (below). Snowplough blades ready

Fig. 10.24 (bottom). Snowplough vee blade

and their purchase must be carefully considered by an authority, who may pay £100 000 for a vehicle that has no other use.

In severe conditions, there is no speedy alternative to a blower when the snow is above 1 m deep. Such a vehicle at work is shown in Fig. 10.25.

As with gritters, snow blowers can either be fixed, purpose-built (Fig. 10.26), or demountable (Fig. 10.27). The advantage with the two shown is that the cutter can be raised or lowered to deal with particularly deep snow. Blowers require particularly skilled operation and much local knowledge when moving through deep snow — as ditches and walls may not be visible. Three other major problems await blowers in deep drift, viz.

Fig. 10.25. Snowblower at work

Fig. 10.26. Purpose-built snowblower

Fig. 10.27. Demountable snowblower

vehicles, trapped animals, and large stones used by drivers to chock vehicles. Any of these can incapacitate a blower, particularly an older one where the cutter is secured by shear bolts to prevent structural damage to itself. The corner of a car presents little challenge; however, more modern types (Fig. 10.26) feature hydrostatic drive of the cutter, which minimizes this problem.

Smaller demountable blowers are available, the smallest capable of being fitted to a motor mower can clear footways and self load into an adjacent lorry. A somewhat larger but very cost effective version can be fitted to a JCB type excavator.

When all items are in use, the final alternative to move snow is a loading shovel, the bigger the better, particularly in a rural area, although when used there is usually an appreciable amount of damage to verges and walls.

It is relevant here to mention fuel, as it is essential that there is an adequate stock of the correct type. A stock of about 3–4 weeks at heavy usage is recommended, and where diesel fuel (the predominant type) is used, a winter grade complying with Class A2, BS 6380,[10.15] should be stocked.

10.10. Operational aspects

10.10.1. General

Flexibility is the keyword, as one of the major problems for the manager of the winter maintenance operation is that he has too much resource, and is criticized for being profligate. Alternatively, he has totally insufficient resource, and serious aspersions are cast about his ability. Having said that, the successful stewardship of winter maintenance gives a great sense of satisfaction to those involved in providing a direct and high profile service to the community.

The primary need is to ensure that somebody is in charge in the field, who has a degree of local knowledge, is fully aware of the plan framework, understands his resources and how to deploy them, commands the respect of his team, is unflappable, and is sufficiently senior to make it happen in the event of need. To be successful, winter maintenance needs pro-active leadership from the front.

Much maligned in the past, but as the need to demonstrate efficiency increases so does the need to maintain an accurate record of what the conditions were, what was done, when, where and by whom, and vitally, what it all cost. Some of the necessary records are

- (a) treatment record (see Fig. 10.28)
- (b) weather forecast and observed
- (c) temperatures forecast and observed
- (d) ice detection record
- (e) wind direction and speed
- (f) road blockages showing lengths and times
- (g) plant available
- (h) plant in repair showing length of time
- (i) salt stock, usage, deliveries and movement
- (j) fuel stocks, usage, deliveries and movement

Winter Maintenance Log   Depot: Date:

Route	Fleet No.	Driver	Time ON	Time OFF	Loads	Remarks/Road Conditions	Time	Temp °C					
								Dry	Rain	Snow	Fog		

Snow   Start   Finish

Fig. 10.28. Typical treatment record sheet

(*k*) labour return — direct employees
(*l*) labour return — indirect employees
(*m*) hired plant return
(*n*) costs and available budget.

It may well be that much of the information is available within the authorities' systems, but the above recommends the necessary information to form a comprehensive record. It is recommended that record keeping at each operational location should be the specific full-time duty of one or more persons.

Part of the records maintained should relate to random checks, by supervisory personnel, of the success or otherwise of treatment, and that the routes laid down are being adhered to. Supervision should also be vigilant that private treatment arrangements do not exist — a large winter maintenance vehicle can do a surprising amount of damage in a public house car park.

Radio communication is vital at all depots and in all operational vehicles, especially where single manning is normal. This will allow drivers to call for assistance, and the direction of back-up and mechanical assistance as well as an up-to-date picture of conditions and problems to be maintained.

In some authorities it is policy to maintain a central control room to co-ordinate the activities across a county; in some cases this is only manned when serious conditions occur and transfer of resources may be required. Even so it is important that the field manager has a manual containing the sources of all possible extra resources together with contact names and details and previously arranged hire rates.

Communications with the media should be considered and an authority policy established, which it is suggested should allow only certain nominated senior people to give information and comment. When conditions are severe, a regular and systematic press statement should be made.

Co-ordination and liaison on a national scale could have many benefits and, whereas this presently is exercised in an ad hoc manner by the police, there may be merit in a highway authority version of the national co-ordination run by the Association of Chief Police Officers.

Operationally it is very desirable that each depot or location from which winter maintenance takes place should have a mechanical services support to provide at least first line repair facilities and a standby system to cope with major problems. This should include the capability of recovery of unserviceable or damaged vehicles to the depot.

Precautionary gritting is a much simpler operation to control than the more dynamic snow clearing problems. At the onset of a major snowfall it is difficult to decide at what point to bring in a shift rota and go on to round the clock working, which may be necessary after the snow has stopped, particularly if high winds prevail. The emergency plan should, however, have foreseen this possibility and established a framework.

In times of serious snowfall, one of the major problems faced by field management is in maintaining an accurate and up-to-date picture of problems on the ground, particularly when there is large scale blockage. In many instances it is difficult to get an accurate picture from the ground and it may be necessary to use a helicopter to carry out an aerial survey. While this will initially appear costly, it is likely to prove cost effective overall as resources can be deployed much earlier to clear blockages.

Operational management must be aware of the two contrasting faces of the public and how amazingly unreasonable and foolhardy people can be. 'You need to clear my road I have a dinner appointment' is not unknown, nor is the sudden incidence of many pregnant women at an imminent stage of labour in isolated locations. Each situation must be judged on its merits as guidance is difficult.

In conditions of heavy snowfall, the needs of the farming community must be attended to. Ensuring that animal feed arrives can be a self help operation by the farmer, which they are usually happy to participate in, but as technology has changed, milk is collected by tanker rather than by churn, and there is usually only two days' storage capacity at the farms.

As temperatures fall, so abnormal problems arise and Fig. 10.29 gives an indication of what may occur in severe conditions; thus, care should be taken to ensure that winter grade fuels are used.

The welfare of the labour force must be given sufficient emphasis and it may be relevant to make some more formal arrangements for welfare facilities than usually obtains. The constant availability of hot drinks, soups and meals is of great benefit when 24 hour working is in progress. Drying facilities should be provided for wet clothes even if only on an ad

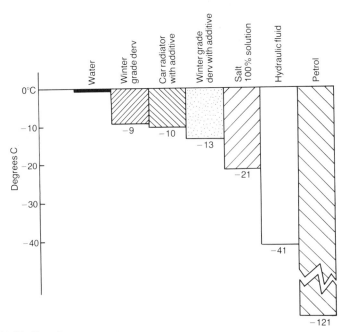

Fig. 10.29. Freezing temperatures

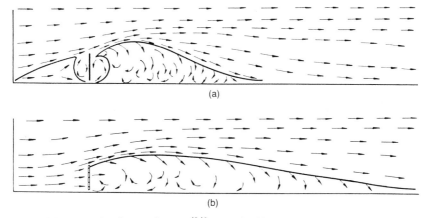

(a)

(b)

Fig. 10.30. Principle of snow fencing:[10.16] typical eddy patterns and drift patterns, about: (a) a solid fence; (b) an open fence

hoc temporary basis. The availability of four-wheel drive personnel carriers is vital in serious conditions as there is little point having set up a shift system to find that drivers cannot get either home or to the depot. In these circumstances it is sensible to arrange a 'taxi' service, using these vehicles for the duration of the emergency.

Care should be taken with the purchase of waterproof clothing, which in times of emergency may be worn for lengthy periods. Cheaper designs and fabrics tend to suffer from serious condensation problems, which, in addition to being uncomfortable to the wearer, can also become dangerous if wind chill factors are high.

Fig. 10.31. Successful snow fencing

10.10.2. Snowfencing

In exposed rural areas, drifting snow can be controlled by the use of snowfencing erected on the windward side of affected areas. The principle behind the fence is dealt with by Hogbin[10.16] and it acts as shown in Fig. 10.30.

A successfully placed fence, usually 15–20 times the height away from a road, can drop the snow short of the road, as shown in Fig. 10.31. A field boundary fence, even a timber post and four-rail type, can cause the snow to drop on the road by the same principles.

Fabrication of a fence can be from traditional materials, e.g. chestnut paling, suitably stayed, and can be left out all year. Alternatively, in some areas the fences are erected and dismantled annually. The advent of plastics and geotextiles has led to several proprietary varieties, which all tend to have the desired void/solid ratio of about 1:1.

10.10.3. Snow disposal sites

In urban areas where it is necessary to pick up snow from the highway, a means of disposal must be arranged, which may be

(a) rivers and waterways — it is usual to have permanent snowgates in parapet walls in several locations throughout a city for the tipping of snow. Prior agreement with the relevant authority is advised
(b) on the verges of rural roads
(c) on tipping sites or derelict land.

Care should be taken when selecting (b) and (c) to ensure no flooding or nuisance is caused.

10.10.4. Drainage

Consideration should be given to known flooding spots when a snowfall is heavy, as rapidly melting snow produces a large run off.

10.10.5. Sub-surface heating

Heating elements can be laid in the surfacing layers of difficult locations although they are extremely expensive, difficult to maintain, and easily damaged. There are probably more non-operational installations than successful ones.

10.10.6. Police assistance

A close liaison should be maintained at all times with the police and when conditions become severe and roads are closed, this can be very helpful. The photograph in Fig. 10.32, taken from a landrover driven by the author, shows a police Range Rover shepherding a family of sightseers in a family saloon out to show their children the snow. A snowblower had passed through this two mile long drift half an hour previously.

Self help is an important resource for the highway authority and should be encouraged. In some rural counties a network of voluntary snow wardens has been established who provide valuable information to the Divisional Surveyor on the local conditions and problems. This can

Fig. 10.32. Police assistance

become a fairly formal resource, which can, by arrangement, mobilize additional local resources in emergencies.

Supplies of salt, either in grit bins, which are usually brightly coloured plastic containers of about 0·5 tonne capacity in urban areas, or heaps of salt on verges in rural areas, can be of benefit to the motorist.

In urban areas care should be taken in the siting of grit bins as they are a regular target for vandals. A degree of restraint may also be required of operational management concerning the abuse of salt from bins. A fairly typical example was a residential estate on which a grit bin was situated and on investigating a complaint from the residents about road conditions it was found that the road was largely impassable, but all the house drives were clear of snow, glistening wet and covered with salt. In urban areas grit bins are usually placed following request and subsequent investigation. They can be a fairly costly resource and in times of snow need continuous replenishment.

10.11. Future developments

As attempts are made to reduce the cost of winter maintenance, developments will take place in several areas.

More accurate weather forecasting will become possible as more authorities invest in ice prediction sensors, particularly the deep probe type. Research into local weather patterns, greater availability of thermal maps and computerized route generation will enable ad hoc routes to be produced on each occasion to optimize gritting operations.

In parallel, there is expected to be a progressive investment in salt storage barns to keep salt dry, and the development of spreaders with wetting technology to minimize salt spread rates on any road conditions.

Winter maintenance will become the subject of tender action, probably with authorities owning the plant; essentially, a form of dayworks contract is envisaged whereby the contractor will be required to supply varying levels of resource to differing time scales. This will require that there is a parallel development in contract management for this operation, mindful of economic problems and constraints. As the practice spreads there will be an increasing confidence in contractors and highway authorities, which will lead to increasing flexibility at reduced costs.

References

10.1. THORNES J.E. *Ice prediction enters a new phase — highways.* D.R. Publications, Croydon, 1988, 37–38.

10.2. AUDIT COMMISSION. *Improving highway maintenance — a management handbook.* Her Majesty's Stationery Office, London, 1988, 35.

10.3. AUDIT COMMISSION. *Improving highway maintenance — a management handbook.* Her Majesty's Stationery Office, London, 1988, 37.

10.4. DEPARTMENT OF TRANSPORT. *Use of salt in removing ice from roads.* Circular Roads 1/76, London, January 1976.

10.5. RENDEL PALMER & TRITTON and HERTFORDSHIRE COUNTY CCOUNCIL. *Pavement Management System Design Study.* Design Study Report, Local Authority Associations/Department of Transport, 1989, B/75.

10.6. PONTING M. Weather prediction systems. *J. Instn Highw. Transpn*, 1984, November, 32.

10.7. PARMENTER B.S. and THORNES J.E. New technology for the winter maintenance of roads. *Mun. Engr*, 1987, February, 7–13.

10.8. PONTING M. Weather prediction systems. *J. Instn Highw. Transpn*, 1984, November, 38.

10.9. CHORLTON E. The use of weather monitoring equipment in the management of highway maintenance. *Mun. Engr*, 1986, October, 254.

10.10. AUDIT COMMISSION. *Improving highway maintenance — a management handbook.* Her Majesty's Stationery Office, London, 1988, 41.

10.11. BRITISH STANDARDS INSTITUTION. *Salt for spreading on highways for winter maintenance. Rock salt.* BS 3247: 1970: Part 1. BSI, London.

10.12. TRANSPORT AND ROAD RESEARCH LABORATORY. *Loss of salt due to rainfall on stockpiles used for winter maintenance.* TRRL, Crowthorne, 1966, LR30.

10.13. DEPARTMENT OF TRANSPORT. *Winter maintenance of motorways and other trunk roads, statement of service and code of practice.* DTp, London, August 1987, 3.

10.14. BRITISH STANDARDS INSTITUTION. *Spreaders for the winter maintenance of roads.* BS 1622: 1976. BSI, London.

10.15. BRITISH STANDARDS INSTITUTION. *Guide to low temperature properties and cold weather use of diesel fuel and gas oil.* BS 6380: 1983. BSI, London.

10.16. HOGBIN L.E. *Snow fences.* Transport and Road Research Laboratory, Crowthorne, 1970, LR362.

Bibliography

COMMITTEE ON HIGHWAY MAINTENANCE. *Marshall Report.* Her Majesty's Stationery Office, London, 1970.

COUNTY SURVEYORS SOCIETY. *Report on ice warning systems.* CSS, June 1985, Report No. 5/2.

COUNTY SURVEYORS SOCIETY. *Winter maintenance manual and code of good practice* (working draft for use in the 1988–89 winter). CSS, Ipswich, September 1989, Report No. 5/12.

DEPARTMENT OF TRANSPORT. *National ice prediction network.* Specification MCE 2020F, DTp, London, August 1987.

Highways Act 1980. Her Majesty's Stationery Office, London.

INSTITUTION OF CIVIL ENGINEERS. Winter maintenance — State of the art report. *Mun. Engr,* June 1984, 65–80.

INSTITUTION OF HIGHWAYS AND TRANSPORTATION and COUNTY SURVEYORS SOCIETY. Improving the service and reducing the costs. *Joint Technical Seminar on Winter Maintenance,* June, 1987.

LOCAL AUTHORITY ASSOCIATIONS. *Highway maintenance — a code of good practice.* LAA, London, 1983.

TRANSPORT AND ROAD RESEARCH LABORATORY. *Salt treatment of snow and ice on roads.* TRRL, Crowthorne, 1968, Road Note 18.

Ice detection systems

ICELERT   — Findlay Irvine Ltd, Peneicuick, Scotland.
SCAN   — Eagle International Equipment Ltd, Petersfield, Hants.
VAISALA   — Vaisala UK, Cambridge.
BOSCHUNG — Rolba Ltd, East Grinstead, West Sussex.
               — FFV Maintenance, Sweden.
               — Malling Kontrol, Denmark.

Organizations engaged in thermal mapping

Meteorological Office, London.
Thermal Mapping International Ltd, Birmingham.
Transport and Road Research Laboratory, Crowthorne, Berks.
Travers Morgan & Partners, London.

Snowfencing materials

Tensar — Netlon Ltd, Blackburn, Lancashire.
Paraweb — ICI Ltd, Harrogate, North Yorkshire.

11

Maintenance of highway structures

Since earliest times transportation networks have been faced with the problem of providing bridges and other structures as an alternative to long and time-consuming detours. Centuries later some of these structures, built from available materials, still exist as a testimony to the effectiveness of their design and construction, and also to their subsequent maintenance.

During the 19th century a massive expansion in railway and canal building resulted in the development of new techniques and the widespread use of metal as a construction material. Further developments followed with the introduction of reinforced, and more recently, prestressed concrete, for all types of building forms. While good design and attention to workmanship can minimize the rate of deterioration, all structures will ultimately require and benefit from some form of maintenance.

The engineer engaged in the task of maintaining structures is faced with a wide range of types, construction materials, repair and inspection methods, and systems for recording and transmitting information. This chapter gives guidance on the day-to-day activities and problems encountered by structure maintenance offices, and reviews some of the latest aids to assist in this specialism.

11.1. Objectives

The process of maintenance is necessary to ensure

(*a*) public safety
(*b*) protection of investment
(*c*) cleanliness
(*d*) an acceptable appearance.

With suitable resources and management, systematic attention to this aspect of engineering will help to counteract the decline in serviceability of structures caused by

(*a*) ageing of materials and variations in age potential
(*b*) use (either as designed or from abuse)
(*c*) accidental damage
(*d*) mismatch between design parameters and field conditions

(*e*) differences between specified and actual construction details and/or materials.

With these responsibilities and variables in mind, the engineer must endeavour to answer the following questions in order to carry out his functions effectively and efficiently.

(*a*) What are the types of structure and how many are my responsibility?
(*b*) What statutory obligations apply?
(*c*) How much evidence exists on their present condition and rate of deterioration?
(*d*) How much money is available?
(*e*) Can the necessary work be prioritized?

Depending on the accuracy and scale of answers to these questions, a plan of action can be prepared aimed at satisfying the four main objectives listed above.

These general considerations will now be developed to illustrate the stages of maintenance and some of the methods used to solve common problems. At all times, management and staff must ensure safety in working methods, in use of materials, and in the design and erection of access arrangements and temporary works. Guidance and references to legislation are given in the Construction Regulations Handbook.[11.1]

11.2. Registration and records

Highway authorities have a duty to maintain structures owned by them or subject to an agency agreement, such as those for which the duty of maintenance has been delegated by the Department of Transport. There is also a duty to ensure public safety, which may necessitate action being taken on structures owned by others if a failure to maintain has led to a hazardous situation. The starting point is the preparation of a comprehensive plan of the highway system within the area of responsibility. This will usually consist of a number of road categories, namely

(*a*) motorways and trunk roads owned by the Department of Transport
(*b*) principal roads owned by county authorities or metropolitan boroughs
(*c*) local roads owned by borough or district authorities
(*d*) privately owned roads.

Careful inspection of this plan, in conjunction with any available maps, listings or previous records, will lead to the preparation of a provisional structures register. Completion of the register will require site visits and considerable research into records of drainage and watercourses since many of these features become obscured by later developments, particularly in urban areas. It is important to realize that it is these often neglected and quite minor structures which become dangerous when overlooked.

ROAD NAME/ STRUCTURE NAME	TYPE CODE	ROAD NO.	UNDER/OVER OR EXTRA DATA	OWNER	BOROUGH REF.	GRID REF.	DATE BUILT	NO OF SPANS	SPAN IN FT	MATERIAL	LOAD CAPACITY & DATE OF ASSESSMENT OR CLEAR HT.	INSPECTION CODE P/S/G/SU
BEVERLEY BRIDGE	BG	A 3	BEVERLEY BROOK	GLC	31/01	214723	1927	1	20	ST/C	HA/45HB 1975	6/0/2/6M
BEVERLEY BROOK BRIDGE		0	OWNER IS WIMBLEDON	C.CON	0				0			
BEXLEY HIGH STR RAIL OVER	K	A 223	RAIL OVER RD	BR	3	495735			0		15FT 3IN CLEARANCE	6/0/2/6M
BEXLEY RD	Y		SEE ERITH RD BR						0			
BEXLEY RD (ERITH STN)	Y	A 220	RAIL	BR-S	N0637	512779			0			
BICKLEY PARK BRIDGE	BB	A 222	KYD BROOK	GLC	5/01	432692	1860	1	10	BWK	TWIN 24T AX(BE4)1975	6/0/2/6M
BICKLEY PARK RD RAIL OVER	K	A 222	RAIL OVER RD	BR	5	432693			10		14FT 10IN CLEARANCE	
BICKLEY POINT	8	A 222	RD.IMPROVEMENT 1982		5Z1524	1-29			0			
BISHOPS BRIDGE RD	Z	A 4206	SEE BISHOPS RD BR	BR-M	32							
BISHOPS BRIDGE RD B	Y	A 4206		BR-M	32 0M19C				0			
BISHOPS ROAD BRIDGE	Y		RAIL			264815						
BISHOPSFORD BRIDGE	BB	A 217	R.WANDLE	GLC	23/04R	263814	1882	3	11	BWK	TWIN 28T AX (BE4)1974	6/0/2/6M
BISHOPSFORD BRIDGE RIVER WALL	BB	A 217	SUPPORTING R.BANK	GLC	23/04R	271678	1882			BWK		6/0/2/6M
BISHOPSFORD BRIDGE E FOOTWAY	BB	A 217	R.WANDLE	GLC	23/04B		1969	3	11	PCU		6/0/2/6M
BLACK DITCH BRIDGE (FERRY LA)	BB	A-503	RIVER LEA	GLC	13/01	347894	1929	3	11	RC-PF	LOAD TRAIN 25T MAX AX	6/0/2/6M
BLACK'S BRIDGE (MAIN RD)A	BB	A 118	BLACKS RIVER	GLC	15/01A	519894	1860	2	1	BWK	TWIN 29T AX(BE4)1975	6/0/2/6M
BLACK'S BRIDGE (MAIN RD)B	BB	A 118	RAPHAEL PARK LAKE	GLC	15/01A		1860	1	31	STONE	4T WHEEL SATISFACTORY	6/0/2/6M
BLACK'S BRIDGE-N WALL(AT ENDS)	BB	A 118	SUPPORTING ROAD	GLC	15/01BP		1860		5	BWK		6/0/2/6M
BLACK'S BRIDGE-S WALL ALONG BL	BB	A 118	SUPPORTING ROAD	GLC	15/01BR		1860	1	14	BWK		6/0/2/6M
BLACKFRIAR ROAD RAIL OVER	K	A 201	RAIL OVER RD	BR	27				0	RC	17FT 8IN CLEARANCE	
BLACKFRIARS PUMPING STATION A	MG	B8000	SUPPORTS IN THAMES	GLC	33/RP44A	316800	1941	M	0	RC		6/0/2/3M
BLACKFRIARS PUMPING STATION B	MG	B8000	PUMP HOUSE	GLC	33/RP4B	315807	1941		0	RC		6/0/2/3M
BLACKFRIARS PUMPING STATION C	MG	B8000	APP.WALKWAY-THAMES	GLC	33/RP44C		1941	1	0	RC		6/0/2/3M
BLACKFRIARS PUMPING STATION D	MG	B8000	DOLPHIN IN THAMES	GLC	33/RP44D		1941		0	WOOD		6/0/2/3M
BLACKHEATH HILL NORTH	RB	A 2	BY HOLLYMOUNT CLOSE	GLC	10/R76N	379767			0			6/0/2/1
BLACKHEATH HILL PUB.CON.	C	A 2	UNDER CEN.ISLAND	10	10				0			
BLACKHEATH HILL SOUTH	RB	A 200	BY HOLLYMOUNT CLOSE	GLC	10/R77S				0			6/0/2/1
BLACKHORSE BRIDGE (EVELYN ST)	BB	A 200	DISUSED SURREY CAN	GLC	22/08	360781	1910	1	42	STEEL	C & U 1970	6/0/2/6M
BLACKHORSE RD STN	Y	A1006	UNDER ROAD	BR-E	22/08B	358893	1910	1	6	STEEL		6/0/2/6M
BLACKWALL BASIN (PRESTON'S RD)	Z	A1206	RAIL	PLA	30 L3756	383802			0			
BLACKWALL LANE	B		THAMES		29				0			
BLACKWALL LANE B	8		SEE BTSA		10	15			0			
BLACKWALL LANE CROSSOVER STORE	AG	A2203	ALTERATION	1976	10Z579				0	ALUMINIUM		6/0/2/6M
BLACKWALL LANE(BTSA)			UNDER VIADUCT	GLC	10/A16				0	RC		
BLACKWALL T.N.EXIT HIGHT GAUGE	AG	A2203	RD.IMPROVEMENT 1969		10Z579	1-14			0			
BLACKWALL TUNNEL A-E WALL TO E	GG	A 102	ATTACHED TO 29/R1	GLC	29/G05	383807	1974	1	12			6/0/2/6M
BLACKWALL TUNNEL B-SLIP RD-N	RG	A 102	SUPPORTING CUTTING	GLC	29/R02	384808	1958		0			6/0/2/1
BLACKWALL TUNNEL N.END STORE	AG	A 102		GLC	29/R02				0			6/0/2/1
BLACKWALL TUNNEL N.NORTH APP	RO		OPEN AREA BY SHAFT	GLC	29/A23				0			6/0/2/6M
BLACKWALL TUNNEL;NEW-MAX HIGHT	KG	A 102	SEE EAST INDIA DKRD		29				0		15FT 6IN MAX HIGHT	
BLACKWALL TUNNEL;OLD-MAX HIGHT	KG	A 102			29/VT3				0		9FT 5IN MAX HIGHT O/S	6/0/2/6M
BLACKWALL TUNNEL-NEW	VG	A 102	SEE UNDER 29/VT3		29/VT1 10/VT3				0			6/0/2/6M

Fig. 11.1. Example of simple computerized structures register (register of all known structures on principal roads in alphabetical order)

Confirmation of ownership for all identified structures is the next stage, and for this the assistance of the Solicitors and Valuers Department is likely to be necessary. Such enquiries are frequently time consuming and may result in confusing situations, such as shared ownership, indistinct boundaries, or agreements in which the responsibility for maintenance is not clear. Meanwhile, the safety of the highway must be ensured, and any necessary works carried out without prejudice to the eventual liability.

Having recorded all structures, as far as possible including pipes and conduits where deterioration and ultimately collapse would jeopardize the fabric of the highway, decisions can be taken as to the form of register most suited to the size of the stock, and the management system to be employed. For many authorities, a manual system has developed in which the records are retained in a number of forms such as a manually compiled and updated register of structures, copies of original 'as constructed' drawings, site construction photographs, site records of material testing, lists of material suppliers, subsequent inspection records, later works carried out as maintenance or modification, records of any monitoring of individual structures, estimates and actual costs of work done, original specifications, historical files, administrative records, load capacity assessment calculations, the location of design calculations and the result of any special investigations.

The existence and accuracy of such records and also the ability to retrieve information from the system forms an invaluable tool for the maintenance team. With advances in technology, some elements may lend themselves to computer techniques from which advantages of speed of retrieval, variations in format and ease of amendment can result. There are significant advantages to be gained from computer systems for owners of large numbers of structures. The current requirement of the Department of Transport is detailed[11.2] in TRMM 2/88 and is designed for incorporation into a database of highway inventory information. Considerable detail is required as indicated in Form BE 13/86 and the aim is to establish comprehensive records from which the stock can be reviewed nationally, and the performance of structural types and elements can be monitored.

The form of inventory record chosen needs to be designed to suit local usage, and the content of the register should be capable of answering common questions posed by members of the public and council members as well as day-to-day operational requirements. It is important to consider the cost of regular review and updating of the system, and to avoid over-elaboration. An example of a simple coded register as used in the London area is shown in Fig. 11.1.

The process of collecting the information is likely to be a mixture of the examination of available records and site verification. The development of hand-held data capture devices offers a convenient method of transferring such data for storage in the system. A further point to be considered when deciding the form of records is the length of time that each section of information needs to be retained. A process of review and updating is necessary to ensure that such information as is retained matches the present construction.

Some records lend themselves to storage in microfilm or microfiche forms, but great care is required to ensure that reductions do not impair the clarity and reproducibility of the available information. To be suitable for microfilming, drawings need to be prepared with this system in mind, including scale reduction markings. Earlier drawings and particularly blueprints and drawings dependent on colour for interpretation are often unsuitable or uneconomic due to the need for enhancement of contrast and fine detail before an adequate photographic quality is obtained.

The advances being made in computer aided draughting techniques will alter the mode of storage for many future records, and the further development of scanning equipment may soon make the copying of record drawings more practicable and effective than present photographic methods.

11.3. Finance

The cost of maintaining structures is a small proportion of the overall budget for highway maintenance. For example, the annual expenditure on principal roads in London in 1985–86 was about £45 million of which less than 5% was used on structures. However, the importance of ensuring that the level of expenditure is appropriate to the identified needs cannot be overstated. In a recent census[11.3] carried out jointly by bridge-owning authorities, it was estimated that £560 to £830 million is needed to restore bridges to full capacity, the majority being needed for those of up to 50 m span built before 1922. The underlying problem is thought to be even larger than this indicates.

Sources of finance for maintenance of highway structures are

(*a*) from government in the form of grants (Rate Support Grant — RSG) and Transport Supplementary Grant (TSG)
(*b*) contributions from rates
(*c*) toll charges, e.g. at the Dartford Tunnel and Severn Bridge
(*d*) special reserves dedicated to bridge maintenance such as the City of London bridge fund
(*e*) fees and charges
(*f*) grants from the European Economic Community.

Authorities acting as agents to the Department of Transport for trunk roads and motorways receive reimbursement in two ways

(*a*) as a fee based on the cost of works done (currently the agreed level is 8% of works cost)[11.4]
(*b*) by direct reimbursement of cost, e.g. principal inspection costs.[11.4]

Agency agreements can also be made between county and local council authorities.

The preparation of annual budgets is usually based on partially detailed schemes to avoid abortive costs, pending the settlement of the budget level and priority of works. On approval of the submitted proposals, the completion of contract documents and the processes of tendering and acceptance take place. For larger works, this process can be prolonged, and under the present procedures, carry over of finance from one year to the next is not permitted. This often leads to difficulties and an alternative system allowing greater flexibility has for some time been sought by experts in the field.

11.4. Legal aspects relating to highway structures

In the course of his/her duties, the maintenance engineer needs to be familiar with a range of legislative documents, both for compliance during operations and for enforcement by the police or others. Extracts from the more commonly occurring clauses are listed below, but it should be remembered that the interpretation and implementation of much of the law requires the advice and help of legal experts. Particular care should be exercised in circumstances relating to roadworks and where the safety of the public or operatives is involved, and which may lead to determination of accident liability.

11.4.1. Transport Act 1968, Ch. 73

Part VIII, Clauses 116–122 of the Transport Act 1968[11.5] outlines the responsibilities of highway authorities in respect of bridge maintenance and agreements regarding carriageway surfacing over bridges. In some cases the conditions include the approach embankment. Difficulties may arise in defining the boundary between 'surfacing' and the supporting structure where these are separately financed. Care should be taken to agree these limits prior to carrying out works or changing the surfacing materials to avoid disputes. For existing cases a sensible compromise, in the absence of a clear definition, may be to agree a boundary separating those members that constitute structural elements without which the deck would be unsafe, and then to regard layers or sheeting above this level as a surfacing finish. Obviously, prior consultation is advisable wherever joint responsibilities are likely to be questioned.

Part V of this Act is designed to ensure that operators using the highway for carriage of goods are subject to control by a system of licensing from authorities appointed by the Ministry of Transport.

11.4.2. Road Traffic Act 1974, Ch. 16

Clause 41 of the Road Traffic Act 1974[11.6] refers specifically to the power of bridge owners to limit the use of a bridge where it has been judged to be weak. Notices indicating the upper limit of capacity are to be provided and placed in advance of the bridge, and this may require further notices at road junctions leading to the bridge to enable alternative routes to be taken by approaching drivers. Failure to observe any such notice lays the offender open to police prosecution or possible civil action by the bridge owner if it can be shown that damage to the structure has occurred as a result of this offence.

Objections to prohibitions can be made to the Minister, an action which can result in re-examination of the reasons for the original restriction.

Clause 42 relates to additional powers conferred on highway authorities and bridge owners responsible for maintenance, permitting variations in loads, which can cross the bridge by a system of individual application and permit (such procedures are discussed in more detail later in the chapter in section 11.5).

Clause 54 confers powers on the police or authorized representatives for the placing of temporary signs in cases of emergency or congestion for a period of up to seven days.

Clause 225 covers powers conferred on the police and highway authorities permitting the weighing of laden vehicles. It should be noted that law enforcement is a matter for the police, but that regular conformity checks are carried out by the Weights and Measures Departments employed by county authorities. Clause 255 defines the method of determining the weight of a motor vehicle. Analyses of actual axle loadings using portable weighing installations indicate that the overloading of vehicles is commonplace, and that the prescribed formulae for estimating the residual life and future life of the structure used in design are likely to underestimate the load effects. The load spectrum for urban traffic is also likely to differ from the standard. The use of the latest equipment and refinements in computerized data-recording devices, which allow the identification of vehicle types and axle spacing, should lead to a closer control of the overloading situation and revisions if necessary in the design criteria. Because of the vulnerability of equipment some care is needed in the choice of sites.

Clause 261 entitles highway authorities to establish and operate weighbridges or to contribute towards the cost of a shared installation.

11.4.3. Public Utilities and Street Works Act 1950

The Public Utilities and Street Works Act 1950[11.7] has a number of implications for structures, such as

(a) the placing and servicing of mains within or attached to structures
(b) services required by the structure such as lighting, power, water supply
(c) works by statutory authorities which could affect the stability of a structure including shafts, trenches, headings or damage and disturbances to arch rings or filling material
(d) possible damage resulting from gas or water leakage such as explosion, overloading due to flooding, or erosion of foundations.

Under the Act, companies are required to give notice of operations in advance of the works commencing, except in the case of emergencies when the highway manager must be informed as soon as is practicable. Under this procedure, notice should then be passed to the maintenance organizations who will assess the effects, if any, on highway structures or the highway generally. Any special precautions needed can then be agreed with the companies involved and a programme of inspection visits prepared. Under the Act, statutory authorities indemnify owners against damage caused by their works, but complications and protracted negotiations can occur, particularly where a number of works are in progress at once. Supervision is a critical factor in many of these situations. Where structures are likely to be affected, the owning authority can choose to carry out some elements of the work itself and recover reasonable costs from the statutory authority.

Protection is also given by this Act to the statutory authorities whose services may be affected by works to structures, for instance bridge strengthening or replacement. Complementary procedures for providing advance notice and agreement of works apply.

This Act has been the subject of an extensive review in recent years, and the findings of the review panel have been published.[11.8]

11.4.4. Motor Vehicles (Construction and Use) Regulations 1978

Motor vehicles manufactured in the United Kingdom are subject to compliance with the Motor Vehicles (Construction and Use) Regulations 1978[11.9] and any subsequent revisions. Regulations of particular concern to the maintenance engineer dealing with structures are

- (a) overall length — articulated vehicle 15 metres (articulated bus 18 metres); public service vehicles 12 metres; other 11 metres
- (b) overall height of public service vehicles 4·57 metres (the height of other vehicles is not prescribed) (regulation 10)
- (c) variations in wheel loading (regulation 11)
- (d) overall width of locomotives 2·75 metres and of motor tractors 2–5 metres (regulation 48); heavy motor car 2·5 metres (regulation 53); motor car 2·5 metres (regulation 57); trailers 2·3 metres except where certain conditions apply, in which case 2·5 metres (regulation 74)
- (e) maximum weight controls (see Table 11.1) (regulations 82–95).

Vehicles not included in these regulations are covered by special procedures when travelling on public roads, given in the *Motor Vehicles Authorisation of Special Types) General Order 1979.*[11.10] Included in this category is some of the machinery used by maintenance engineers, such as carriageway surfacing machines (pedestrian controlled), large earth-moving equipment, vehicles fitted with movable platforms, track-laying plant and large cranes. Such vehicles are subject to alternative controls on width, length, overall weight, axle and wheel loads, and in some cases are subject to speed restrictions.

11.5. Abnormal indivisible loads

Abnormal indivisible loads[11.10] are a class of load which, when mounted on specialized vehicles, exceeds the total, axle or wheel loadings normally permitted on public roads, or which exceed dimensions prescribed for length or width as laid down in the *Construction and Use Regulations.*[11.9] Such special cases may require the removal of street furniture at junctions or corners and can involve the temporary strengthening or bridges or the use of purpose-designed air cushions that are fitted to trailers to distribute the load uniformly. Major items such as transformers, boilers, large cranes and certain military equipment, which need to use the road system to reach their destinations, often fall within this category.

Table 11.1. Treatment of previously painted steelwork (from BS 5493: 1977)

Surface conditions	Surface preparation	Teatment (see clause 54.1, notes (a)–(e))
1. Basically sound paint with slight deterioration but no rusting	Wash down only, if (a) Bristle-brush and dust-down, if (b)	(a) No coating required (b) Recoating required by legislation or by appearance requirements. Apply one or two finish-coats as required
2. Paint exhibiting marked chalking or exposing previous finish	Wire-brush* and dust-down	One coat of undercoat and one finish-coat as necessary
3. Thin film, blistering, pinhead rusting > RE7†	Scrape and wire-brush*	Prime rusted areas, build-up film thickness, with undercoat and finish-coat overall
4. Sound film, but with rusted areas less than 25% of area	(a) Rusted areas; remove rust by best means available. See clause 53 (b) Sound paint: nil, if patching is adequate (c) Sound paint: wire-brush if finish-coat is required	Patch-prime bare metal Apply undercoat and finish-coat(s)‡ Apply one or two coats as necessary
5. Sound film, but with rusted areas greater than 25% of total. Thin film, rusting > RE7†	Removal all coating and rust by best means available. See clause 53	Build-up with new system of primer, undercoat, and finish

* For certain hard finishes wire-brushing may not be adequate.

† RE7 is taken from 'Échelle Européenne de degrés d'enrouillement pour peintures antirouille', obtainable from the Paintmakers Association, Prudential house, Wellesley Road, Croydon, Surrey.

‡ It is a matter of judgement whether to patch isolated rusted areas or to patch and overcoat the whole. In the latter case it is sometimes desirable, if time permits, to apply additional undercoats to bring the patches to a similar thickness to the surrounding areas, before overcoating the whole surface.

The proposed route is circulated to all highway and bridge owners by the haulier and also to the police in each area along the route. The responsibility for notification lies entirely with the haulier, who also provides a signed indemnity against damage to all owners. The period of notice (excluding weekends and public holidays) for consideration of proposals varies according to the magnitude of the load

(a)   exceeding *Construction and Use Regulations*, but not exceeding 76 200 kg: two days
(b)   exceeding 76 200 kg, but not exceeding 152 400 kg: six days
(c)   exceeding 152 400 kg: by negotiation.

Special inspections should be carried out by engineering staff before, during and after the passage of the load if calculations indicate that the load will induce critical stresses in the structure or if loads of a similar weight have not previously been carried by the structure or have passed without observation. Further advance agreements are required for loads where the width exceeds 6·1 m, the length exceeds 27·4 m or any combination of the above weights and dimensions. In addition, the police require notice of loads between 4·3 m and 6·1 m.

Hauliers have invested considerable finance in special equipment to cope with important loads which cannot be broken down or transported by means other than on the highway. The most commonly used item is the multi-axle 'well trailer' on which each axle will often have four or more wheels. Such trailers are sometimes of a modular form giving flexibility in the type of load that can be handled. The 'air cushion trailer' mentioned above is designed to spread the effect of the total load by means of air

Fig. 11.2. Footbridge span damaged by overheight vehicle despite escort

pressure within an enclosing skirt, thereby reducing the local effects of axle or wheel loading. The Department of Transport has been willing to accept that this form of relief results in a one-third reduction of the unassisted loading effect up to a maximum relief value of 152 400 kg.

The agreed route should be surveyed and stopping points and a time schedule determined. Most loads of this type are accompanied by a police escort. Since the height of loads is not controlled by legislation these surveys need to pay particular attention to any obstructions over the highway. Despite this care, bridges are regularly hit and damaged, in many cases by inadequately secured hydraulic booms which can demolish lighter structures (Fig. 11.2).

11.6. Staffing levels

Organizations with a relatively small stock of structures may have difficulty in providing the necessary support services, especially as the work load is likely to fluctuate and vary greatly in nature and complexity. Consideration should then be given to letting contracts for defined aspects of work, such as

(*a*) inspection and load-carrying capacity assessments
(*b*) design of improvement or strengthening works
(*c*) testing of materials
(*d*) monitoring.

Of particular relevance to staffing levels for structural maintenance is the need to respond to emergency situations at all times. This aspect must be incorporated in any policy and contract documents, defining the nature and times of response expected and the method of payment for labour and plant acting in a standby capacity or outside normal working hours. The effectiveness and economy of the chosen method has to be capable of demonstration, and at the outset has to provide comparison between tenders.

11.7. Access

Inspection and maintenance of structures usually involves the provision of access platforms such as scaffolding of either a temporary, mobile, or more permanent nature. Since the enactment of the Health and Safety at Work Act and closer public interest in the prevention of pollution, the responsibilities of all involved in maintenance work have become more sharply defined. Contract documents need to specify the requirements for access including the operations to be performed on the access platforms and the anticipated loadings. This aspect is particularly important where more than one group of people are involved, as for instance when inspections are followed by repair works or painting.

The future needs of maintenance should be considered at the design stage and where possible fixings for future scaffolding should be built in. If such fixings are installed at a later date, attention to the position of reinforcement is necessary, especially where prestressing tendons are involved. Commonly used methods of access are as follows.

Fig. 11.3. Close boarded scaffold to arch bridge

Fig. 11.4. Scaffold to suspension bridge tower bearings

Fig. 11.5 (above). Inspection from barge-mounted hydraulic arm

Fig. 11.6 (right). Access to suspended lighting — road closure due to weight restriction and safety requirements

11.7.1. Scaffolding

Scaffolding must be erected in accordance with *Construction* (*Working Places*) *Regulations 1966*.[11.11] When fixed to the structure, care must be taken to allow for thermal movements or deflections. The close-boarded platform may also need to be sheeted to protect the public or to stop pollution of waterways below. Where navigable waterways are crossed, any reduction in the normal headroom has to be agreed in advance with the authority concerned and warnings displayed, and there may be a requirement to provide an approved waterman and safety boat. Similar advance precautions will apply to railways and highway clearances. Attachment to items such as bridge parapets must not be done without checking the ability of the structure to carry applied loads, especially where cantilevered platforms are being constructed (Figs 11.3 and 11.4).

11.7.2. Hydraulic lifts, underbridge inspection platforms, etc.

First, the specification of the proposed machine should be examined in terms of geometry and load-carrying capacity in the available positions, and this information compared with the shape of the structure and the positions to be reached, taking into account the operations to be performed and the necessary equipment and activity loads. Critical aspects are likely to be

(*a*) the effects of increasing depth at arch springings
(*b*) the need for extra depth between arch ribs or deck beams
(*c*) the ability of footway cantilevers to carry outrigger jack loads
(*d*) the acceptability of possible traffic restrictions while the equipment is in use.

The estimated cost of using this type of platform should then be compared with alternative means of gaining access. These platforms have

Fig. 11.7. Purpose-made access gantry to bridge soffit

Department of Transport

Trunk Road / Motorway Structure Inspection Report

Structure No. | 1 5 / M 3 (S) _ _ _ E S / 2 Ø Ø . Ø _ / A 1 S

Grid Ref. | 3 2 4 7 1 | 1 2 6 5 4 |
| E | N |

| | R. Type | Kilom. | Spur/r |

Agent Authority | Barsetshire

Structure name | Proudie Lane

Date of Inspection | 1 4 . S E P . 1 9 8 7 |

(eg. 15 - JUN - 1987)

Type of Inspection G ☑ P ☐ S ☐   Inspected by | J. Blogg |
(Please tick)

Defect Assessment

	Estimated Cost	Extent	Severity	Work recc. & Priority	Comments
1. Foundations					
2. Inverts or Aprons					
3. Fenders					
4. Piers or Columns	—	A	1	-	
5. Abutments	—	B	2	N	Minor Cracks on N. Abutment
6. Wing walls					
7. Retaining walls or Revetments					
8. Approach Embankments					
9. Bearings	11,000	C	4	H	Sliding Bearing on Pier 2 rusted and seized
10. Main beams / Tunnel portals / Mast	25,000	B	3	M	Corrosion to Category II - SD 18/83
11. Transverse beams / Catenary cables					
12. Diaphragms or bracings					
13. Concrete Slab	—	A	1	-	
14. Metal deck plates / Tunnel linings					

	Estimated Cost	Extent	Severity	Work recc. & priority		Comments
15. Jack arches						
16. Arch ring / Armco						
17. Spandrels						
18. Tie rods						
19. Drainage systems	5,000	B	3	R	H	Clear the blocked drains on Abut. & Piers
20. Waterproofing	30,000	-	-	A	L	New waterproofing
21. Surfacing	40,000	B	2	C	L	If item 20 is carried out
22. Service Ducts						
23. Expansion Joints	2,000	B	2	C	L	Replace the rubber sealant
24. Parapets / Handrails	-	A	1	-	-	
25. Access gantries or walkways						
26. Machinery						

Reasons for priority allocation

5. Bearings on Pier 2 need urgent replacement - H

15. Clear the drains before next winter - H

10. Steel Work painting already programmed in 88/89 Budget - M

20, 21 & 23 Early action will reduce Life Time Cost - L

Fig. 11.8 (facing page and above). Department of Transport inspection report form BE 11/86

NAME OF BRIDGE DOG'S LANE   DTp BRIDGE No. M999/876   NATIONAL GRID REF. [ZR] 99732 | 00-422

LOCATION OF BRIDGE BARSDIGE BARSETSHIRE COUNTY   AGENT AUTHORITY BRIDGE No. M 999/56

AGENT [for bridge structure] BARSETSHIRE   File Reference(s)   PYNF No.

AUTHORITY [for road surface] -do-   HQ [ ]   RO (Tp) [ ]   DB KEY No. 95000   Trunk Road Classification No M 999

BRIDGE OWNER SECRETARY OF STATE FOR TRANSPORT

M999 A5053   Road under   Date of Construction 1984

Road / Railway / Canal / River Road ✓   Is Bridge scheduled as an Ancient Monument? [N]

Name of Navigation AVON CANAL   Design Office PVH & PARTNERS
and/or BRITISH WATERWAYS

Drainage Authority
                                        Railway Bridge No. SO41
                                        CANAL
                                        Is River tidal [X]

Names of statutory   navigable [X] /(link bus)

undertakers having   1 No. 150 DIA. G.P.O. CABLE
                     1 No. 150 DIA. ELECTRICITY CABLE

services on bridge   *Delete as necessary

Min Headroom Clearance under*/over Motorway*   7.0 OVER CANAL SPAN 5.3
/Trunk Road carriageways   N. BOUND/W.BOUND   6.1 OVER RAILWAY SPAN 5.3
                                S. BOUND/E.BOUND

Design loading H.A. +45 UNITS H.B.

Special loading/restriction

Construction Details

Deck Materials (e.g. Insitu PSC) 1. END SPANS - VOIDED INSITU A.C.   2. INT. - PRETENSIONED/PRESTRESSED M.BEAMS + INSITU R.C. SLAB

Type of Construction (e.g. Solid Slab) 1. END SPANS - VOIDED   2. INT. - BEAM & SLAB

Form of Deck (e.g. Propped (cantilever) SIMPLY SUPPORTED

End Supports (e.g. Skeleton Abutment) N.END - C/LEVER ABT.   S.END - BANK SEAT

Intermediate Supports (e.g. Slab Wall) TEE HEAD R.C.COLUMNS

Nature of Foundations (e.g. Caissons) N.END SPREAD   ALL OTHERS PILED

	Manufacturer	Type
Joints	THORMACK LTD	ASPHALTIC PLUG
Bearings	ANDRE - ELASTOMERIC	MONOPLATE & MULTIPLATE
Parapets 2. R.C. OVER RAILWAY SPAN	1. BRITISH STEEL	1. P.1 / 1. P.1.G OVER RAILWAY SPAN
Waterproofing	EXPANDITE	FANGUARD
Prestressing System	'M. BEAMS'	STANDARD

Paint System: Parapet P.78/GALVANISED/ACRYLATED RUBBER/CROWN DECORATIVE PRODUCT
Internal
External

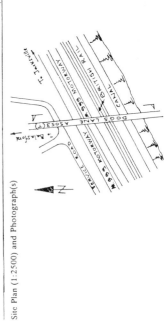

Site Plan (1:2500) and Photograph(s)

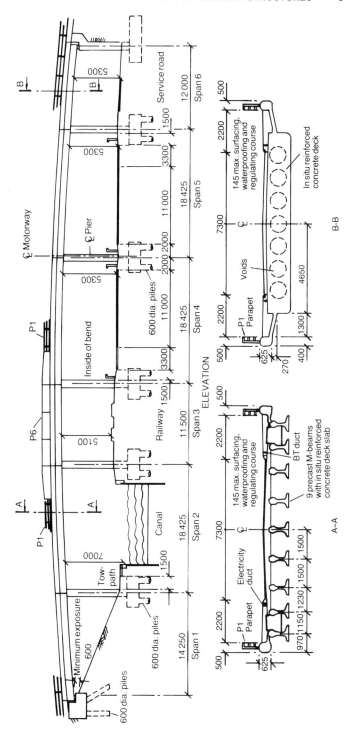

Fig. 11.9 (facing page and above). Department of Transport bridge registration form 'Roads 277'.

Structures Database – Input Sheet

● Please do not fill in the shaded boxes.

Structure File

● St Key `[W,A,T,S,]`
● Name `[D,O,G,'S, ,L,A,N,E,]`
● Class `[R]` ● Rnum `[A,5,2,]` ● R Type `[ ]`
● Kilom `[1,8,7,.,2,]` ● Spurr `[ ]` ● Spurr `[ ]` Jnno `[ , , ]`
● St Type `[2]` ● Road `[M,5,3,2,]`
● Grid (E) `[5,2,2,3,2]` ● Grid (N) `[0,0,4,3,2]`
● Year `[1,9,8,4]` ● Region `[0,3,0,3]`
● County `[1,3,0,0]` ● District `[1,3,0,2]`
● Maint Agent `[1,5,0,0]`
● Maint Region `[6,9,0,1]`
● Sid `[ ]`
● Owner `[ ]`
● Agent Ref `[A,2,2,2,/,5,6]`
● Cert Ref `[ ]`
● Detunked `[ ]`

Other/Services File

● Headroom `[ , , , ]`
● Comments 1 `[ ]`
● Comments 2 `[ ]`

Retaining Wall File

● No of Panels `[ , , ]` ● Length of Wall `[ , , , ]`
● X Ref `[ ]` ● Prestress `[ ]`
● Structural Form `[ ]` ● Material `[ ]`
● Construction Type `[ ]` ● Designer `[ ]`

Panels/Independent Lighting File

● Panel/Mast No
● Panel/Mast Length
● Panel/Mast Height
● Foundations

Bridge File

● Nospan `[6]` ● Load 1 `[7]` ● Load 2 `[ ]`
● Bridge Type `[1,]` ● Paint Sys `[2]`
● Designer `[1,2,0,]` ● Defect `[2]`
● Bridge Length `[ , , , ]` ● Variations `[2]`
● Services `[ , ,C, ]`
● Microfilm `[ ]`

Sign Gantry File

● No of Spans `[ ]`
● Material `[ ]`
● Length `[ , , , ]`
● Designer `[ ]`
● Headroom `[ , , , ]`
● Paint Sys `[ ]`

Tunnel File

● Construction Type `[ ]`
● Form of Deck `[ ]`
● Mat 1 `[ ]` ● Obst 1 `[ ]` ● Length `[ , , , ]`
● Mat 2 `[ ]` ● Obst 2 `[ ]` ● Width `[ , , , ]`
● Headroom `[ , , , ]` ● Max Gradient `[ , , ]`
● Lane Width `[ , , , ]`
● Hilliness `[ , , ]` ● Bendiness `[ , , , ]`
● Design Speed `[ ]` ● Tunnel Type `[ ]`
● Light `[ ]` ● Vent `[ ]` ● Pump `[ ]`
● Emergency Services `[ ]`
● Obstacle `[ ]`
● Int Pavement `[ ]`
● Lining/Finish `[ ]`
● Carriage Way `[ ]`

Small Culvert File

● No of Spans `[ ]` ● Material `[ ]`
● Variations `[ ]` ● Designer `[ ]`
● Length `[ , , , ]`
● Width `[ , , , ]`
● Defect `[ ]` ● Construction Type `[ ]`
● Skew `[ , , ]`

Lighting File

● No of Masts `[ ]`
● Type of Lighting `[ ]`
● Foundations `[ ]`
● Manufacturer `[ ]` ● Material `[ ]`
● Paintsys `[ ]`
● Lighting DB Ref `[ , , , ]`
● XRef to Roads `[ , , , ]`
● Length of Scheme `[ ]`

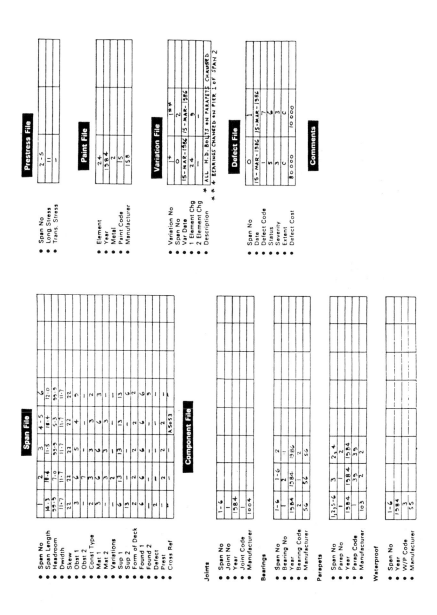

Fig. 11.10 (facing page and above). Department of Transport structures database input sheet BE 13/86

BRIDGE	PRINCIPAL GENERAL	INSPECTION REPORT	M1

Please forward to:
GLC (TD/C/M) Room 517
The County Hall SE1 7PB

From London Borough of ....

Date of this examination ....Date of last examination............................

GLC Structure Ref. No ....Road Class No ....

Name of Bridge/Road ....Type of Construction ....

Over/under ....Construction Date....................................

Item No.	Item Description	Condition G Good F Fair P Poor	Remarks
1	Foundations		
2	Invert/Aprons		
3	Cutwater		
4	Fenders		
5	Piers/Columns		
6	Abutments		
7	Wing/Training Walls		
8	Embankment		
9	Drainage of Structure		
10	Main Beams		
11	Bearings		
12	Transverse Beams/Diaphragms		
13	Crosshead		
14	Troughing/Buckle Plates		
15	Jack Arches (Brick/CI/Steel)		
16	Bracings/Cross ties		
17	Deck Concrete		
18	Expansion Joints		
19	Brick Arch (a) Springing		
20	(b)Rings		
21	(c) Face/Voussoirs		
22	Spandril Walls		
23	Tie Rods		
24	Waterproofing		
25	Paintwork		
26	Parapets (a) Steel		
27	(b) Brick		
28	(c) Concrete		
29	Mesh Screens		
30	Access Manholes & Covers		
31	Carriageway/Footway Condition		
32			

Fig. 11.11 (above and facing page). Example of simple bridge inspection report form

DETAILED CONDITION REPORT AND ACTION REQUIRED

Item No.		Estimated cost
	Total cost £	

Engineer's report reqd. on Items Nos ....

Details of work carried out since previous inspection:

Inspection by ....

Report examined by .... (Engr.) Date ....

Date of next examination ....

(M 13215)

considerable potential and have been developed in a wide range of dimensions allowing them to be successfully adapted for mounting on railway bogies or aboard barges (Figs 11.5 and 11.6).

11.7.3. Purpose-built access

In its simplest form this could be the provision of fixed ladders or step-irons and adequate manholes permitting access to hollow beams and other voids within structures. The problems of maintenance can be eased when designing the structure, if attention is given to the access required. In some cases, the provision of movable gantries, supported on fixed tracks or the lower flanges of bridge beams, can really ease the problem of inspection and routine maintenance (Fig 11.7). Repair operations and even normal use by traffic can lead to the accumulation of toxic fumes, and the access arrangements should allow for the possible use of breathing apparatus, e.g. when sizing manholes, as well as for adequate clearances for personnel carrying tools.

11.8. Inspection

Inspections are a routine part of structural maintenance, and should be planned to be comprehensive, but also to minimize wasted journey times. It is recommended that the frequency of inspection should be geared to the known condition of the stock of structures, and divided into categories related to the degree of detail required and the grade of engineer or inspector appropriate to each category. Agent authorities acting for the Department of Transport are required to adhere to procedures detailed in Departmental Standard BD 22/84,[11.12] in which inspections are described as

(a) *superficial* — undertaken by inspectors or other staff during regular visits to site. The object is to report any obvious damage or deficiencies which could affect traffic or lead to rapid deterioration
(b) *general* — in which engineering staff inspect representative parts of the structure and submit a report on form BE 11/86
(c) *principal* — in which engineering staff inspect all parts of the structure closely and report on forms BE 11/86, form roads 277 and input sheet BE 13/86
(d) *special* — which require engineering staff to inspect specific features, perhaps as a result of reported collision or flooding. Findings are reported on form BE 11/86.

The forms shown have been designed for input into a database. Examples of these forms are shown in Figs 11.8–11.10.

A comprehensive booklet *Bridge Inspection Guide*[11.13] has been issued by the Department of Transport giving advice, examples and photographs of the many aspects of bridge maintenance. Authorities may choose to extend the same routine to their own structures to give uniformity and simplify staff training. For owners not engaged in agency work for the Ministry, it is recommended that a comparable system be developed to ensure that all structures receive periodic inspection and recorded reports from which a programme of prioritized work can be prepared. Such programmes are used together with cost estimates to demonstrate the level of repair works needed and to compare the urgency with other demands made on the available finance.

Typical frequencies for inspections are

(a) superficial: daily–weekly
(b) general: one–two yearly
(c) principal: not less than once in ten years
(d) special: as required, or for cast iron bridges six monthly.

Authorities developing their own systems for inspection records are often able to develop a simpler format, such as the example shown in Fig. 11.11.

Simple equipment will normally be adequate for the inspection and recording of many defects in structures, such as a selection from the following list as the need arises: measuring tapes, spirit level, plumb bob and line, straight edge, inspection mirror, thermometer, wire brush, chipping hammer, pocket knife, camera, binoculars, notebook and inspection report forms. The inspector may also require back-up services for excavation, for access plant and for reasons of safety.

More complex investigations are likely to involve specialist services in carrying out examinations and interpreting the results. A comprehensive review of such methods is beyond the scope of this book, but can be found in the *OECD Bridge Inspection Guide Part IV*.[11.14]

The costs of carrying out inspections for Ministry owned structures are reimbursed in two ways as follows. Superficial and general inspections are

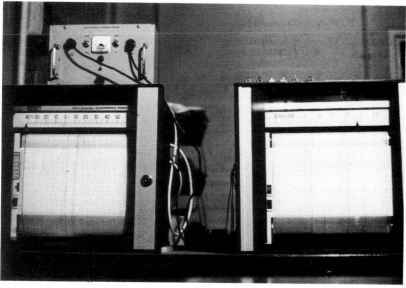

Fig. 11.12. Electronic recording equipment used to monitor deflections and temperature of weak bridge continuously

included in the percentage fee repaid on the overall cost of repair works done. At present the percentage is 8% for works not exceeding £0·5 million. Principal and special inspections are directly reimbursable. Details of the terms of agreement for agency works are given in the *Second Schedule Parts 1/A/6, B/2* and *C/4* with regard to highway structures and their inspection.[11.15]

11.9. Monitoring

Monitoring becomes necessary in order to collect data concerning the performance of an existing structure. Examples of typical monitoring situations are

(a) newly constructed (say, for the first three years)
(b) load-restricted or borderline capacity bridges
(c) cast iron bridges
(d) large and/or complex types
(e) concrete structures suspected of alkali–aggregate reaction
(f) structures in area of subsidence
(g) structures with known progressive problems.

The form of monitor can include one or more of the following

(a) span and level measurement
(b) alignment
(c) movement of bearings or expansion joints
(d) crack behaviour
(e) shape changes
(f) groundwater levels
(g) corrosion potential
(h) before and during any modification to the structure or nearby works.

The results may be presented as tables, graphs, diagrams and in some cases using oscilloscopes or electronic print-out methods (Fig. 11.12).

An example of specialized monitoring is the periodic soundings taken to detect evidence of scour at bridge piers, river walls and above tunnels under rivers.

11.10. Assessment

Current bridge design loading is prescribed[11.16] in BS 5400: Part 2:1978 and the requirements of the Department of Transport are detailed[11.17] in Departmental Standard BD 14/82. For many years prior to this standard, design criteria in BS 153: Part 3A were used, with some variation permitted according to the availability of alternative routes for the heaviest vehicles.

Existing bridges may have been assessed depending on their perceived condition and importance, but not until the late 1960s, after an appraisal of railway bridges, was a determined effort made to establish the condition and load-carrying capacity of the national stock of bridges. Known as 'Operation Bridgeguard', this assessment was based on a code prepared by the Ministry of Transport and was mandatory for agents dealing with Ministry owned bridges and commended for use on all other bridges. The code covered a method of assessment for the simpler structures with recommendations on stresses to be used for a range of materials, together with tables and charts for use in determining the maximum axle load that was recommended for a given arch bridge. This review, which took many years to implement, led to a number of responses being found necessary

(*a*) the imposition of vehicle weight limits for weak bridges
(*b*) diversion of traffic
(*c*) temporary bridging
(*d*) relief of critical members by traffic control.

These immediate steps were often unacceptable in the longer term, and a programme of repairs, strengthening or complete replacement was mounted. Even today many of these 'temporary' measures are still in service due largely to financial constraints. The assessment code was revised and reissued in 1973 under the same terms. Meanwhile successive amendments of the *Construction and Use Regulations*[11.9] under which vehicles are made in the United Kingdom, have changed the total weight

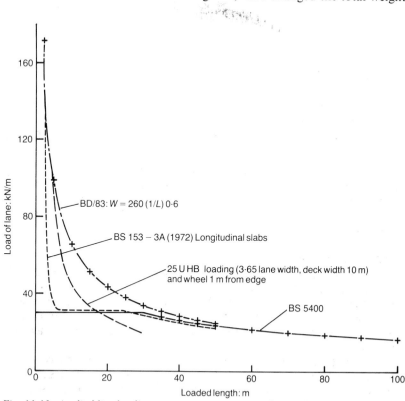

Fig. 11.13. *Applied live load/span curves: comparison of HA udl loading as given by BS 5400: Part 2, cl. 6.2.1 and BD/83 cl. 7.4.2*

and configuration of axles permitted to use the highway without special consent to the present maximum of 38 tonnes. To take account of these changes and to incorporate some of the revisions in design crtieria, a new assessment code (BD 21/84)[11.18] was developed and issued by the Department of Transport in 1984, and an explanatory document (BA 16/84) was issued.[11.19] Again, the implementation of the code is mandatory for Ministry owned structures. There is some reluctance among bridge owners to follow the previous course and extend the assessments to all stock, since a recent estimate came up with a total of some £600 million, mainly to be spent on pre-1922 bridges of up to 50 m span.

A comparison of the applied live load/span curves is shown in Fig. 11.13 for the more recent documents mentioned above.

11.11. Measurement of works

Much of the work done on highway structures will be the subject of prepared contracts using the Institution of Civil Engineers Standard Method of Measurement[11.20] and Conditions of Contract.[11.21] Such contracts will have contract drawings if appropriate, a specification, and a Bill of Quantities itemizing the necessary works. However, situations sometimes arise in maintenance activities where the above approach is not practicable due to the uncertainties about repairs and the possible need for emergency action. In these circumstances, allowance must be made in the system of measurement for part of the work to be the subject of an agreed labour, plant and materials schedule. A basis for this can be the Schedule of Dayworks prepared by the Federation of Civil Engineering Contractors. It is important that the form and content of any schedule is agreed in advance and that it provides a clear basis for tendering and demonstrable audit capability. A purely 'cost plus' arrangement is not usually acceptable to the client organization or the district auditor, except for small elements that do not lend themselves to detailing and could not be foreseen. There are several features of a maintenance contract which require special consideration.

(a) The type of work frequently involves a mixture of skills akin to 'do-it-yourself' and may also be on a small scale. The Dayworks Schedule does not cater for the experienced 'handyman' category suited to this situation.

(b) The appointed contractor or direct labour organization is required to respond at short notice throughout 24 hours all year round to deal with accident damage and emergencies.

(c) The organization has to have the necessary potential in plant and materials on call within an agreed timescale. Some of the plant items may be outside the scope of the Dayworks Schedule or may need to be used under conditions not envisaged by the Schedule, in which case agreement of rates, preferably in advance, is necessary. It may also be prudent to ensure that plant is duplicated for sensitive items where a mechanical breakdown would be critical in terms of time and/or public safety.

11.12. Expansion joints and bearings

11.12.1. General

These semi-mechanical accessories are often the focal point for most frequent attention and can rarely be expected to have a service life equal to the structure itself. While there are exceptions to this, their cost can become prohibitive. The maintenance engineer will therefore be faced with repair and replacement at intervals in the lifespan of the structure. The following attributes should be aimed for in choosing such replacements

- (*a*) to accommodate all movements of the structure
- (*b*) to withstand all predictable loadings
- (*c*) not to impart unacceptable stresses to the structure
- (*d*) to be silent and vibration free in operation
- (*e*) to give reliable operation throughout the expected temperature range
- (*f*) to be sealed against water or foreign matter or make provision for their disposal
- (*g*) to resist corrosion and withstand attack from chemicals and grit to facilitate easy inspection, maintenance and repair.

In addition, expansion joints should

- (*a*) not present a skidding hazard or danger to traffic such as cyclists or animals
- (*b*) have good riding characteristics.

The setting of joints and bearings during construction or replacement depends on the anticipated temperature range, the temperature at the time of placing or casting the deck and the materials used. The following coefficients of thermal expansion have been used in major constructions

- (*a*) for metal structures

$$11 \cdot 7 \times 10^{-6} \text{ per } °C \ (6 \cdot 5 \times 10^{-6} \text{ per } °F)$$

- (*b*) for concrete structrues, the value varies depending on the type of aggregate used, some typical values being

$$13 \times 10^{-6} \text{ per } °C \ (7 \cdot 2 \times 10^{-6} \text{ per } °F)$$

for gravel aggregate and

$$8 \times 10^{-6} \text{ per } °C \ (4 \cdot 4 \times 10^{-6} \text{ per } °F)$$

for limestone aggregate.

Further guidance is given in Table 12A of BS 5400: Part 2.[11.16]

11.12.2. Expansion joints

Depending on the anticipated movement of the bridge deck, joints may be categorized according to movement capacity.

Group 1. Joints in group 1 have a relatively small capacity (less than 50 mm), catered for by buried joints formed with various flashing fabrics over compressible joint fillers, the whole being covered by road surfacing material with or without its own mesh of reinforcement. For walls the joint filler is usually pointed with a semi-elastic filler which adheres to the sides of the joint (the depth/width ratio of pointing and the detailing need to be in accordance with the suppliers instructions).

Group 2. Joints in group 2 are in the range 50–150 mm and cover a wide range of bridge types and sub-divided decks of steel and concrete construction. Earlier joints were generally a sliding plate or interlocking comb form, bolted, welded or cast into the deck. Often these designs included copper or canvas 'U'-shaped water bars. In the post-war period, developments in materials have led to extruded neoprene types aimed at low maintenance, noise-free and competitively priced joint types.

Group 3. Joints in group 3 cope with movements in excess of 150 mm, which take many forms, usually requiring complex bridging arrangements to sustain an acceptable running surface under all conditions of movement.

For work on trunk roads and motorways, the Department of Transport has issued a list of approved joint types.[11.22]

Consider the maintenance needs of each category.

Group 1 involves little routine treatment, and breakdown of the joint will become evident by observation of either leakage through the joint and/or disruption of surfacing, usually commencing with reflective cracking. Leakage is never good but may be assessed for significance, e.g. in terms of effects on the structure, usage of space below the structure and the serviceability of the drainage system, which should be installed at all movement joints. Often quite minor details such as the provison of effective drips at the deck edges can counter the adverse effects of water penetration at the joint. Some relief can be obtained by sealing surface cracks with pouring grade sealants and this helps to counter the effects of frost, but such measures are likely to be needed frequently and certainly before each winter. Ultimately, the renewal of the joint will become necessary, and the cost of this can be expected to occur several times within the life of the surfacing (say three or four times within 20 years). It is strongly recommended that careful records be kept of the specification, installation photographs, temperature and movement patterns wherever possible and particularly when previously untried materials or methods are involved. From these, the effectiveness of the chosen system can be judged and the designer can be furnished with information on which to base future installations or to revise existing designs.

Group 2 types are usually more accessible, at least from the carriageway, and signs of wear, undue deformation or detachment may be obvious from routine inspection. The most common problems relate to

(a)   loosening of fixings to the deck
(b)   damage to neoprene inserts
(c)   blockage of drainage channels
(d)   delamination of elements of the joint
(e)   seizure or jamming of components due to corrosion and/or accumulation of compacted detritus (Figs 11.14–11.18).

Fig. 11.14. Expansion joint — teeth under cover plate choked with compacted detritus

Fig. 11.15. Expansion joint — sheared holding down bolts

Fig. 11.16. Expansion joint — repair method using splicing sleeves and machined recesses to underside of base plate

Fig. 11.17. Expansion joint — repair method using purpose-made grooved boxes for holding down bolts fixed with epoxy mortar

Fig. 11.18. Expansion joint — tightening down repaired expansion joint top plate bolts

Some of these problems occur or are exacerbated because of inattention to regular cleansing and flushing out of the joint and the associated drainage routes. Stones and metal components falling from vehicles become lodged in the clutch of some joints causing local damage as the joint closes. Routine cleansing of the carriageway by sweeping vehicles is unlikely to keep many types of joint clear and in fact can result in material being swept into the joint. The maintenance programme should locate and provide for special attention to all joints that are likely to be sensitive to blockage.

Group 3 joints require similar care to the above, and may also need periodic lubrication or replacement of working parts subject to wear. This can require partial or even full closure of carriageways and consequently must be planned in advance to minimize traffic disruption. For relatively major works of this type, the fabrication of bridging units to span the joint while critical reconstruction takes place may relieve some of the traffic problems.

All joints need careful attention during installation and may require special jigs to maintain the required clearance between shoulders (Figs 11.19 and 11.20). A further type of joint uses materials such as epoxy resin or specially designed concrete mix reinforced with strands of chopped wire to form the shoulders. These types can be critical in both constituents and the dimensions specified, as can asphaltic joints, and they should be installed by specialists. In fact the skill required and problems arising from faulty workmanship dictate that all expansion joint works should be performed by fully experienced staff under close engineering supervision.

Fig. 11.19. Expansion joint — accurate alignment of position welded steelwork with small sections of Maurer D75 joint

As part of his/her duties, the maintenance engineer should consider the monitoring of expansion joint movements seasonally in the early life of the structure and compare performance with the designer's expectations. Ideally, the initial settings and movements during the construction stages of the contract will be recorded by the resident engineer and furnished to the maintenance organization as part of the handover documents. Any inexplicable behaviour of the joint should be discussed with the designer and favourable performance should also be fed back to assist in the choice of future components.

Further guidance is given in the *Specification for Highway Works*.[11.23]

11.12.3. Bearings
The maintenance of bearings falls into two aspects

(*a*) confirmation that the performance agrees with the designer's assumptions over a range of climatic conditions and sometimes loading conditions

(*b*) routine maintenance such as lubrication, cleaning and servicing, depending on the type and materials forming the bearing.

Of critical importance in carrying out these functions is accessibility, and the designer must ensure that bearings can be reached for servicing and inspection. Since most bearings have a life expectancy of between 25% and 50% of the present design life for the deck (125 years), provision must also be made for a means of replacement, such as built-in jacking arrangements and/or reinforcement of the deck to permit eccentric localized loading near bearings.

Fig. 11.20. Expansion joint — temporary steel bridge pieces used for final positioning of Maurer D75 joint

During construction, bearings of the roller or sliding type will usually need a preset to allow for the difference between designer's mean and actual temperature at the time of final fixing of the top plate. Careful recording of such measurements by the resident engineer and their transmission with other construction records to the maintenance organization will provide the basis for accurate assessment of the performance of the bearing. This can be vital in determining possible reasons in the event of later failure.

Many bearings require lubrication, and it is of course necessary for the recommendations of the designer/manufacturer to reach operational staff. This seemingly obvious need is all too often overlooked until trouble manifests itself in the form of seizure and possible shearing of fixings and surrounding construction. A maintenance manual should be incorporated in the bridge files covering all such semi-mechanical features and their prescribed needs.

Not all problems arise from malfunction or expiration of the bearings and inspection following accidents such as collision, fire or flooding must include a careful examination of bearings to check for abnormal displacement, impact damage or other deterioration. For example, fire damage to neoprene bearings will at best shorten the remaining period of serviceability and in serious cases will require early replacement. Other cases where bearings are at risk are lightweight footbridges that are subject to collisions and bridges over tidal waterways where ships have become lodged on a rising tide. Clearly the maintenance engineer must be aware of the form of bearing in each case, and the way in which it is intended to operate or be replaced.

Many proprietary bearings make use of the exceptionally low coefficient of friction properties of polytetrafluoroethylene (PTFE), which can give considerable reductions in the forces transmitted to columns and abutments. Values in the range 0·02 to 0·045 are obtainable, with variations related to the magnitude of the applied loading, the speed of sliding, and also the nature of the structure and the total movement to be accommodated. From a practical point of view, this material has a good service life if protected from undue contamination, and requires no maintenance. It is important to ensure correct alignment of the sliding surfaces.[11.24]

A recent bearing failure at a major London suspension bridge required extended traffic restriction while investigation and replacement of the failed steel rollers were carried out. Available space dictated the use of multiple small hydraulic jacks, and the existing saddle was finally supported on offset laminated rubber pad bearings with outriggers attached to the structure, using stressed high tensile steel through bolts. The performance of the finished work was load tested using a series of double decker buses, and bearing movement were recorded. Some aspects of the work, carried out with the assistance of consulting engineers are illustrated in Figs 11.21 and 11.22.

Elastomeric bearings, when properly fixed and designed, will not require routine maintenance. Occasionally, due to misplacement, overloading, damage or excessive deflections, this type of bearing will suffer delami-

Fig. 11.21 (above). Bridge bearing replacement — system of small hydraulic jacks placed between failed existing roller bearings, with pipe harness and load gauge (Hammersmith Bridge 1985)

Fig. 11.22 (right). Bridge bearing replacement — new offset mountings for replacement pad bearing outriggers (Hammersmith Bridge 1985)

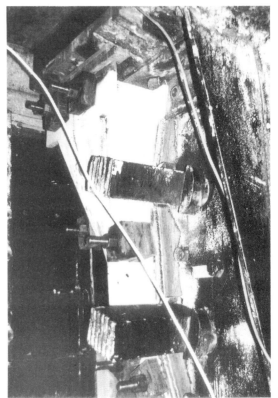

nation. The degree of damage will determine the stage where replacement becomes necessary.

Guidance is given in BS 5400: Part 9[11.25] (and explanatory notes BD 20/83)[11.26] and the *Specification for highway works.*[11.27]

11.13. Waterproofing

The need to protect bridge decks from water ingress, and particularly water-borne corrosive contaminants, such as de-icing salts, used on the carriageway, is now fully recognized. Similarly, areas such as piers, columns and abutments subject to spray from vehicles need to be considered when specifying materials and finishes. This has not always been the case, and as recently as the 1960s bridges were built without a waterproofing membrane.

To be effective, a membrane system needs to be as many of the following as possible: impervious, flexible, durable, stable, light, replaceable, repairable, capable of shaping, capable of jointing, inexpensive, transportable, compatible, safe to use, adhesive, immune to weather, quick to lay and resistant to temperatures of wearing course materials during laying.

A number of tests have been designed to evaluate some of the properties listed. In brief these are

(*a*) mandril test for cracking at $-5°C$
(*b*) water vapour permeability — as for Canadian DPC test 13–15 g/m²/day
(*c*) water absorption — test for seven days with chloride salts on one side and distilled water on the other
(*d*) water pressure — under 6 metre head
(*e*) tests for the effects of moisture and time on curing times
(*f*) crack tolerance — test on cracked block under controlled conditions
(*g*) chisel impact test (this includes any specified protection): a 10 mm × 1 kg chisel is dropped 40 times in different places. On a scale the results are graded 1 (no effect) to 5 (puncture) and the material is judged acceptable if an average value of 3 is achieved
(*h*) self-protective capacity: the test sample is spread with crushed aggregate and loaded to 25 kg/cm² (equivalent to wheel load intensity). The results are judged as for the chisel impact test
(*i*) tensile bond — material is applied to the manufacturer's specification and pulled off, and the load achieved is noted.

To ensure successful waterproofing the designer must

(*a*) ensure adequate falls and drainage outlets to avoid water traps
(*b*) ensure adequate ventilation to avoid condensation traps
(*c*) ensure continuity of the membrane
(*d*) avoid any unnecessary penetration of the membrane for fixings
(*e*) give attention to all edge details to provide a seal or an upstand with tuck-in
(*f*) specify an appropriate surface finish to take the membrane

(g)   specify requirements for the protection of the membrane during and after laying.

During construction or at a later date when replacement of the membrane system becomes necessary, the critical aspects to be borne in mind are adherence to manufacturer's instructions and programming the works to avoid the typical last minute rush, which can lead to faults in application and damage to the membrane.

In the maintenance context, faulty waterproofing is usually discovered during inspections by the presence of leaks or staining of the structure. Tenants of space below the structure are also quick to report any obvious leakages. Difficulties in repair arise because the actual point of ingress for leaks is seldom at the position where the leak becomes evident. For most membranes, the making of satisfactory joints is also difficult to achieve. Add to these problems the traffic disruption associated with bridge deck repairs and the access difficulties caused by service pipes and cables placed after the membrane was first laid, and some idea of the complexity of the task is gained.

In some instances these problems are further compounded by the original work having been subdivided by construction sequences, and even between different contractors and owning authorities. This can lead to protracted arguments where liability for faults is in dispute. Bearing in mind the small relative cost of the waterproofing membrane and the vital part played by it in the long-term serviceability of the main structure, it makes sense to choose a high quality product and to supervise properly the installation and aftercare to sustain its integrity. Remember that this item is one of the few where performance is judged as a success or failure, although the consequences of failure may not become evident for some time.

In all but the simplest cases, the tracing of faults is a process of elimination commencing with

(a)   establishing the source of water
(b)   defining the drainage regime and confirming that it is functioning or, if it is not, rectifying it
(c)   using methods such as controlled die testing to locate the point of initial leakage and the route taken through the structure.

The consequences of faulty waterproofing have to be considered in each case and a course of action decided upon. In some situations the economic conclusion may be merely to observe the rate of deterioration. In cases where the leakage causes potential problems, such as in locations where the water could freeze and create a traffic hazard or lead to unacceptable staining or significant corrosion, the immediate corrective measure could be to install half round channels within the road surfacing thickness or behind finishes, leading the water away via small gauge pipes. Of course, such measures are only a palliative, and have to be viewed in terms of the possible longer-term adverse effects of the water penetration. Rarely can any action taken from within the structure or from the underside of it be more than cosmetic in its effectiveness.

Ultimately, the cost and disruption of surface removal and the replacement of the membrane may have to be faced in the interests of preserving the satisfactory service life of the structure. In investigating water problems, some of which create accumulations within, for instance, box beams, the possibility of leaks around and through street furniture should not be overlooked. Also in this context, the maintenance programme should include regular internal inspections and checks on the freedom of flow through internal diaphragms and similar potential dams.

The Department of Transport have issued guidance on waterproofing membranes for bridge decks and similar locations in BE 27,[11.28] which includes a list of products acceptable for use on their structures. Further information is given in the *Specification for Highway Works*.[11.29]

11.14. Protective treatments

Most structures constructed in steel will benefit from protective treatment, the purpose of which is to preserve the underlying material and also to enhance the appearance. In the maintenance context, much of the treatment is applied to surfaces that have already received coatings, and the first requirement is to determine the conditions of the existing surface and its constituents. Preliminary steps are

(*a*)   to identify existing materials
(*b*)   to assess the condition in terms of adherence and surface condition, and estimate the proportion of the surface that is breaking down as a percentage of the whole
(*c*)   to examine the areas of breakdown and to try to discover reasons, e.g. corrosion, water seepage, faults in protective film or in application
(*d*)   to determine the condition of the underlying metal surface.

Research has shown that surface preparation is the most important single factor in achieving an acceptable life span for paint systems (the most commonly used treatments) and that even inferior materials will outlast a higher quality system when applied to a carefully prepared surface.

The most serious damage to structures often occurs in places that are difficult to reach and inspect, and preparation may also be hampered once construction has been finished. The designer can assist by giving attention to the following aspects of design

(*a*)   the accessibility of components for labour and the normal maintenance processes, typically difficult areas being at bridge bearings and expansion joints
(*b*)   the avoidance of sharp edges, angles and projections on which it will be difficult to achieve the required paint film thickness
(*c*)   the avoidance of water and dirt traps.

Corrosion may be of a general nature related to the condition of protective coatings and the degree of exposure to moisture and contaminants, or it can take the form of localized pitting resulting from the development of cell action. The former case is less urgent but should nevertheless receive treatment before reaching a stage where expensive surface preparation becomes unavoidable. Where pitting has occurred, counter-measures should be adopted as soon as practicable, since this type of deterioration can develop rapidly into structural weakness by acting as a focal point for corrosion cracking, particularly in association with high or fluctuating stress levels.

Guidance in the design of paint systems is given in BS 5493: 1977,[11.30] which takes account of the location, importance, degree of exposure, life expectancy and accessibility of relevant components. Illustrations of good and bad practice in the detailing of members are included. For maintenance purposes, the engineer is faced with a wide variety of conditions and material specifications previously adopted. The action needed may vary, for example, between the following:

(a) to do nothing except to keep under review and inspection
(b) to carry out local repairs such as patch painting
(c) to prepare the surface and to apply a two-coat treatment to otherwise sound existing paintwork (to change colour scheme or to improve the appearance and extend useful life)
(d) to remove a failing paint system and to prepare the underlying metal surface by means of grit blasting, flame cleaning or mechanical abrading, and to apply a designed system aimed at satisfying life expectancy criteria.

The choice of system will be conditioned by the following factors

(a) the present state of the existing surface and an estimate of the residual life, particularly in critical and exposed areas
(b) the need for structural repairs requiring access platforms
(c) accessibility now compared to at a later stage in the case of known developments
(d) any perceived changes in the environmental conditions affecting the structure including pollution, usage, vandalism.

In arriving at a suitable specification, the compatibility of materials has to be verified, together with any precautions needed to satisfy the Health and Safety at Work Act, and a comparison of the respective costs of alternative treatments and their advantages should be carried out.

Referring to BS 5493, Table 3 Part 17 emphasizes the vulnerability of certain roadside features such as bridge parapets, guard railings and similar items in close proximity to the carriageway splash zone. It is recommended that such items be galvanized prior to further treatment. Figure 1 of the Standard indicates a minimum thickness of between 50 and 100 μm for a 'life to first maintenance' of ten years over a range of exposure conditions. Section 5 deals specifically with many of the problems and requirements of maintenance activities. Among advisory items is the need to keep adequate records of the treatments used. This becomes especially important when dealing with expensive systems from which a long life is expected. Also, the importance of quite minor details in producing an effective job underlines the quality of training needed for both appliers and inspectors of the protective system, and the care required from the initial designers of the construction. Tables 11.1 and 11.2, taken from the Standard, indicate a range of typical treatments which might be considered.

For smaller bridges, especially those over water, the underside of the deck and internal beams may be best protected using chlorinated rubber paint. For larger bridges the appearance may be a controlling factor and in fact the use of light colours can help to draw attention to areas of corrosion at an early stage during general inspections.

The preparation of existing structural elements before resurfacing is confined to

(a) hand and mechanically assisted methods such as wire brushing, chipping, needle guns and similar equipment driven by compressed air or electricity
(b) flame cleaning (for sections thicker than 5 mm only)
(c) either wet or dry process grit blasting

In all cases the surface is then thoroughly washed and allowed to dry before applying primer paint or an undercoat. Many situations severely limit the choice of method due to access difficulties and the decision as to the most appropriate method will include consideration of cost, the control required for safety, and anti-pollution measures. On large structures, the method may vary from place to place and due to variations in

Fig. 11.23. Fire damage to bridge soffit — underside of prestressed concrete bridge beams damaged by 20 minute exposure to fire

Table 11.2. Site treatment of previously metal-coated steelwork (from BS 5493: 1977)

Initial condition	Present condition	Surface preparation	Replacement of metal where required	Paint treatment over	
				Sprayed metal	Galvanizing
Bare metal coating	Areas of corrosion and/or some rusting of substrate*	If metal is to be replaced, blast-clean	Spray metal to appropriate specification, see table 3	Not normally necessary. If overcoating is required, see table 3 and clause 11.3	
		If metal not to be replaced, clean corroded areas by best means available	Not applicable	Build-up cleaned areas with suitable paint system and, preferably, apply chemical-resistant finish overall	Build-up cleaned areas with suitable paint system and, preferably, apply chemical-resistant finish overall
	Areas with some white corrosion products	If decoration required wash to remove salts, using stiff brush if necessary. Remove loose material with non-metallic brush	Not applicable	Apply sealing coat and chemical-resistant finish for maximum life	Apply suitable surface pretreatment followed by, preferably, chemical-resistant finish
		If decoration not required, no action is necessary		Not applicable	
	Areas in sound condition	If decoration is required, wash to remove salts, using a non-metallic brush	Not applicable	Apply suitable paint which should be chemical-resistant for maximum life	Apply suitable surface pretreatment; follow by suitable paint which should be chemical-resistant

Sealed or painted metal coating	Areas of corrosion of some rusting of substrate	If decoration not required, no action is necessary	Not applicable		See table 3 and clause 11.3, consider one or two coats overall. preferably chemical-resistant
		If metal is to be replaced, blast-clean	Spray metal to appropriate specification, see table 3	See table 3 and clause 11.3, consider one or two coats overall. preferably chemical-resistant	See table 3 and clause 11.3, consider one or two coats overall. preferably chemical-resistant
		If metal not to be replaced, remove corrosion product by best method available	Not applicable	Build-up cleaned areas with suitable paint. Apply one or two coats overall, preferably chemical-resistant	Build-up cleaned areas with suitable paint. Apply one or two coats overall, preferably chemical-resistant
	Areas with some degradation of paint, dissipation of sealer, or loss of adhesion of either	Remove loose material with non-metallic brush	Not applicable	Apply further coats of paint or sealer, preferably chemical-resistant	Apply further coats of paint or sealer, preferably chemical-resistant
	Areas in sound condition	If decoration is required, dust-down	Not applicable	As above	As above
		If decoration is not required, no action is necessary	Not applicable		

*It should be confirmed that the apparent rusting emanates from the substrate.

the pretreatment needed. As a general guide, areas of existing paintwork exhibiting more than 0·5% corrosion breakdown should be cleaned back to bare metal, chamferring the edges of sound paint and following with a full protective system. For many years the standard treatment for steelwork included a red lead primer since this has a proven tolerance to a degree of rusting. However, this paint involves both a health risk to operatives and to the environment when abraded. Alternative primers are therefore recommended for current work, one of the most effective being zinc phosphate. When dealing with painted surfaces, precautions to be taken include the wearing of face masks, bagging and care in the disposal of abraded detritus and general hygiene before meals.

Paints are applied either by brushing or spraying methods, each having advantages. The advantages claimed for brushing methods are that they

(a) give a greater film thickness (provided that surface roughness and the profile of projections are sympathetic)

(b) assist in the disturbance of dust or moisture (where control is not of the best standard)

An equally satisfactory job can also be achieved by airless spraying provided that the shape of the members does not lead to 'shadowed' areas such as around rivet heads.

11.15. Fire risk

The design of buildings takes account of the effects of fire damage. In the case of bridges, risks may develop which can lead to serious damage, e.g.

(a) from accidents to vehicles on or below the bridge

(b) as a result of fires in flammable materials, stored or used in areas under elevated roads or bridge approaches.

Controls are therefore necessary to reduce the possibility of fire damage and it is often the responsibility of the maintenance organization to ensure by regular inspection that the risks are minimized. The following aspects need attention

(a) control of the development and usage of space below and adjacent to any highway structure

(b) consideration of measures needed to protect structural members such as additional cover to steel, encasement, or protective finishes such as sprayed vermiculite.

The advice of fire prevention officers should be sought and records kept of the presence of dangerous substances, notices being displayed outside premises as appropriate.

Whenever fire damage occurs, careful inspection and assessment of the resulting damage is necessary. Concrete strength falls rapidly when temperatures rise above 300°C and it is likely to be severely affected if temperatures reach 600°C. Damage occurs after quite short periods of exposure; in one case a 20 minute fire in a cabin below deck level caused spalling beyond deck reinforcement (Fig. 11.23). Colour changes occur in the concrete, which indicate the likely extent of damage and this can be interpreted by an expert. As spalling progresses, this leads to faster heat penetration, and depending on the loading at the time of the fire, reinforcement can be affected and permanent deformations may result. Prestressed members can be seriously weakened if the temperature of the tendons rises to 400°C.

Following a fire of any significance, traffic control may be needed to reduce live loading until such time as expert assessment of the damage has been done and any necessary remedial works completed. The ability of emergency services to reach all parts of a structure and the availability of adequate facilities such as hosereels, sand buckets and means of communication is vital. Contingency planning for difficult sites, such as long elevated roads, tunnels and underpasses where accidents lead to rapid traffic congestion, should be part of the maintenance procedures.

11.16. Investigatory methods

Faced with the problems of deterioration and damage, maintenance engineers need to determine the residual strength of structural members. During the assessment process, described in section 11.10, estimates are made of the likely quality of the original materials, which are then adjusted to allow for loss of section or perceived condition. For the majority of structures this process is satisfactory, but for more complex structures perhaps subjected to unknown increases in the anticipated design stresses, a more comprehensive form of assessment may be warranted.

Usually this entails controlled loading of the structure either by static methods such as kentledge or anchored tension rods and a jack system, or by dynamic loading from the passage of loaded vehicles. During the loading, measurements of deflection, strain gauge readings and load cell values taken at predetermined positions may be taken and an analysis of the actual behaviour can be compared with the expected theoretical values. The validity of such testing depends on the accuracy of knowledge concerning the placing and nature of the constituent materials and components. The importance of collecting and preserving this sort of information at the time of construction is emphasized, and in the absence or incompleteness of such data further steps are likely to be necessary including some of the following tests

(a) Schmidt hammer — used to give an indication of comparative concrete uniformity or a guide to the compressive strengths by correlation with known strengths

(b) various pull-out and pull-off tests designed to produce tensile 21failure from which the compressive strength may be estimated

(c) ultrasonic pulse velocity measurements from which an indication of density and the possible presence of voids or cracks may be deduced

(d) radiography using a radioactive source to produce a radiograph or readings which can indicate the position of reinforcements, tendons, or voids within the concrete; the thickness to be penetrated is critical since time of exposure increases very rapidly with thickness and becomes impractical beyond about 0·5 metre (using a ^{60}Co source)

(e)   pulse echo readings used to detect flaws in metal components

(f)   core testing usually of 100–150 mm dia. cores cut from selected positions which when crushed can be related to an equivalent 28 day standard cube strength

(g)   half cell potential measurements to indicate the likelihood of reinforcement corrosion

(h)   direct drilling to introduce an endoscope into voids such as tendon sheaths, cavity walls, or other confined spaces; the positioning of the initial holes must be done with care to avoid damage, and further information may be extracted by analysing the drilling products.

Further information on some of these tests is given in BS 6089: 1981.[11.31]

11.17. Cracks

Most structural materials will show the presence of cracks after a period of time or loading. It is necessary for those engaged in maintenance to detect and make judgements about the significance of such cracks and to implement any resulting repair treatments.

Reinforced concrete has an inherent system of cracks once loaded and the designer limits the size and distribution of these cracks in areas of tensile stress by the positioning and quantity of steel reinforcement. Such cracking can develop early in the life of the concrete due to a number of causes, e.g.

(a)   thermal shrinkage due to heat of hydration

(b)   care taken during curing operations

(c)   restraint from shuttering

(d)   restraint from previously cast sections at horizontal construction joints

(e)   abrupt changes in cross-section or proportions of reinforcement

(f)   inappropriate striking times or support systems for formwork

(g)   weather conditions and drying shrinkage.

Once developed, these cracks may increase in size or new cracks may occur due to stress concentrations resulting from settlement of the structure, overloading, errors in design or construction, chemical reactions within the concrete or steel such as alkali–aggregate reaction and corrosion, respectively, each of which can set up bursting forces leading to cracking and spalling of surfaces.

During inspection, the discovery of cracks raises questions which the inspector or maintenance engineer must attempt to answer, e.g.

(a)   Can the cause of the crack be identified?

(b)   Is the position or pattern of cracking indicative of a major problem?

(c) Is the crack or its cause of structural significance?

(d) If so, what immediate steps are necessary to ensure safety?

(e) What longer term measures are necessary to preserve the integrity of the structure?

The scale and severity of the cracking will influence the repair treatment and may also prompt discussions with the designer. It is often advisable to monitor cracks over a period to establish the degree of activity under varying load and climatic conditions. This can be done using vernier scales between fixed points, Demec gauges, or simple mortar patches sometimes bridged by glass. Disruption due to alkali–aggregate reaction appears as a pattern described as 'map cracking' and confirmation requires chemical analysis of sample drillings. Corrosion cracking will usually be apparent from rust staining and the straightness of the cracks, often at regular intervals matching the spacing of bars or links. The Transport and Road Research Laboratory have developed techniques for assessing the proneness of areas of concrete to corrosion attack.

In brickwork and masonry, cracks are the result of tensile or shear forces beyond the capacity of the constituent materials. Typically, a crack will follow bedding and joints and depending on the cause may also show transverse displacement. Again these symptoms of distress need to be investigated to establish the cause if possible, and particularly in the case of arch bridges and retaining walls. Guidance in the recognition and significance of such cracks is given in *Bridge inspection guide*.[11.13]

Having located and determined the significance of the crack the next step is to try to eliminate or reduce the cause and to institute a programme of longer-term monitoring to confirm the effectiveness of remedial measures. Persistent flow of water through cracks, especially in underground structures, can be difficult to deal with as it usually indicates a breakdown in the waterproofing system and can involve considerable pressure. Corrective treatment needs to stem the flow and then have the capacity to accommodate thermal or deflection movements. Among the treatments that can be considered are

(a) sealing with a fast setting mortar followed by pointing with a polysulphide filler. The crack will usually need enlargement and shaping to form a rebate for this treatment

(b) bridging the crack with neoprene strip bolted to each side and forming an elastic channel leading water away to a drain. This has been used successfully for a major underpass roof, but is suitable only for relatively straight cracks.

The fine cracks normally present in concrete can become prominent where surfaces receive further treatment such as grit blasting to give an exposed aggregate finish. This also makes the repair more conspicuous and difficult to mask (Fig. 11.24). If it is deemed necessary and beneficial to try to seal such cracks, the following methods are available

(a) resin fillers introduced through nipples installed along the crack

(b) pressure or vacuum system using specialized grouting materials.

Fig. 11.24. Repairs to cracked subway walls — repairs to shrinkage cracking made more obvious by textured finish. Note also vandal resistant lighting fittings

For other situations, dealing with cracks may require the breaking away of areas of deteriorated, loose or 'hungry' concrete, e.g. where steel has corroded causing spalling. The most important aspect of carrying out such repairs is the preparation of the repair areas. Often this will necessitate cutting back behind the reinforcement to remove all porous concrete, cleaning the steel, priming the surfaces and adopting careful replacement methods to return to the original profiles. Such work requires expertise, and a number of firms specialize in such concrete repair techniques. For some situations, the use of resins and polyester materials is acceptable and effective, but these materials will behave differently to the concrete and may therefore be unsuitable aesthetically.

Cracks in metal components may be the result of fatigue, overstress, impact damage, embrittlement or design features such as notched sections and corrosion traps. Inspection methods include visual dye testing and sonar detection techniques, and on discovery all such cracks should be carefully investigated and fully reported. Repairs may be undertaken using the appropriate grade of welding rod provided that all necessary precautions have been taken (see section 11.18), or the affected member may have to be replaced or relieved by introducing duplicate strengthening. A specialist method of stitching across crack with purpose-made keys is also available and this has been successfully employed to repair important cast iron bridge features.

11.18. Welding

Site welding of existing structures is a difficult and potentially damaging operation for the following reasons

(a) determination of the stress variation in each member to be welded is uncertain

(b) changes in stress induced by the welding operation or changes in shape can affect stress concentrations

(c) lack of fit of superimposed or replacement materials

(d) problems of position or access affecting the quality of the weld

(e) unknown factors such as fatigue life, crack propagation and the consistency of metallurgical properties affecting the weld area

(f) the practicability of temporary loading relief on members to be treated.

Consideration of such factors is necessary before embarking on repairs by welding techniques, and consultation with the designer of the structure and experts in welding is strongly advised. Controlled sampling and non-destructive testing to locate cracks or deficiencies in the construction materials may also be necessary. For work of this type, the training of inspectors and the testing of welders for the appropriate level of skill is of crucial importance.

As design methods develop, leading to changes in the load ratios for certain types of structure and in the effects of fatigue, it is likely that maintenance engineers concerned with the more advanced designs will require techniques and inspection systems capable of monitoring more closely the performance of welded construction, and designers need to consider the means of access to all parts of such structures.

11.19. Drainage of structures

The drainage of structures is essentially a matter for the designer, and care is needed in detailing to ensure that water and contaminants, e.g. resulting from accidental spillage, from actions such as the spreading of de-icing salts or from maintenance processes, can be effectively directed away from the structure without causing damage. Many situations are encountered where such detailing has either been inadequate or where, perhaps due to a lack of maintenance, the system of drainage has failed to perform its function properly. Typical examples are as follows.

(a) On the uphill side of expansion joints, particularly in footway areas, water accumulates below surfacing or in filling material. The provision of a gully should be made and levels adjusted using concrete filling to direct water towards the gully or its back entry.

(b) Ponding within hollow structures can occur when maintenance of outlets is neglected, when outlets are not provided on the assumption that leakage will be absent or due to the faulty positioning of outlets and disturbance during concreting operations. Such faults need correction and can require the provision of pumping equipment and drilling of the structure. Diaphragms and stiffeners are prone to cause these problems.

(c) Areas around bankseat bearings, especially when associated with expansion joints, are often constructed without sufficient thought for later maintenance, and the design should provide access to give visibility and to allow cleansing with normally available equipment.

(d) Pipes embedded in the structure must be provided with ample rodding eyes at bends.

(e) Attention must be directed to the routine requirements of pumping machinery and the cleansing of grit traps designed to protect them. In critical situations standby equipment should be installed or be readily available.

(f) Drains should be sized not only for capacity but also with the potential for blockage in mind, and the maintenance of gratings, strainers and gully covers assists in minimizing choking.

(g) Manholes and covers must be designed with safety in mind and, for deeper chambers, allowance for the possible use of breathing apparatus has to be made. The position of access covers, where carriageway siting is unavoidable, should be adjusted to minimize interference with traffic lanes.

(h) For bridges, the designer is limited in the choice of drainage furniture, and the demands of the structure and its appearance often result in the absence of grit traps at carriageway level and gradients in the pipework close to the self-cleansing limits. Such locations are outside the scope of routine cleansing machines and the maintenance engineer must arrange for additional measures such as hand cleaning and jetting of the system.

(i) Small-scale items of street furniture fabricated in hollow sections should be checked for accumulations of water since such items could be damaged in freezing conditions.

(j) Discharge points should be checked to ensure that water is deflected away from structural members.

(k) Deck edges should always be provided with a drip channel to control the effects of weather staining.

11.20. Tunnels and underpasses — special problems

11.20.1. Communications

The advantages of a continuous form of radio link have been stressed by the police in the case of long tunnels. This can be provided by the installation of a leaky feeder system throughout.

Emergency telephone points, designed to be vandal resistant by dispensing with handsets, need to be provided at frequent intervals in positions that are accessible but safe for stranded drivers. Closed circuit television may also be an advantage, in relaying information on traffic to a central control room with continuous monitoring (see Chapter 6).

11.20.2. Cleansing

Cleansing requires regular attention and will normally be done at night to minimize traffic disruption. The build up of oily residues on the surfaces can be difficult to remove and may require a two-stage operation — first spraying with a detergent solution to break down and emulsify the oil, then flushing and cleaning with purpose-designed scrubbing equipment. The shape and features within the tunnel may control the practicability of mechanized cleaning. One alternative is the use of high pressure water jetting equipment. However, care is needed to control the effective surface pressures to avoid damage to the structure finishes.

Due to the effects of channelled traffic, a build up of oil-bound detritus often occurs on the carriageway. This also is difficult and expensive to remove, and must be tackled regularly to reduce the risk of skidding accidents, particularly for two-wheeled vehicles. A number of methods have been tried including mechanical flails, grit blasting, chilled shot blasting and hand scraping. Hand scraping was found to be most effective where an appreciable thickness of deposit had accumulated.

11.20.3. Ventilation

Ventilation may rely on the ram effect of traffic, or may also require a controlled fan-assisted system, depending on the length of the tunnel. In addition to the periodic maintenance of the machinery, inspection and cleaning of all ducts is necessary, care being required to protect staff from dust hazards. Most systems have automatic smoke and carbon monoxide level monitoring, which needs to be regularly checked. In the event of

Fig. 11.25. Vehicle height control showing variation in safe clearance between lanes. Continuous maintenance of suspended tubes required

prolonged traffic stoppages, instructions to drivers to switch off engines may be needed.

11.20.4. Lighting

Lighting produces several maintenance problems as a result of being vulnerable to damage and usually needs frequent checking and replacement of outages, especially in areas such as portals where boost lighting ensures a safe transition from daylight conditions. The design of fittings needs to take account of the likely methods of cleansing to be employed for the tunnel.

11.20.5. Drainage

Most tunnels rely on pumped systems, and maintenance of the protective features such as grit traps and filters is a critical factor in preserving the equipment.

11.20.6. Traffic control

The control of traffic is vital in the tunnel situation. Most tunnels have individual by-laws specifying the nature of controls which may include

(a) a limit on vehicle dimensions
(b) control of specified goods that are permitted to use the tunnel, e.g. petroleum products, dangerous chemicals and explosives limits on vehicle weights.

Such by-laws have to be backed up by systematic checking against abuse and commonly there will also be physical controls such as height gauges and lane curtains. Where present, these features are subject to regular damage and must be inspected and repaired as part of a programme of routine maintenance, at least on a weekly basis or after reported accidents (Fig. 11.25).

11.20.7. Resources

The access difficulties associated with tunnels and the sensitivity to stoppage require that emergency procedures are prepared and labour and equipment made available at short notice. Contingencies include the removal of damaged vehicles, demolition and removal of tunnel finishes involved in accidents, clearance of drains and dealing with random breakdown of services and structural elements. To minimize the effects of repairs, a programme of regular close inspection is essential.

A range of skills is necessary to cover mechanical, electrical and civil engineering aspects. In larger installations, there is a need for resident staff and, whether directly employed or under contract, the terms of reference, response times and instructions for dealing with emergencies must be clearly defined.

11.20.8. Fire risk

Despite the careful regulation of traffic using tunnels, there will remain a risk of fire from fuels normally carried in vehicles, or from faults developing in the necessary services through the tunnel. Attention must therefore be given to the provision and maintenance of fire fighting equipment such as hosereels, sand buckets and extinguishers.

11.21. Pedestrian subways

The maintenance of pedestrian subways is mainly concerned with the

(a) replacement and repair of lighting
(b) cleansing and repair of drainage, including pumps if fitted
(c) removal of graffiti and redecoration
(d) cleaning and repair of signs
(e) random repairs to guardrails, handrails, door furniture, stair treads and the treatment of leaks and damage to the structure — much can be done at the initial design stage to limit the future costs of maintenance in these areas.

11.21.1. Lighting

Lighting requires periodic replacement of expired lamps, and inspections should be performed weekly. This will usually entail a separate routine from street lighting, which may be scouted from a vehicle. Local policy often governs the periods of illumination, as does the length of the subway barrel, some systems being capable of having half the units lit during daylight, or being controlled by light-activated switches. All fittings must be vandal resistant and this is assisted by placing them in the corners of subway ceilings or within the roof structure. Translucent covers should be impact and flame resistant, and wiring is best protected by embedding ducts within the structure.

11.21.2. Drainage

Drainage is often designed for small flows, and consequently is prone to blockage. Gratings need to be removable, but should be bolted in place. Despite this, cast iron covers are broken and become hazards to pedestrians if not quickly repaired. Lack of attention to drainage sumps and grit traps soon leads to deterioration in pumping plant or the blockage of outlets followed by flooding. Pedestrians seeking alternative routes can then be at risk.

11.21.3. Graffiti

Graffiti adorn many public thoroughfares (see Fig. 11.26) and can be offensive and even intimidating in the confines of a subway. Finishes should be designed with cleansing in mind. Solvents and cleaning fluids are effective on hard tiled surfaces, but less so on small mosaics where permanent staining of the jointing material detracts from the appearance. Transparent and decorative coatings applied to original finishes can also screen graffiti and present a less difficult surface for future cleaning. Particularly obstinate staining may require the use of water jetting equipment, but care is needed to control the pressure and jetting distances used otherwise damage to the underlying surface and finishes can result.

Fig. 11.26. Graffiti disfiguring pedestrian subway walls, and general litter which can block drainage channels

A series of tests using conventional paint strippers was conducted by the Greater London Council's Scientific Branch[11.32] from which the following conclusions were drawn.

(*a*)   Paint strippers (largely of the methylene chloride type) can effectively remove graffiti, but results are affected by the age of the paint film, the type and colour of the paint used, the composition of any previously applied surface coating, and the nature of the substrate, i.e. composition, porosity, texture, etc.

(*b*)   The effect of using such strippers can be to create contrasting 'clean areas' which may deface the appearance of the structure.

(*c*)   Care is needed in the choice of brushing equipment because bristle brushes may not remove paint effectively, but wire brushes can be too harsh for some surfaces, e.g. soft brickwork and some concrete surfaces. Trials using non-ferrous wire brushes may be an alternative.

(*d*)   The skill, interest and experience of the operatives are significant factors whatever process is used, and this work should not be left to casual labour.

11.21.4. Sign maintenance

Sign maintenance follows the general procedures described in Chapter 7 and is mainly concerned with subway complexes where clear directions can be important. Routine maintenance will be simpler and most cost-effective if all such equipment forms part of a comprehensive inventory, internally illuminated signs being treated in the same way as lighting described above.

11.21.5. General repairs

General repairs are matters of inspection, assessment of significance and costing for possible inclusion in a programme of works. Matters affecting public safety, such as damaged stair treads, loosened copings or exposed wiring must receive urgent attention. Leaks in subways are often difficult to deal with satisfactorily and can be expensive. Establishing the source of water can be beneficial (i.e. repair of leaking pipes or faulty drainage), but often the path of water through the structure and its protective membrane defies all efforts. Superficial sealing on the inside with the possible provision of ducts to lead the water to drainage outlets may be the only economic solution.

Areas attracting a high incidence of vandalism include timber doors, lightweight false ceilings and expensive furniture such as bronze handrails. Replacement of such fittings by heavy duty or less theft-provoking materials may be the only viable answer. In winter conditions extra emphasis on the type of walkway finish is needed, together with drainage maintenance, particularly on ramps and stairs. Accidents or complaints should be recorded and steps taken to improve areas showing proneness to risk.

Many of the above items are aimed at ensuring an acceptable environment within a subway system. Public confidence needs support in these unpopular highway features, and steps to improve security, such as improvements in lighting standards, better signing and in some cases the provision of convex mirrors at corners, can encourage the public to use them rather than attempting to cross roads on the surface. A policy of high maintenance standards is also a positive move towards an acceptable environment.

11.22. River structures

There are particular problems with river structures associated with flowing water, e.g.

(*a*)   scour of foundations
(*b*)   removal of cover due to changes in bed levels
(*c*)   silt affecting drainage outlets
(*d*)   penetration and deterioration of joints
(*e*)   access and safety aspects
(*f*)   inspection difficulties below water level.

The programme of inspection and methods used must ensure that damage and changes are detected at an early stage and steps taken to sustain structural stability. Among the measures employed are the following.

(*a*)   Periodic soundings — either manual or sonar recordings — are carefully related to an established reference grid. From this information a record of the behaviour patterns and tidal or current effects can be gained and action taken where changes likely to adversely affect structures become apparent. In addition to using opportunities when water levels are lowered, the employment of specialist divers equipped with underwater video cameras may be necessary. Attention to safety aspects is necessary, particularly in fast flows and adjacent to bridge piers

(b) Remedial actions may include replacement of eroded material using tremied concrete, or by the construction of a temporary dam by steel sheeting or sand bagging (for shallow situations), the deposition of rock fill to replace eroded bed levels, or dredging and excavation of silted areas.

11.23. Bridge parapets

Bridge parapets are designed to criteria specified in Department of Transport document BE 5.[11.33] In the maintenance context, the important feature is the ease of replacement, particularly of holding down arrangements after collision damage. Most steel guardrails and parapets are galvanized and painting may become a maintenance task, in which case the surface has to be primed with a mordant solution prior to painting to neutralize and key the zinc coating.

Among the problems encountered with parapets are

(a) ingress of water into posts, which unless drain holes are provided at the lowest point, can freeze and burst the post

(b) top rails on which children may be tempted to balance

(c) a tendency for cracks to develop in parapet concrete at post socket positions.

11.24. Footbridges

Footbridges over the highway are generally of light construction, designed for the situation, or fabricated from units such as military trestling. Occasionally a facility is provided for horses. These structures can be owned by

(a) a highway authority

(b) a local authority in connection with housing estates, schools, etc.

(c) private concerns, e.g. where bridges join shopping or office development and span the highway.

The last category requires the owner to obtain permission to erect the structure, under Section 176 of the Highways Act 1980,[11.34] and be responsible for its maintenance.

Because of their vulnerability to traffic, an additional height clearance of 17 ft 6 in (5·33 m) is specified in Department of Transport Memorandum BE 14[11.35] with a further increase to 20 ft (6·01 m) for those on high load routes. Regular damage is, however, common, and requires a quick response from the maintenance organization. Among the questions to be considered are the following.

(a) Is collapse threatened?

(b) Can the carriageway remain in service, or is temporary closure by the police necessary?

(c) Can the footbridge remain in service, and if not, what alternative route is available and safe for pedestrians?

A detailed inspection of the structure must be carried out to identify all resulting damage including

(a) fractured, distorted or impaired structural elements
(b) displacment or damage to bearings and shear pins
(c) distortion of supporting columns, approach stairs or ramps
(d) damage to holding down bolts
(e) displacement or breakage of drainage, handrails, expansion joints or electrical supplies
(f) in the case of concrete bridges, any fractured and loose concrete to be removed and the presence of cracks noted.

The serviceability of the bridge then has to be determined from an appreciation of the damage and the degree of impairment. This may require full structural assessment. Quite often the removal of the main span is necessary where damage is obvious and substantial. Temporary measures apart from closure may entail the introduction of makeshift splices or propping using scaffolding if space permits.

A peculiarity of stairs and landings is the heavy wear that occurs due to foot traffic. Many recent footbridges have anti-slip surfaces applied at the factory, but after a few years part or all of such surfaces need repair. Techniques to do this include

(a) local patching with epoxy resin and grit
(b) applied felt laid on bituminous adhesive, having an anti-slip top surface (this method may conveniently cover the central walkway, or can be tailored to the shape of the deck)
(c) application of mastic asphalt, which provides good protection for the underlying structure
(d) substitution of plywood deck panels surfaced and sealed with resin and calcined bauxite.

Care is needed to ensure that tread nosings are securely fixed and that the drainage of the structure is not adversely affected by such repair works.

11.25. Sign gantries

Sign gantries can be of two types

(a) free standing spans
(b) spans combined with other structural elements such as retaining walls or an underpass.

The type of construction will depend on the distance to be spanned, the nature of signing and equipment to be supported (and the consequent maintenance requirements) and the type of carriageway to be crossed, which can affect the access and height clearances needed.

Currently all such gantries constructed over trunk roads and motorways are subject to the criteria in Technical Memoranda BE 1/78[11.36] and BE

$14^{11.35}$ which specify a minimum headroom for design of 5·7 m and for maintained headroom of 5·41 m.

Most gantries will be of steel or aluminium alloy materials, constructed in girder or hollow section format. Maintenance painting will be periodically necessary for steel types, and thought needs to be given to access, particularly where traffic flows are critical. For lightweight structures it may be practical to lift the span off for maintenance.

Damage to sign gantries occurs most often from

(a) impact, often from overheight vehicles, uncontrolled crane and earthmoving plant jibs, etc.
(b) collision with supporting columns or frames
(c) wind damage to signs
(d) vandalism
(e) weathering.

Being of relatively light construction, regular inspection is recommended and detailed examination of all structural elements should be done following any reported collision.

Attention to hollow sections where water can accumulate is needed, and care is required in resealing cover plates and access manholes removed for inspection. The functioning of all drains should be verified.

The safety of the public and the workforce must be ensured during overhead works, giving attention to

(a) safety harnesses with attachment points or rails
(b) kick boards
(c) temporary sheeting over mesh walkways to prevent loose tools, nuts and bolts from falling
(d) ventilation of all enclosed sections prior to entry
(e) isolation of electricity supplies
(f) clearance distance from all traffic
(g) advance warnings and coning off of work lanes.

11.26. Retaining walls

Routine maintenance of retaining walls, generally of concrete or brick construction, involves

(a) repairs to pointing
(b) repairs to expansion joint fillers
(c) removal of weed growth
(d) clearance of drain holes
(e) removal of graffiti.

Such work is itemized during inspections and incorporated in a programme as permitted by available finance.

If, however, inspections or reports indicate undue movments in a wall such as differential forward movement at joints, angular rotation or non-uniform settlement of a section of a wall, then the cause of such movement and its significance must be established. Depending on the seriousness of the movements, remedial actions to be taken could include the following

(*a*) short-term or long-term monitoring for level, line and inclination
(*b*) relief of surcharge loading on the wall
(*c*) improvements of the drainage behind and through the wall
(*d*) removal and replacement of defective or damaged material
(*e*) strengthening of foundations by underpinning or piling.

Of course, the steps to be taken will also be related to the type of wall as originally designed, and the importance of records and consultation with designers is emphasized.

In parts of the country, long lengths of 'dry walling' exist, extending in some cases to considerable heights. This form of wall is a traditional type of construction in which flat stones are selected and graded in size, and stacked vertically or to a batter without bedding or jointing. Such walls often defy analysis, and regrettably many are suffering the effects of age and perhaps heavier loading, leading to much repair work.

Many walls adjacent to the highway are privately owned, typically cellar walls in urban areas. The owner has a duty to sustain support to the highway, including during reconstruction.

11.27. Bailey bridges

Bailey bridges are a unit form of metal bridging, developed for military use and capable of many permutations to suit particular span/load ratios. For the maintenance engineer faced with the problem of a weak bridge situation, such units may provide a solution (Fig. 11.27), e.g. where

Fig. 11.27. Temporary use of Bailey bridge units

(*a*) the bridge deck is found to be weak
(*b*) abutments are weak and need relieving
(*c*) carriageway widening requires an alternative route for pedestrians
(*d*) traffic loading is reduced by converting an existing bridge into a one-way traffic system.

Such bridges are usually of a temporary nature and can lead to noise complaints. Regular checking and tightening of connections and replacement of worn timber chesses is necessary. If such a structure remains in service for a long period under heavy use, inspection should include careful examination of welds for the development of fatigue cracks.

Deck covering can be of metal or timber, and to ensure adequate skid resistance an effective surface, comprising epoxy resin and grit, can be applied either directly or on panels of sealed plywood.

11.28. Health and safety

Staff and management engaged in maintenance operations must ensure personal and public safety in the use of equipment and working methods. Obligations are set out in the Health and Safety at Work Act 1974[11.37] and the Factories Act 1961.[11.38] Other useful guides are the *Construction regulations handbook*[11.1] and the *Supervisors safety handbook*.[11.39]

Each authority and contracting organization is advised to prepare a policy statement covering aspects of health and safety. This is likely to comprise advice to employees and managers similar to the following.

11.28.1. General

The safety of all employees is of great importance, and it is the policy of the contracting organization to promote this aim by

(*a*) the provision and maintenance of plant, systems and working environments that are safe
(*b*) the provision of appropriate instruction, training, supervision and information
(*c*) the conduct of operations in such a way as to ensure that the surrounding areas and the people therein are not exposed to any risk to health or safety
(*d*) arranging for and participating in joint consultation with employees' representatives on matters concerned with the achievement of the aims of this policy.

11.28.2. Employees

It is the responsibility of all employees while at work

(*a*) to take all reasonable care for the health and safety of themselves and of all other persons who may be affected by their actions
(*b*) to co-operate with management in complying with all statutory provisons, rules and codes of practice
(*c*) to use all safety equipment and protective clothing provided and to be responsible for its safe keeping while in their possession

(*d*) to familiarize themselves with the accident reporting, first aid, fire, flood and bomb procedures appropriate to their place of work.

11.28.3. Management

It is the responsibility of line managers to ensure, so far as is practicable, that all work is done in a safe manner. This aim is to be achieved by

(*a*) familiarity with the safety policy
(*b*) regular and detailed inspections of plant, operations and work areas
(*c*) ensuring that staff for whom they are responsible are adequately trained, instructed and supervised and are aware of the potential hazards of their work
(*d*) ensuring that suitable protective clothing and equipment is available and worn or used whenever necessary
(*e*) the prompt investigation of all accidents involving personal injury or damage to property or equipment and all 'near miss' incidents to discover their cause
(*f*) ensuring in the event of an accident that all necessary report forms are properly completed and submitted
(*g*) taking all necessary steps for the introduction of new equipment and processes to ensure compliance with safety requirements.

Some typical circumstances encountered in maintenance work which require special precautions are

(*a*) abrading painted surfaces, particularly old red lead paints
(*b*) working in noise
(*c*) entering confined spaces
(*d*) entering sewers or places likely to be infested by rats, where a risk of contracting Weil's disease exists (such staff should be provided with warning cards to alert their doctor to such risks)
(*e*) lifting methods
(*f*) use of safety harnesses
(*g*) use of safety boats
(*h*) use of inflatable protective jackets
(*i*) use of safety helmets
(*j*) use of gas detection equipment
(*k*) working on glass fibre compounds
(*l*) demolition of asbestos items
(*m*) use of epoxy resins
(*n*) working on fast roads
(*o*) working on scaffolds.

Procedures should be developed to cover personnel on site visits, particularly where they are out of sight from the highway, e.g. in culverts, box beams or within bridge abutments. In some cases, prior notification to the Health and Safety Executive is needed for operations, for example when proposing to use radioactive isotopes in carrying out X-ray examinations of a structure.

Acknowledgement

The author wishes to thank Mr Geoffrey Mallett for the loan of the slide used in Fig. 11.7.

References

11.1. ROYAL SOCIETY FOR THE PREVENTION OF ACCIDENTS. *Construction regulations handbook*, 8th edn. RoSPA, London, 1970.

11.2. DEPARTMENT OF TRANSPORT. *Trunk roads and motorway structures.* Department of Transport Records and Inspection, TRRM 2/88.

11.3. COUNTY SURVEYORS SOCIETY and DEPARTMENT OF TRANSPORT. *National bridge census.* DTp, London, 1987.

11.4. DEPARTMENT OF TRANSPORT. *Agency Agreement 1985* (based on *Circular Roads 10/78*).

11.5. *Transport Act 1968.* Her Majesty's Stationery Office, London, Chap. 73.

11.6. *Road Traffic Act 1974.* Her Majesty's Stationery Office, London, Chap. 16.

11.7. *Public Utilities and Street Works Act 1950.* Her Majesty's Stationery Office, London.

11.8. HORNE M.R. *Roads and the utilities.* Report, Her Majesty's Stationery Office, London, 1985.

11.9. *Motor Vehicles (Construction and Use) Regulations 1978.* Her Majesty's Stationery Office, London.

11.10. *Motor Vehicles (Authorisation of Special Types) General Order 1979.* Her Majesty's Stationery Office, London.

11.11. *Construction (Working Places) Regulations 1966.* Her Majesty's Stationery Office, London.

11.12. DEPARTMENT OF TRANSPORT. *Inspection and records of highway structures.* Departmental Standard BD 22/84.

11.13. *Bridge Inspection Guide 1984.* Her Majesty's Stationery Office, London.

11.14. ORGANISATION FOR ECONOMIC CO-OPERATION AND DEVELOPMENT. *OECD Bridge Inspection Guide Part IV.* Her Majesty's Stationery Office, London.

11.15. DEPARTMENT OF TRANSPORT. *Second Schedule Parts 1/A/6, B/2 and C/4.* DTp, London, 1978.

11.16. BRITISH STANDARDS INSTITUTION. *Specification for loads.* BS 5400: Part 2: 1978. BSI, London.

11.17. DEPARTMENT OF TRANSPORT. *Loads for highway bridges. Departmental Standard BD 14/82.*

11.18. DEPARTMENT OF TRANSPORT. *The assessment of highway bridges and structures. Departmental Standard BD 21/84.*

11.19. DEPARTMENT OF TRANSPORT. *Explanatory Notes BA 16/84.* Advice Note, 1984.

11.20. INSTITUTION OF CIVIL ENGINEERS. *Civil Engineering Standard Method of Measurement*, 2nd edn. Thomas Telford, London, 1985.

11.21. INSTITUTION OF CIVIL ENGINEERS, *Conditions of Contract*, 5th edn. Thomas Telford, London, 1986.

11.22. DEPARTMENT OF TRANSPORT. *Expansion joints for use in bridge decks.* BE 3/72.

11.23. *Specification for Highway Works.* Her Majesty's Stationery Office, London, 1986.

11.24. TRANSPORT AND ROAD RESEARCH LABORATORY. *Low friction sliding surfaces for bridge bearings — PTFE weave.* TRRL, Crowthorne, 1967, LR 101.

11.25. BRITISH STANDARDS INSTITUTION. *Bridge bearings.* BS 5400: Part 9: 1983. BSI, London.

11.26. DEPARTMENT OF TRANSPORT. *Bridge bearings* (use of BS 5400: Part 9: 1983). *Departmental Standard BD 20/83.*

11.27. DEPARTMENT OF TRANSPORT. *Specification for Highway Works Series 2100.*

11.28. DEPARTMENT OF TRANSPORT. *Departmental Standard BE 27.* Waterproofing of bridge decks.

11.29. DEPARTMENT OF TRANSPORT. *Specification for Highway Works Series 2300 and notes for guidance NG 2300.*

11.30. BRITISH STANDARDS INSTITUTION. *Code of Practice for protective coating of iron and steel structures against corrosion.* BS 5493: 1977. BSI, London.

11.31. BRITISH STANDARDS INSTITUTION. *Guide to assessment of concrete strength in existing structures.* BS 6089: 1981. BSI, London.

11.32. *Report on the removal of graffiti.* Greater London Council, Scientific Branch. Bulletin no. 64, 2nd series, item no. 3, 1973.

11.33. DEPARTMENT OF TRANSPORT. *The design of highway bridge parapets. Departmental Standard BE 5.*

11.34. *Highways Act 1980.* Section 176, Her Majesty's Stationery Office, London.

11.35. DEPARTMENT OF TRANSPORT. *Headroom standards. Departmental Standard BE 14.*

11.36. DEPARTMENT OF TRANSPORT. *Design criteria footbridges and fine/signal gantries. Departmental Standard BE 1/78.*

11.37. *Health and Safety at Work Act 1974.* Her Majesty's Stationery Office, London.

11.38. *Factories Act 1961.* Her Majesty's Stationery Office, London.

11.39. FEDERATION OF CIVIL ENGINEERING CONTRACTORS. *Supervisors safety handbook.* FCEC, London, 1970.

11.40. DEPARTMENT OF TRANSPORT. A schedule of design documents relating to highway bridges and structures. *Schedule TAS,* Dec. 1983.

Appendix. Schedule TAS (December 1983) A[1.40]: Schedule of design documents relating to highway bridges and structures

British Standards

BS 153: Part 3A   Specification for steel girder bridges (see BE 1/77)

BS 5400   Steel concrete and composite bridges

Part 1:	1978 — General statement (see BD 15/82)	
Part 2:	1978 — Specification for loads (see BD 14/82)	
Part 3:	1982 — C.P. for design of steel bridges (see BD 13/82)	
Part 4:	1978 — C.P. for design of concrete bridges (see BD 17/83)	
Part 5:	1979 — C.P. for design of composite bridges (see BD 16/82)	
Part 6:	1980 — Specification of materials and workmanship, steel (see BD 11.82)	
Part 9:	1983 — Bridge bearings (see BD 20/83)	
Part 10:	1980 — C.P. for fatigue (see BD 9/81)	

BS 5628:   Part 1:   1978 — Unreinforced masonry

BS 5930:   1981 — Site investigations

BS 6031:   1981 — Earthworks

British Standard Codes of Practice

CP 112 Part 2   The structural use of time

CP 114 Part 2   Reinforced concrete in buildings (see Tech. Memo BE 1/73)

CP 116 Part 2   The structural use of precast concrete (see Tech. Memo BE 1/73)

CP 118   The structural use of aluminium
CP 2   Earth retaining structures
CP 2004   Foundations

DTp publications (HMSO)
Railway construction and operation. Requirements, structural and electrical clearances (1977)
Railway construction and operation. Requirements for passenger lines and recommendations for goods lines 1950 (Reprinted 1970)
Roads in urban areas and metric supplement (as amended by TA 32/82)
Layout of roads in rural areas and metric supplement (as amended by TA 28/82)
Specification for road and bridge works and notes for guidance (1976 edition) including supplement No. 1 (1978)
Traffic signs manual, Chapter 13, Part 8 — Wind loading on sign plates
Simplified tables of external loads on buried pipelines (1970)

Miscellaneous
Circular Roads No. 61/72 — Routes for heavy and high abnormal loads

Technical Memoranda (bridges)
BE 5   The design of highway bridge parapets (4th revision)
BE 14   Headroom standards
BE 23   Shear key decks
BE 27   Waterproofing and surfacing of bridge decks
BE 29   MOT/C & CA bridge beams
BE 3/72   Expansion joints for use in highway bridge decks
BE 4/72   Street lighting columns of steel construction
BE 1/73   Reinforced concrete for highway structures (1st revision 9/8/73) (for the design of rigid buried structures only)
BE 3/73   The assessment of highway bridges for construction and use vehicles (to be used for pre-1922 structures or where directed by TAA)
BE 1/74   The independent checking of erection proposals and temporary works details for major highway structure on trunk roads and motorways
BE 5/74   High alumina cement concrete
BE 7/74   Lateral loading on piled foundations
BE 5/75   Rules for the design and use of Freyssinet concrete hinges in highway structures
BE 8/75   Painting of concrete highway structures
BE 5/76   Evaluation of highway structures
BE 1/77   Standard highway loadings (relevant parts for the design of rigid buried structures and sign/signal gantries only)
BE 7/77   Departmental standard (interim) motorway sign/signal gantries
BE 8/77   Use of DTp bridge paint manual
BE 1/78   Design criteria for footbridges and sign/signal gantries
BE 3/78   Reinforced earth retaining walls and bridge abutments for embankments

Highways Technical Memoranda
11/70   Site investigation procedure
H 9/71   Cross section design of road verges and central reserves on or under bridges
H 1/72   Manual of standard highway designs — rural motorways

H 5/72   Notes on the treatment of old filled mine shafts and disused shallow coal workings
H 9/73   Safety fences (excl. specification clauses)
H 10/75   Clearances to bridges on dual 2 lane roads
H 14/76   Noise barriers — standards and materials

Interim Memoranda (bridges)
IM 4   Pulverised fuel ash, back filling to structures
IM 5   Formation of continuity joints in bridge decks

DTp standards on traffic engineering and control
TD 2/78   Pedestrian subways — layout and dimensions
TD 3/79   Combined pedestrian and cycle subways — layout and dimensions
TD 9/81   Road layout and geometry. Highway link design

DTp standards on bridges and structures
BD 2/79   Technical approval of DTp highway structures on trunk roads and motorways
BD 5/80   Standard bridges
BD 6/81   Approval in principle and calibrating of computer programs for use in DTp highway structures on trunk roads and motorways
BD 7/81   Weathering steel for highway structures
BD 9/81   Implementation of BS 5400 Part 10, CP for fatigue
BD 10/82   Design of highway structures in areas of mining subsidence
BD 11/82   Specification for structural steelwork
BD 12/82   Corrugated steel buried structures
BD 13/82   Design of steel bridges — use of BS 5400 Part 3: 1982
BD 14/82   Loads for highway bridges — use of BS 5400 Part 2: 1978
BD 15/82   General principles — use of BS 5400 Part 1: 1978
BD 16/82   Design of composite bridges — use of BS 5400 Part 5: 1979
BD 17/83   Design of concrete bridges — use of BS 5400 Part 4: 1978
BD 19/83   Standard bridges
BD 20/83   Bridge bearings — use of BS 5400 Part 9: 1983
BD 28/87   Early thermal cracking of concrete
BD 30/87   Backfilled retaining walls and bridge abutments. Circ. Rds 2/80
BS 8004   Foundations
BS 5400   Part 4: 1984 C.P. for design of concrete bridges, as implemented by BD 24/84

DTp standards on highways
HD 2/79   Specification for road and bridgeworks — rolled asphalt wearing course
HD 3/80   Specification for road and bridgeworks — texture depth of bituminous surfacings for high speed roads
HD 4/80   Specification for road and bridgeworks — rolled asphalt wearing course, cold weather working
HD 6/80   Specification for road and bridgeworks — dynamic compaction (end result specification)

The Authors

J. K. Atkinson, CEng, MICE, MIHT

Ken Atkinson trained initially with a contractor and then moved to local government after completing his national service. He carried out a series of major bridge, underpass and riverside road improvement schemes as Resident Engineer and served in the design office and in the project engineering team at the Greater London Council, working on bridge and general road design issues and the co-ordination of multi-million pound road projects. In 1972 he took up the post of Section Head in the specialized area of maintaining metropolitan road structures within London, and progressed to Assistant Chief Engineer in charge of all maintenance functions prior to the dissolution of the GLC in 1986. He has represented the GLC at conferences and bridge assessment panels and was a member of the Transport and Road Research Working Party on Highway Maintenance Research.

He takes an active interest in training and has lectured both in the UK and abroad. He has presented papers on bridge maintenance topics to the annual Institution of Highways and Transportation Workshop, the Rubber Institute and the Royal Institute of Public Administration.

Since leaving the GLC Ken Atkinson has undertaken a number of appraisal, assessment and management reviews in the capacity of consultant and has used the broad experience gained during his career in helping to compile this manual on highway maintenance.

W. P. F. Heather, BA, FIHT, MIAT

Bill Heather has worked in the blacktop industry for 27 years. He started as a management trainee with Constable Hart. He moved to ARC and has been employed by Associated Asphalt for the past 14 years where he has been involved in line management for contracting and production. He is currently the Technical Services and QA Manager. He is responsible for the technical assessment of new products and processes in the UK and overseas.

K. W. Huddart, MA (Cantab), CEng, FICE, FIEE, FIHT, FInstP

Ken Huddart is a physicist and electrical engineer who initially worked on extra high voltage systems. For 20 years with the Greater London Council he was responsible for traffic control systems, including the introduction of innovative traffic signals maintenance operations and contracts. He was finally Chief Traffic Engineer.

He is now working as a traffic engineering consultant in his own right and with the MVA consultancy. His projects include the traffic control of light rail transit in Hong Kong and the UK, and direction signposting for London's primary routes.

A. Lilley, MPhil, CEng, MICE, FIHT

Alan Lilley now runs his own consultancy, having spent most of his working life with the Research and Development Division of the Cement and Concrete Association. In 1970 he was awarded a master's degree for a thesis on cement stabilized materials.

His research areas included studies on the repair of concrete pavements — an area of work with which he is still concerned, believing that in the UK, as in the USA, there will be a growing need for work of this type as the existing pavements become ever older and more heavily trafficked. He is perhaps best known for his work on various forms of small element paving.

B. L. Parker, CEng, MICE, MIHT, AMCST

Len Parker started his career in 1952, joining Sir Donald Bailey's team at MEXE where he developed soil stabilization techniques for forward air-field construction. After service in the RAF he was engaged on road and airport construction in Iran, and subsequently on a variety of projects including buildings, dams and harbour works. In 1958 he joined Scott Wilson Kirkpatrick and Partners and spent the next ten years on the design and construction of motorways in the UK and international airports in the Middle East.

In 1969 he joined Cumberland County Council and was involved in the latter stages of the construction of the M6, including aspects such as reclamation works, coast erosion and geotechnics. In 1974 he was appointed Senior Group Engineer jointly serving Surrey County Council and the South Eastern Road Construction Unit with responsibility for geotechnical and materials engineering. He currently holds the position of County Materials Engineer at Surrey County Council where he has initiated major developments in pavement assessment systems.

D. I. Pearson, CEng, MICE

Derek Pearson has spent 15 years engaged in a wide range of design and construction projects on highways, bridges, drainage, sewage disposal and waterworks. While employed by the West Riding County Council, in 1974 he gained a diploma in management studies at Sheffield Polytechnic. Subsequently he specialized in highway maintenance and held operational appointments with Sheffield County Council and South Yorkshire County Council before spending five years in the headquarters. He returned to Sheffield County Council in 1986 where he is currently Chief Engineer Highway Maintenance and responsible for highway maintenance on an urban network of 2000 km.

D. G. Powell, BSc(Eng), PhD, CEng, MIMechE, FIHT, MREAAA
David Powell is at present a Senior Lecturer in Civil Engineering at Queen Mary College, University of London, and in addition acts as a consultant and expert witness specializing in highway and vehicle problems and accident investigations.

In 1979 David Powell was visiting Professor of the International Association of Traffic and Safety Sciences in Japan, and from 1982 to 1986 he was co-ordinating project director on a joint study programme funded by the EEC on the engineering aspects of highway/traffic safety with the National Technical University of Greece, Athens. He has also been a member of the Road Safety Advisory Committee of the London Borough of Tower Hamlets and has been author or co-author of 60 technical publications.

His particular areas of interest include skid resistance of road surfaces, highway maintenance and vehicle dynamics under emergency conditions.

N. Zuman, IEng, FILE
Bert Zuman started his career in public lighting in 1950 in Crawley, Sussex, during the early years of the development of Britain's first generation of New Towns. In 1967 he joined Hertfordshire County Concil to take responsibility for the newly created street lighting section and he is now Group Engineer (Lighting, Electrical and Mechanical). In 1968 he pioneered competitive street lighting maintenance contracts. He joined the Institution of Lighting Engineers in 1960 and has been the author of a number of papers on various lighting subjects.

Index